The Writer's Craft

W9-CZS-141

Grammar and Usage Practice Book

Orange Level
Grade 9

McDougal Littell Inc.

A Houghton Mifflin Company
Evanston, Illinois   Boston Dallas Phoenix

Special Features of the Grammar and Usage Practice Book

- It contains a wealth of skill-building exercises in grammar, usage, capitalization, and punctuation.

- Each page focuses on one topic or skill. A brief instructional summary is followed by comprehensive reinforcement exercises.

- Key words and phrases are highlighted for greater clarity and ease of use.

- Each page corresponds to a part in the pupil text for easy reference.

- Grammar lessons are leveled. Form A introduces the skill. Form B extends the skill with more advanced exercises.

- Skills Assessment sheets may be used by the student for self-diagnosis and additional practice or by the teacher as a check for understanding.

- A proofreading practice activity is provided for each Grammar and Usage Handbook.

ISBN 0-8123-8855-0

4 5 6 7 8 9 10 – MDO – 99 98

Contents

Grammar and Usage Handbook

29 The Sentence and Its Parts

The Complete Sentence	1
Kinds of Sentences	3
Complete Subjects and Predicates	5
Simple Subjects and Predicates	7
Verb Phrases	9
Subjects in Unusual Positions	11
Objects of Verbs	13
Subject Complements	15
Compound Sentence Parts	17

30 Writing Complete Sentences

What Is a Sentence Fragment?	19
What Is a Run-on Sentence?	21

31 Using Nouns

What Is a Noun?	23
Kinds of Nouns	25
The Uses of Nouns	27
The Plurals of Nouns	29
The Possessives of Nouns	31

32 Using Pronouns

What Is a Pronoun?	33
Personal Pronouns	35
The Cases of Personal Pronouns	37
Reflexive and Intensive Pronouns	39
Demonstrative Pronouns	41
Indefinite Pronouns	43
Interrogative Pronouns	45
Relative Pronouns	47
Agreement with Antecedents	49
Indefinite Pronouns as Antecedents	51
Vague Pronoun References	53
Problems with Pronouns (I)	55
Problems with Pronouns (II)	57
Problems with Pronouns (III)	59

Skills Assessment 1: Sections 29–32	61

33 Using Verbs

What Is a Verb?	65
Helping Verbs and Main Verbs	67
Transitive Verbs and Main Verbs	69
Active and Passive Voice	71
Principal Parts of Regular Verbs	73
Principal Parts of Irregular Verbs (I)	75
Principal Parts of Irregular Verbs (II)	77
Principal Parts of Irregular Verbs (III)	79
Verb Tense	81
Progressive Verb Forms	83
Avoiding Shifts in Tense	85
Using the Right Verb (I)	87
Using the Right Verb (II)	89

34 Using Modifiers

Adjectives	91
Nouns and Pronouns as Adjectives	93
Adverbs	95
Using the Correct Modifier	97
Using Modifiers in Comparisons	99
Using Correct Comparisons	101
Problems with Modifiers (I)	103
Problems with Modifiers (II)	105

	Skills Assessment 2: Section 33–34	107
35	**Using Prepositions, Conjunctions, and Interjections**	
	What Is a Preposition	111
	Prepositional Phrases as Modifiers	113
	Conjunctions	115
	Subordinating Conjunctions	117
	Interjections	119
36	**Reviewing Parts of Speech**	
	The Parts of Speech	121
37	**Using Verbals and Appositives**	
	Gerunds	123
	Participles	125
	Infinitives	127
	Misplaced and Dangling Modifiers	129
	Appositives	131
38	**Making Subjects and Verbs Agree**	
	Agreement in Number	133
	Compound Subjects	135
	Indefinite Pronouns	137
	Other Agreement Problems	139
	Skills Assessment 3: Sections 35–38	141
39	**Clauses and Sentence Structure**	
	What is a Clause?	143
	Adjective Clauses (I)	145
	Adjective Clauses (II)	147
	Adverb Clauses	149
	Noun Clauses	151
	Sentence Structure (I)	153
	Sentence Structure (II)	155
	Sentence Structure (III)	157
	Using Clauses Correctly (I)	159
	Using Clauses Correctly (II)	161
	Using Clauses Correctly (III)	163
40	**Capitalization**	
	Proper Nouns and Proper Adjectives	167
	Geographical Names	169
	Organizations, Events, and Other Subjects	171
	First Words and the Pronoun *I*	173
41	**Punctuation**	
	End Marks	175
	The Comma (I)	177
	The Comma (II)	179
	The Comma (III)	181
	The Comma (IV)	183
	The Comma (V)	185
	The Semicolon and Colon	187
	The Dash	189
	The Hyphen	191
	The Apostrophe	193
	Quotation Marks (I)	195
	Quotation Marks (II)	197
	Quotation Marks (III)	199
	Skills Assessment 4: Sections 39–41	201
	Proofreading Practice for Handbooks 29-41	204
	Answer Key	217

The Complete Sentence

A **sentence** is a group of words that expresses a complete thought. A group of words that does not express a complete thought is a **sentence fragment.**

A. Identifying Sentences and Fragments

Write **S** for each group of words that is a sentence. Write **F** for each sentence fragment.

1. Rock music blared across the dance floor. _____

2. By the end of the set, the drummer. _____

3. The kids began to mingle after the first few songs. _____

4. Rachel could barely hear. _____

5. The first dance since starting high school. _____

6. The greater the tempo of the music. _____

7. It had taken the freshmen a month to make the decorations. _____

8. Lee had a difficult time finding her friends in the crowded gym. _____

9. The hardest part of going to the dance. _____

10. When the last song was over. _____

B. Writing Complete Sentences

Add a word or group of words to make each fragment a complete sentence.

> **Example**   A symbol. **The Maple leaf is a national symbol in Canada.**

1. Signing up for football. _____

   _____

2. On a ranch in Wyoming. _____

   _____

3. The skateboard at the end of the sidewalk. _____

   _____

4. Working in the garden. _____

   _____

5. Questions on the test. _____

   _____

The Complete Sentence

A. Identifying Complete Sentences

Write **S** for each group of words that is a sentence. Write **F** for each sentence fragment.

1. Some American colonists sympathetic to the British moved to Canada as news of the coming revolution spread.   _____

2. An important British colony, giving the British bases on the continent.   _____

3. Staying behind, other supporters of King George III.   _____

4. They were called Tories.   _____

5. About a fourth of the American colonists were loyal to the crown.   _____

6. Families were torn by the question.   _____

7. Entering the war and costing lives.   _____

8. This was not an easy decision to make.   _____

9. Sacrifice for unknown results.   _____

10. If you had been a colonist in 1776, you would have had the same dilemma.   _____

B. Completing Sentences

Imagine that you work as an archaeologist in Egypt. You have decoded a portion of a writing sample shown below. It is now your job to supply the missing words. On the lines below, rewrite the sample, using five complete sentences.

> praying to the gods for a good harvest year . . . from the Nile River . . . because most of the country is desert . . . By the end of the flooding . . . Once the crops have been gathered . . . We will celebrate the harvest by . . .

_____

_____

_____

_____

_____

_____

_____

_____

Kinds of Sentences

There are four kinds of sentences. A **declarative sentence** makes a statement. An **interrogative sentence** asks a question. An **imperative sentence** gives a command. An **exclamatory sentence** expresses strong emotion.

A. Identifying Kinds of Sentences

Identify each sentence below as **DEC** for declarative, **INT** for interrogative, **IMP** for imperative, or **EXC** for exclamatory. Add the proper punctuation mark at the end of each sentence.

1. Where is the Baseball Hall of Fame _____

2. In Greek mythology, Mercury was the messenger of the gods _____

3. How exciting it is to watch trapeze artists _____

4. Do you know what the Dewey Decimal System is _____

5. That's incredible _____

6. Look in the card catalog for a book on Amelia Earhart _____

7. What country gave the Statue of Liberty to the United States _____

8. Dallas, Texas, ranks seventh among the nation's ten largest cities _____

9. Don't try to change my mind _____

10. New England's Shaker communities cared for homeless children _____

B. Writing Different Kinds of Sentences

Label each sentence below as **DEC** for declarative, **INT** for interrogative, **IMP** for imperative, or **EXC** for exclamatory. Add the proper punctuation mark. Then write a sentence of your own of the same kind.

> **Example**   Please help me with this algebra problem. **IMP**
> **Be sure to study for the algebra quiz on Friday.**

1. The Dutch artist van Gogh is famous for his bold use of color _____

_____

2. Does Jim's part-time job interfere with his homework _____

_____

3. What a spectacular view you have of the lake _____

_____

4. Talk with someone who shares your interests _____

_____

Kinds of Sentences

A. Identifying Different Kinds of Sentences

Imagine that you receive a phone call. You are asked to baby-sit for the little boy next door. Below is the conversation. Place the correct punctuation mark at the end of each sentence to show whether it is declarative, interrogative, imperative, or exclamatory. (The punctuation mark should be inside the closing quotation marks.)

"Is this John "
"Yes "
"Would you like to baby-sit for Justin "
"OK "
"I would be willing to pay you extra, since it's short notice "
"That would be great "
"Do you have any baby-sitting experience "
"Well, I do have a little brother "
"I will be gone for four hours Are you sure that you would like to baby-sit "
"Yes, Mrs. Murray "
"Terrific Can you be here at 6:30 "
"That will be fine I'll see you then "

B. Using Different Kinds of Sentences in Writing

Write a dialogue that you, as the baby sitter, might have with Justin. Unfortunately for you, Justin is a difficult child. Try to use at least one of each of the following types of sentences: declarative, interrogative, imperative, and exclamatory. Remember to begin a new paragraph each time the speaker changes. Enclose each speaker's words in quotation marks. Use the correct punctuation at the end of each sentence, inside the closing quotation marks.

_____

_____

_____

_____

_____

_____

_____

_____

_____

_____

_____

_____

Complete Subjects and Predicates

Every complete sentence contains a subject and a predicate. The **subject** of the sentence is the person, place, thing, or idea about which something is said. The **complete subject** is all the words in the subject part of the sentence. The **predicate** tells something or asks something about the subject of the sentence. The **complete predicate** is all the words that express an idea about the subject.

A. Identifying Complete Subjects and Predicates

Draw a vertical line between the complete subject and the complete predicate in each of the following sentences.

Example   Ten of us boys | joined the freshman choir.

1. Many people mispronounce the words *library* and *February*.

2. The crowd swayed with the rhythm of the cheerleaders' chant.

3. A major earthquake devastated San Francisco in 1906.

4. Michiko has an exotic collection of seashells.

5. The majestic Rocky Mountains rose in the distance.

6. A dromedary, a camel with one hump, is used for racing.

7. Elaine is traveling to Denver on the *California Zephyr*.

8. The countries of Central America have a complex history.

9. Tall people have an advantage in basketball.

10. Abraham Lincoln's vision of democracy endures.

B. Using Complete Subjects and Predicates

Identify each fragment below by writing **S** if it can be used as a complete subject or **P** if it can be used as a complete predicate. Then add the missing part to make a sentence.

1. The umpire _____. _____

2. _____ noticed the open window. _____

3. An alert officer _____. _____

4. The man with the moustache _____. _____

5. _____ surprised many people. _____

6. Dangerous currents _____. _____

7. _____ have decreased dramatically. _____

8. The other team _____. _____

9. _____ built a cabin last summer. _____

10. A professional stunt man _____. _____

Orange Level, Copyright © McDougal, Littell & Company

Handbook 29   The Sentence and Its Parts   **5**

Complete Subjects and Predicates

A. Using Complete Subjects and Predicates

Write how each of the following groups of words could be used: **CS** for a complete subject or **CP** for a complete predicate. Then use each group of words to write a complete sentence, adding a complete subject or complete predicate as necessary.

> **Example** The fierce winds   **CS**
> **The fierce winds knocked down several power lines.**

1. The flowers on the ledge _____ . _____

2. _____made everyone laugh. _____

3. The tiny extraterrestrials _____ . _____

4. _____felt proud and relieved. _____

5. The last express train _____ . _____

B. Using Complete Subjects and Predicates

Imagine that you have taken notes in science class. As you review your notes, you will rewrite them in complete sentences. Write the following notes as five sentences that have complete subjects and predicates.

> Tortoises, turtles—changed little through time. The term *tortoise*—refers to land species. *Turtle*—to aquatic. Some tortoises enormous—weighing over 500 pounds—often have long life spans. Example—Galapagos tortoise, up to 150 years.

_____

_____

_____

_____

_____

_____

_____

_____

_____

Simple Subjects and Predicates

The **simple subject** is the key word or words in the complete subject. The **simple predicate,** or **verb,** is the main word or words in the complete predicate. The verb tells what the subject of the sentence is or does.

Identifying Verbs and Their Simple Subjects
Underline the simple subject once and the verb twice.

Example   The <u>inventor</u> of the phonograph <u>was</u> Thomas Edison.

1. Loud chatter in a movie theater bothers many viewers.
2. Williamsburg is a restored colonial town in Virginia.
3. The band usually practices its routines every day after school.
4. Visitors to Vermont enjoy the scenic beauty of the state.
5. A committee of students designed the homecoming float.
6. The most complete dictionary in the room is on Shawn's desk.
7. Hostels are places of shelter for travelers.
8. In Spanish class, Anita played flamenco music on her guitar.
9. Ms. Voorhees, from the Village Florist, arranged fresh flowers in vases.
10. This auditorium was the location of many exciting programs.
11. The swimmers demonstrated racing dives.
12. The long-awaited gourmet restaurant opens on the lakefront Saturday.
13. After the fire in our oven, we installed smoke detectors in our apartment.
14. The captain of C Company requested a volunteer to take the mission.
15. Two excellent bands play dance music on both levels of the club.
16. Meredith was the first person to complete the test so quickly.
17. The computer screen flashed with bizarre messages.
18. I remember the vintage clothing store on the corner.
19. The new luxury hotel downtown offers special rates for the first weekend of the season.
20. Marianne always travels through Canada during her summer vacation.
21. David presented a paper at the state conference last month.
22. The bus stalled this morning on its way to the station.
23. Sharon's boss announced a new company policy regarding vacation time.
24. Your new poster is on the table in the living room.
25. Gian Lorenzo Bernini was one of the most talented sculptors in seventeenth-century Italy.

Simple Subjects and Predicates

A. Identifying Simple Subjects and Verbs

Underline the simple subject once and the verb twice in each of the following sentences.

1. The Boston Marathon is an annual twenty-six mile race.

2. Many runners come from all over the world to take part in this race.

3. The race begins in a suburb of Boston.

4. The finish line is downtown near the Boston Public Library.

5. The night before the race, many runners eat either pasta or other complex carbohydrates.

6. Complex carbohydrates give runners energy and stamina.

7. During the race, some runners hit "the wall" after twenty miles.

8. Some racers simply stop at this point of exhaustion.

9. Approximately six thousand people enter the competition each year.

10. Despite the tension and exhaustion, many of these contestants return again and again.

B. Using Subjects and Predicates

Write sentences on the lines below by adding both a subject and a predicate to each fragment. Do not use the fragment as the subject of the sentence.

1. Five hot dogs on the grill. _____

_____

2. The broken laundry machine. _____

_____

3. The dense forest. _____

_____

4. The fire alarm. _____

_____

5. Her scientific experiments. _____

_____

Verb Phrases

A verb made up of two or more words is called a **verb phrase.** A verb phrase consists of a **main verb** and one or more **helping verbs.**

I *must tell* you our good news.

The contestant *could have won.*

Common helping verbs are shown below.

be (*and its forms:* am, are, is,
was, were, being, been)

have (*and its forms:* has, had)

do (*and its forms:* does, did)

can	may	will	shall	must
could	might	would	should	ought

Identifying Verbs and Verb Phrases

Underline the simple subject once and the verb or verb phrase twice in each of the following sentences. Remember that some of the common verbs can also be used as main verbs.

Example   Alan must have left the cellar door open.

1. The kookaburra is a bird with a laughlike call.

2. My friend is recruiting sponsors for the walkathon.

3. *Orthodontics* comes from the Greek words for "straight" and "tooth."

4. Jane Marple had solved the crime.

5. Thoreau lived at Walden Pond for twenty-seven cents a week.

6. The counselor at school could have given you job information.

7. I will need a pair of snowshoes for my trip north.

8. A stamp with an error has more value than a perfect one.

9. The polka has long remained a popular folk dance.

10. Tony may have been selling tickets for the concert.

11. Karen was waltzing on ice skates a moment ago.

12. Eddie may have met you during the last class outing.

13. That storm must have been a frightening one.

14. Those four students bike to school most days.

15. My dad had been waiting at the bus stop for well over an hour.

16. The librarian went into the stacks for these volumes.

17. Mr. Vincent does want both newspapers today.

18. Janet claimed the gray wool gloves as her lost pair.

19. She can do her best work under pressure.

20. Nobody could see through the steamy windows.

Verb Phrases

A. Using Verbs and Verb Phrases

Write sentences on the lines below by adding a predicate to each subject. The predicate should contain a verb phrase—a main verb used with one or more helping verbs.

1. Telephones with special features _____

_____

2. Long-forgotten memories _____

_____

3. Our natural environment _____

_____

4. Photography _____

_____

5. Recent inventions _____

_____

B. Using Verb Phrases in Writing

Imagine that you have been awarded a scholarship to a summer course that offers college credits. It is a fiction writers' workshop. Your classmates are friendly, imaginative, and witty. You will be sending the scholarship committee a summary of your experience. On the lines below, rewrite your rough notes as a paragraph of five sentences for your report. Include some verb phrases.

> an unusual type of class . . . the instructor's enthusiasm . . . a typical student . . . interest in the workshop . . . criticism of one's work . . . professional writers . . . talent and humor . . .

_____

_____

_____

_____

_____

_____

Subjects in Unusual Positions

The subject of a sentence usually comes before the verb. However, in some sentences part or all of the verb comes first. To find the subject, first find the verb. Then ask *who?* or *what?* before the verb. The answer is the subject of the sentence.

> Into the room walked Tony.   verb = walked
> *Who walked?* Tony   subject = Tony

In an imperative sentence, the subject is an understood *you.*

Finding Subjects in Unusual Positions

In the following sentences, underline the simple subject once and the verb twice. If the subject is understood, write **You** in parentheses in the blank.

1. Write home as soon as possible. _____

2. There is an exhibit of Ray's photographs at the bank. _____

3. Does Francine play tennis on the school team? _____

4. Always check your answers on a test. _____

5. Here are the tickets to the concert. _____

6. How much money did the group raise for charity? _____

7. On the front door hung a large wreath. _____

8. There will be a meeting of the French Club on Thursday. _____

9. In Lancaster County, Pennsylvania, are many Amish families. _____

10. Here is the key to the mailbox. _____

11. Into the rain forest went the photographers. _____

12. Save me a place in line. _____

13. There was too much noise backstage. _____

14. Has Lauren heard this new compact disc? _____

15. What did Anna tell you? _____

16. To your left is the mansion of the governor. _____

17. Start the music immediately after the show. _____

18. Is Phyllis coming to the rehearsal tonight? _____

19. There were six bridesmaids in the wedding procession. _____

20. Where have you been since this morning? _____

Subjects in Unusual Positions

A. Writing Sentences

In the following sentences, underline the simple subject once and the verb twice. Then rewrite each sentence so that the subject comes before the verb.

1. There is a new movie opening at the cinema next Friday.

2. All along the road stood large, colorful billboards.

3. Here are the latest statistics on the health risks of smoking.

4. In the apartment down the hall lives a woman from Czechoslovakia.

5. There are several cars parked across the street.

B. Writing Sentences

Rewrite these sentences, following the directions in parentheses. Underline the simple subject of your sentence once and the verb twice. If the subject is an understood *you*, write **you** in parentheses after your sentence.

> **Example**   The books are here (Begin with **Here**.)
> **Here** <u>are</u> the <u>books</u>.

1. A message for you is on your desk. (Begin with *There*.)

2. The snapshots from our vacation are here. (Begin with *Here*.)

3. Ken's mother bought a personal computer. (Change the sentence to a question.)

4. You must send your entry to the radio station. (Change this to an imperative sentence.)

5. Under the bridge is a popular swimming area. (Begin with *There*.)

Objects of Verbs

A **direct object** is a word that receives the action of an action verb.

The class presented a *gift*. (*Gift* is the direct object.)

A sentence that has a direct object may also have an **indirect object.** An indirect object tells *to whom?* or *for whom?* or *to what?* about an action verb.

The class presented the *school* a gift. (*School* is the indirect object.)

Recognizing Objects of Verbs

Write the direct object from each sentence below in the blank at the right. Then underline any indirect objects that appear.

Example   Sonya read <u>us</u> a long story.   **story**

1. Residents near this airport dislike the noise. _____

2. Janeen built her parents a table in shop class. _____

3. Did the biology lab receive new equipment this year? _____

4. Robots are replacing people in some factories. _____

5. Mr. Lawrence has been teaching students Latin for twenty-nine years. _____

6. The freshmen collected boxes for the homecoming bonfire. _____

7. Did you write your aunt in Colorado a letter? _____

8. The Lee family gave the exchange students a welcoming party. _____

9. Carl Lewis won four gold medals in the 1984 Summer Olympics. _____

10. According to legend, Betsy Ross sewed the first flag of the United States. _____

11. Rafael is making his sister a costume for the class party. _____

12. Jack, did you catch a trout at Pine Lake last week? _____

13. The inspector noticed the mud on the taxi driver's boot. _____

14. Some people took cameras to the air show. _____

15. Jen gave her cousin a framed picture for her birthday. _____

16. Josh tied the knot much too tightly. _____

17. Did the mechanic inspect the brakes after the accident? _____

18. Will you save me a seat at the concert? _____

19. Our uncle sent us tickets for the play at the community center. _____

20. Karen offered me her extra umbrella. _____

Objects of Verbs

A. Identifying Objects of Verbs

identify the function of the boldfaced word in each sentence below. Write **DO** for direct object and **IO** for indirect object. If the word is neither the direct object nor the indirect object, write **N.**

> **Example**   Cora writes *poetry* for a literary magazine.   **DO**

1. Mark sings in the adult *choir.* _____

2. The travelers left some *money* behind when they ran to catch their train. _____

3. The firefighters entered the *house* through the back door. _____

4. The pianist played the *king* a beautiful sonata. _____

5. Alex paints *landscapes* in oils. _____

6. Gabi translated the *letter* from my pen pal in Germany. _____

7. The height of the steep cliff terrified *him.* _____

8. Gail told *me* the story of the people who built this ship. _____

9. Saul doesn't know about the committee's *decision.* _____

10. What gave *you* that idea? _____

B. Using Indirect Objects

Underline the direct object in each sentence below. Then rewrite each sentence, adding an indirect object.

1. My trip with Outward Bound last year taught self-confidence.

_____

2. Elena told her plans for the long summer.

_____

3. Dave brought a souvenir from his trip to Nova Scotia.

_____

4. Jenny showed the way to the new restaurant.

_____

5. The guide gave interesting information about the caverns.

_____

Subject Complements

A **linking verb** does not describe an action. Instead, it links the subject with another in the sentence. This word is called the **subject complement.** The verb *be* is the most common linking verb. Other frequently used linking verbs are shown below.

appear	grow	smell
become	look	sound
feel ·	seem	taste

Two kinds of subject complements complete the meaning of linking verbs. They are predicate nominatives and predicate adjectives.

A *predicate nominative* is a noun or pronoun that follows a linking verb and that identifies, renames, or explains the subject.

Dinosaurs were *reptiles.*

A *predicate adjective* is an adjective that follows a linking verb and that modifies or describes the subject.

That fashion model looks *attractive.*

Identifying Linking Verbs and Subject Complements

In the following sentences, underline the linking verbs once and the subject complements twice.

Example   Apple cider <u>is</u> <u>tart</u>.

1. An earthquake is a sudden movement of part of the earth's crust.

2. Dill pickles taste good with corned beef sandwiches.

3. David appeared calm backstage.

4. Sara is quarterback on the girls' football team.

5. The Continental Divide is part of the Rocky Mountains.

6. These photographs seem blurry.

7. After the long hike through the canyon, we felt tired.

8. The winners of the citizenship awards are friends of mine.

9. This is she.

10. The sunset over the mountains looked beautiful last night.

11. The pretzel tastes salty.

12. My brother is a cashier at Goodwin's.

13. Next season I will be captain of the team.

14. The sky appears cloudy today.

15. Dolphins are very intelligent creatures.

16. Both sides are being stubborn about this issue.

17. The casserole in the oven smelled delicious.

18. Steve will become an architect after graduation.

19. Before the season tournament, the team grew tense.

20. Barbara seemed very excited about the concert.

Subject Complements

A. Identifying Types of Subject Complements

In each of the following sentences, underline the linking verb once and the subject complement twice. Then, in the blank, write **PN** if the subject complement is a **predicate nominative** or **PA** if it is a **predicate adjective.**

> **Example**   My uncle <u>is</u> a gym <u>teacher</u>.   **PN**

1. Li has become an excellent mathematician. _____

2. Buffalo Bill Cody was a scout for the United States Army. _____

3. The popcorn smells delicious. _____

4. Indira Gandhi was the first female leader of India. _____

5. It is I. _____

6. The last locker in this row looks bigger than the others. _____

7. Has George Washington's birthday remained a legal holiday? _____

8. The family car has become quite dilapidated. _____

9. Jamie, my little brother, is afraid of water. _____

10. Alaska is the only state without a motto. _____

B. Using Subject Complements

Rewrite each of the numbered items in the passage below with a new subject complement. Underline your new subject complement. If it is a predicate nominative, write **PN** after the sentence. If it is a predicate adjective, write **PA.**

> **(1)** Our camping trip last summer was a great experience. **(2)** Once we reached the campsite, we felt relaxed. **(3)** The site, next to the river in a small clearing, looked perfect. **(4)** The wind in the trees sounded peaceful, **(5)** and the water in the river was clean. **(6)** The wild blueberries we found tasted fresh.

1. _____

2. _____

3. _____

4. _____

5. _____

6. _____

Compound Sentence Parts

The word **compound** means "having two or more parts." Subject, verbs, and complements can be compound. The parts of a compound are usually joined by one of these conjunctions: *and, or, but.* When a compound has three or more parts, the parts are separated by commas.

> *Bob, Carmen,* and *Jeff* worked on the model engine. (compound subject)
> Shirley *wrote* the play and *acted* in it. (compound verb)
> Stephanie visited *Copenhagen* and *Stockholm* last summer. (compound direct object)
> Bill offered *Margot* and *Suzanne* a ride to the beach. (compound indirect object))
> Is that instrument a *violin* or a *viola?* (compound predicate nominative)
> The climbers looked *hot* and *tired.* (compound predicate adjective)

Identifying Compound Sentence Parts

Underline the compound parts of the following sentences. Label the compound parts **S** for subject, **V** for verb, **DO** for direct object, **IO** for indirect object, **PN** for predicate nominative, or **PA** for predicate adjective.

>   **S**   **S**
> **Example**   <u>Sid</u> and <u>George</u> are Eagle Scouts.

1. Hayrides and quilting bees are old American traditions.

2. Edgar Allan Poe wrote stories and poems.

3. The only rags left in the closet were damp and moldy.

4. The Ambassador Bridge joins the United States and Canada.

5. Kangaroos and koalas are two of Australia's unusual animals.

6. Sacajawea showed Lewis and Clark the way to the Pacific Ocean.

7. Come and join us at the park on Friday afternoon.

8. Kim is manager and captain of the team.

9. Mrs. Sousa sanded and varnished the antique table.

10. Most employers demand neatness and punctuality from their employees.

11. Selma's designs for the costumes were original, practical, and affordable.

12. Thomas Jefferson was an architect, an inventor, and a writer.

13. Ms. Wise paid Luis and Jill their salaries.

14. Through the use of vaccines, scientists have conquered smallpox and polio.

15. Berlin and Dresden are two German cities that were badly damaged in World War II.

Compound Sentence Parts

Writing Sentences with Compound Parts

Rewrite each of the following sentences, making the part indicated in parentheses compound. Make sure the subjects and verbs agree in number.

> **Example**   I love soccer. (subject)
> **Jess and I love soccer.**

1. We returned the books to the library. (direct object)

   _____

2. The fireworks sparkled in the dark summer sky. (verb)

   _____

3. Maria sent me a post card. (indirect object)

   _____

4. In this part of the country, the winters are long. (predicate adjective)

   _____

5. The only typewriter for sale at the flea market was broken. (predicate adjective)

   _____

6. The news shop on the corner has various magazines. (direct object)

   _____

7. After the meeting, the secretary will file a report. (verb)

   _____

8. John found an old photograph in the attic. (direct object)

   _____

9. Ellen studied all day at the library. (subject)

   _____

10. The students in the last four rows are sophomores. (predicate nominative)

    _____

A **sentence fragment** is a group of words that is only a part, or fragment, of a sentence. A sentence fragment does not express a complete thought.

A. Identifying Sentence Fragments

For each complete sentence, write **S** in the blank. For each sentence fragment, write **F** in the blank.

1. Saw a comet in the sky. _____

2. The pandemonium after the victory. _____

3. Where was she? _____

4. Rocketed past the corner and disappeared. _____

5. Bryan struggled to complete the project on time. _____

6. Has traveled to Europe and Africa. _____

7. That's right. _____

8. Kept reading far into the night. _____

9. Just around the corner. _____

10. I'm satisfied. _____

B. Changing Fragments to Sentences

Add a subject, a verb, or both to make each of the following fragments a complete sentence. Use appropriate capitalization and punctuation.

1. Fell asleep at the movies

_____

2. Finally, the superintendent of the apartment building

_____

3. Slumped on the dugout bench

_____

4. An enormous crowd of anxious spectators

_____

5. Because the lake had dried up

_____

What Is a Sentence Fragment?

A. Identifying and Revising Fragments

Determine which of the following groups of words are complete sentences and which are fragments. After complete sentences, add the appropriate punctuation mark and write **Correct** on the blank line. Make fragments into complete sentences by adding appropriate words and punctuation.

1. Chosen in the first-round draft _____

2. The phone rang twice _____

3. Riding a dirt bike _____

4. During the thunderstorm _____

5. Highways during the winter _____

6. Lucy at the library _____

7. The music is over _____

8. Became king of the tiny country _____

9. Are you there _____

10. At the bottom of the application _____

B. Rewriting Sentence Fragments

Imagine that you have just finished reading an article on the Aboriginal people of Australia and have taken notes. To save time, you used sentence fragments. Rewrite the notes below, using five complete sentences.

> Aboriginal people first in Australia. Lived in north over 20,000 years. Some still in area. Now national park—record of traditions, history there in rock paintings. Youth losing interest in paintings, stories. Culture being lost.

_____

_____

_____

_____

_____

_____

_____

What Is a Run-on Sentence?

A **run-on sentence** occurs when two or more sentences are strung together without punctuation or are separated by only a comma. Run-on errors can be corrected by using a period, a semicolon, a semicolon and a conjunctive adverb, or a conjunction.

Run-on	Ray had lost his house key he was locked out.
Correct	Ray had lost his house key. He was locked out.
Correct	Ray had lost his house key; he was locked out.
Run-on	Chris is on vacation, she won't be joining us.
Correct	Chris is on vacation; therefore, she won't be joining us.
Correct	Chris is on vacation, and she won't be joining us.

A. Identifying Run-on Sentences

Identify each sentence as either **Run-on** or **Correct.**

1. Driving was fun there wasn't much traffic. _____

2. The rookie running back carried the ball, he made a touchdown. _____

3. Kendra chose her courses wisely. _____

4. All watched the launching it was spectacular. _____

5. One disc jockey reads letters he also jokes with callers. _____

6. The paddle-wheel steamboat still operates it's the *Delta Queen.* _____

7. A motorcycle turned into the alley it skidded on the gravel. _____

8. Glass is a common, inexpensive material with many practical uses. _____

9. Tony wants bigger biceps he lifts barbells every day. _____

10. I heard the term *a mackerel sky* for the first time today. _____

B. Correcting Run-on Sentences

Correct the following run-on sentences by using correct punctuation and capitalization.

1. Last summer we camped we had the best vacation ever. _____

_____

2. We saw an old Hitchcock film, it was a classic thriller. _____

_____

3. Diane tried to skate backwards, she ended up with a badly sprained arm. _____

_____

4. Burnett noticed the leaves of the bush he realized that it was a poisonous plant. _____

_____

What Is a Run-on Sentence?

A. Correcting Run-on Sentences

Rewrite the following run-on sentences by using correct punctuation and capitalization.

1. Russia sold Alaska to the United States the price was two cents an acre.

_____

2. Paul's brother works for United Airlines, he's a flight attendant.

_____

3. Court stenographers must listen well they must also type rapidly.

_____

4. Eyes are delicate organs have them examined every two years.

_____

5. *Dendrophobia* is a medical term it means "fear of trees."

_____

B. Identifying and Correcting Run-on Sentences

Imagine that a reporter for your school's newspaper submitted the following play review. In five complete sentences, rewrite the review, eliminating the run-on sentences.

> The senior production of Shakespeare's *Macbeth* was fantastic the stars were all members of the senior class some juniors played supporting roles. It is clear that the students put in a lot of time, they must have rehearsed for many weeks. The stage crew deserves credit, too, the sets, lighting, costumes, and makeup were all exceptional the hard work of the entire cast and crew paid off.

_____

_____

_____

_____

_____

_____

_____

Orange Level, Copyright © McDougal, Littell & Company

22   *Handbook 30   Writing Complete Sentences*

Kinds of Nouns

A **common noun** is a general name for a person, place, thing, or idea. A **proper noun** names a particular person, place, thing, or idea. A **concrete noun** names an object perceived through the senses; an **abstract noun** names something that cannot be perceived with the senses. A **collective noun** names a group of people or things. A **compound noun** contains two or more words.

Common Nouns	avenue, city, statue
Proper Nouns	Fourth Avenue, Rome, Statue of Liberty
Concrete Nouns	book, computer, boat
Abstract Nouns	wisdom, courtesy, honesty
Collective Nouns	crowd, jury, team
Compound Nouns	real estate, thumbprint, son-in-law

A. Identifying Kinds of Nouns

Identify each boldfaced noun as **common, proper, concrete, abstract, collective,** or **compound.** Each noun will fit at least two categories.

1. Many **groups** are concerned about **changes** in the sizes of fish in the Amazon. _____

_____

2. Certain fishing **practices** and increased **demand** have resulted in smaller and

fewer fish. _____

3. This **trend** could affect the **food chain** in the entire region. _____

_____

4. Other changes have come to the basin of the **Amazon** and its **tributaries.** _____

_____

B. Using Different Kinds of Nouns

Rewrite each sentence, completing it with the type of noun that is shown in parentheses.

1. The (collective) decided to sponsor the amendment. _____

_____

2. My grandfather's (common, abstract) is to live to the year 2020. _____

_____

3. (Proper) is the name of a city in California. _____

_____

4. (Abstract) may influence the result of an examination. _____

_____

Kinds of Nouns

A. Identifying Kinds of Nouns

On the lines below, list the nouns in the numbered sentences. In parentheses after each, identify the noun as **PRO** for proper, **COM** for common, **CON** for concrete, **ABS** for abstract, **COLL** for collective, or **COMP** for compound. All of the nouns can be identified in at least two ways.

(1) Lincoln began life as a poor boy who had little formal education. (2) His family moved to Illinois, where he began studying law. He served in the United States House of Representatives. Later, he became a candidate for the Senate but lost the election to Stephen Douglas. **(3)** During this campaign, however, Lincoln won national fame by debating Douglas on the subject of slavery. Lincoln went on to become President, but shortly after his inauguration, the Civil War began. **(4)** As commander-in-chief, Lincoln directed the war with efficiency and calm strength. **(5)** Eventually, he saw the conflict come to an end.

1. _____

2. _____

3. _____

4. _____

5. _____

B. Using Different Kinds of Nouns

Rewrite each of the following sentences, replacing each boldfaced noun with the kind of noun given in parentheses. You may need to add, subtract, or change the articles (*a, an, the*) in some sentences.

1. The snorkeler saw an **object** (concrete) near the **swimmer** (proper). _____

_____

2. **Denise** (common) admired the **beauty** (concrete) beneath the water's surface. _____

_____

3. A good snorkeler has **fins** (abstract) and a **mask** (abstract). _____

_____

4. Only a **fraction** (compound) of our group went snorkeling in the **bay** (proper). _____

_____

5. Another **person** (collective) agreed to take a **ride** (abstract). _____

_____

The Uses of Nouns

A noun may act as a **subject** of a verb, as a **direct object** that receives the action of a verb, as an **indirect object** that tells *to whom?* or *for whom?* or *to what?* or *for what?* about an action verb, or as a **predicate nominative** that follows a linking verb.

A. Identifying How Nouns Are Used

Identify the boldfaced noun in each sentence as **S** if it is used as a subject, as **DO** if it is used as a direct object, or **IO** if it is used as an indirect object, or as **PN** if it is used as a predicate nominative.

1. Hurricanes are violent ***storms*** that form over warm oceans. _____

2. Most ***hurricanes*** that hit the United States form in September or October. _____

3. Meteorologists give ***hurricanes*** names, such as Adam or Anna. _____

4. In the Gulf of Mexico, hurricanes cause tremendous ***damage.*** _____

5. A hurricane that struck Bermuda in 1987 uprooted many ***trees.*** _____

B. Using Nouns in Different Ways

Write a sentence using each group of nouns below. Then identify the way you have used each noun by writing **S** above the nouns used as subjects, **DO** above direct objects, **IO** above indirect objects, and **PN** above predicate nominatives. Vary your sentences to use nouns in all four ways.

      Example   Ms. Clark, worker

              S   **PN**
      Ms. Clark is a postal worker.

1. Lee Corporation, computer operators _____

_____

2. doctor, patient, medicine _____

_____

3. Bud Hopkins, cars _____

_____

4. Rosa Ruiz, customers, appliances _____

_____

5. Ms. Schwartz, forest ranger _____

_____

The Uses of Nouns

A. Using Nouns in Different Ways

Imagine that you are editing an article about aspirin for a journal. You notice that every sentence begins with the word *aspirin* and that this word is the subject of each sentence. Your job is to make the sentences more interesting by using the word *aspirin* in different ways. Rewrite each numbered sentence, using the word *aspirin* as a direct object (DO), an indirect object (IO), or a predicate nominative (PN). Identify the way you use the word each time by writing **DO, IO,** or **PN** above it. You may have to add or subtract words to rewrite some sentences.

> **(1)** Aspirin is one of the most common medicines. Aspirin is cheap, easily obtained, and generally not harmful to adults. **(2)** Aspirin is kept in the medicine cabinets of most families. **(3)** Aspirin often is taken for colds, fevers, or headaches. Aspirin may have another use, scientists think. Aspirin can help prevent heart trouble in healthy individuals. Aspirin works by inhibiting the body's production of chemicals that contribute to the formation of blood clots. **(4)** Aspirin and its side effects must be given special consideration, however, by doctors whose patients have digestive problems. Aspirin can cause serious side effects because its acid contributes to ulcers and other disorders of the digestive system. **(5)** Aspirin should not be taken frequently, except under a doctor's supervision.

1. _____

2. _____

3. _____

4. _____

5. _____

B. Using Nouns in Different Ways in Writing

Write a paragraph stating what you think is the most important medical discovery of our time. Vary your use of nouns to include subjects, direct and indirect objects, and predicate nominatives. Identify these nouns by writing **S, DO, IO,** or **PN.** Draft your paragraph on a separate sheet of paper; then write the final version on the lines below.

_____

_____

_____

_____

_____

_____

_____

The Plurals of Nouns

To form the plural of most nouns, just add -s: *dogs, hills*. When the singular noun ends in *s, sh, ch, x,* or *z,* add -es: *buses, bushes, birches, taxes, waltzes*. When the singular noun ends in *o,* add -s or -es: *autos, echoes*.

When the singular noun ends in *y* with a consonant before it, change the *y* to *i* and add -es: *juries, parties*. When a vowel comes before the *y,* just add -s: *driveways, alleys*.

For most nouns ending in *f* or *fe,* change the *f* to *v* and add -s or -es: *leaves, wives*.

Some nouns, such as *deer* and *sheep,* have the same form for both singular and plural. Other nouns, such as *tooth* and *woman,* form their plurals in special ways: *teeth, women*.

If a compound noun is written as one word, change the last word in the compound to its plural form: *truckloads, grandchildren*. Otherwise, change the most important word to the plural form: *fathers-in-law, attorneys general, flight attendants*.

Forming Plural Nouns

Write the plural form of each of these nouns in the appropriate blank. Use a dictionary to ensure correct spelling.

1. elephant _____

2. lady _____

3. snowman _____

4. monkey _____

5. footstep _____

6. cameo _____

7. moose _____

8. fish _____

9. glass _____

10. roof _____

11. sofa _____

12. raspberry _____

13. toy _____

14. life _____

15. bunch _____

16. box _____

17. ferry _____

18. banjo _____

19. brush _____

20. staff _____

21. dress _____

22. knife _____

23. hero _____

24. fly _____

25. tomato _____

26. dwarf _____

27. son-in-law _____

28. tooth _____

29. pushup _____

30. enemy _____

31. cattle _____

32. thief _____

33. child _____

The Plurals of Nouns

A. Using Plural Nouns

Fill in each blank in the following sentences with the plural form of the noun given in parentheses.

1. Property _____ will almost certainly be raised again this year. (tax)

2. Two _____ fought on the Plains of Abraham in Canada. (army)

3. Those steep _____ are made of limestone. (cliff)

4. The Parkers have three _____. (grandchild)

5. They were accused of being _____ to the smuggling operation. (party)

6. The furniture _____ from Denmark were being shipped in huge containers. (cargo)

7. The buds on the trees will soon develop into _____. (leaf)

8. How many _____ do you have? (sister-in-law)

9. The recipe calls for two _____ of flour. (cupful)

10. Some _____ now provide realistic habitats for their animals. (zoo)

B. Using Plural Nouns in Writing

Write the plural of each boldfaced noun. If necessary, use a dictionary to check your spelling.

    (1) Five **oboe,** three **bass,** and two **piano** had been placed in the recording studio. **(2)** Musical **score,** including several series of songs, lined all the **bookshelf.** **(3)** Two audio **technician** placed **microphone** to avoid **echo.** **(4)** The **pianist** were **brother-in-law** of the **maestro** who wrote the songs. **(5)** Folk **rhythm** and **melody** in minor **key** gave the recording **session** diversity.

1. _____

2. _____

3. _____

4. _____

5. _____

The Possessives of Nouns

Possessive nouns show ownership or belonging and are formed in one of the following ways: (1) If a noun is singular, add *'s*. (2) If a noun is plural and ends with *s*, add just an apostrophe. (3) If a noun is plural but does not end in *s*, add *'s*.

A. Forming Possessive Nouns

Write the possessive form of each of the following nouns in the appropriate blank.

1. bicyclist _____
2. students _____
3. year _____
4. tree _____
5. Dennis _____
6. bus _____
7. oxen _____
8. writers _____
9. sheep _____
10. minibike _____

11. lawyers _____
12. Los Angeles _____
13. the Jacksons _____
14. lady _____
15. group _____
16. knives _____
17. sailors _____
18. teacher _____
19. library _____
20. children _____

B. Using Possessive Nouns

Write in the blank the possessive form of the noun boldfaced in each sentence.

1. That **boy** mother taught him to make bread. _____

2. Three trophy **winners** exhibits were fuchsias. _____

3. You may buy **gentlemen** gloves at that shop. _____

4. **Galileo** discovery was controversial. _____

5. **Miss Thomas** explanation was enlightening. _____

6. The **monkeys** cages are cleaned twice a week. _____

7. This **wineglass** stem contains a spiral pattern. _____

8. Each **year** end brings nostalgic thoughts. _____

9. The **knights** lances were solid oak. _____

10. There is a **travelers** rest stop in two miles. _____

The Possessives of Nouns

Using Possessive Nouns

Fill in the blanks with the possessive form of the noun in parentheses.

1. The _____ clothes were scattered all over the room. (girls)

2. We are picking up _____ parents at the airport. (Kim Soo)

3. The _____ car is being repaired. (Andersons)

4. _____ family came to the United States from Peru. (Carlos)

5. _____ shells consist of nine narrow bands. (Armadillos)

6. Our _____ estimated population is 242 million. (nation)

7. Many _____ homes were destroyed by the flood. (families)

8. The _____ faces showed their fatigue. (men)

9. Did _____ essay win first place? (James)

10. The school _____ decision was applauded. (board)

11. Do you remember Samuel _____ pen name? (Clemens)

12. Our _____ organization is fighting a rent increase. (tenants)

13. Fire destroyed the _____ summer feeding grounds. (deer)

14. Thomas _____ ideas influenced many other thinkers. (Hobbes)

15. _____ jobs are often highly stressful (Secretaries)

16. Have you heard about the _____ vacation? (Curtises)

17. Several ducks wandered into the _____ pen. (geese)

18. The _____ scent terrified the impala. (lioness)

19. Do you think that "To Autumn" is _____ best poem? (Keats)

20. YWCA stands for Young _____ Christian Association. (Women)

21. We care for our _____ pets while they are away. (neighbors)

22. Some of _____ plots are based on his life. (Dickens)

23. A small boat followed in the _____ wake. (ferry)

24. The _____ manager quarreled with the umpire. (Yankees)

25. Mrs. _____ little daughter opened the door. (Marx)

Personal Pronouns

Personal pronouns change form to refer to the person speaking **(first person)**, the person spoken to **(second person)**, and the person or thing spoken about **(third person)**. First- and third-person pronouns also change form to show singular and plural.

	Singular	**Plural**
First Person	I, me, (my, mine)	we, us (our, ours)
Second Person	you (your, yours)	you (your, yours)
Third Person	he, she, it	they, them
	him, her, it	(their, theirs)
	(his, her, hers, its)	

A. Identifying Personal Pronouns
Underline the personal pronouns in the following sentences.

1. I will rake the leaves after school.

2. Irene says she wants to become a commercial pilot.

3. We want to help you with your work.

4. Are the gerbils yours or theirs?

5. Between you and me, I think she has a chance to make the Olympic team.

B. Understanding Personal Pronouns
On the line provided, identify each boldfaced pronoun as **first person, second person,** or **third person.** Then write **S** if the pronoun is singular and **P** if it is plural.

Example: *We* think Jason will be able to improve *his* pitching.
We—first person, P; his—third person, S.

1. Anticipating the first snowfall, Carolyn and Katy waxed *their* skis. _____

2. "Have *you* spoken to Jean about the change in plans?" *I* asked Rene. _____

_____

3. The steam from the copper kettle made a hissing sound as it escaped. _____

_____

4. Should *we* invite *them* to *your* performance, Janet? _____

_____

_____

5. *His* arguments against the proposal were as convincing as *mine.* _____

_____

Using Personal Pronouns in Writing

Rewrite the numbered sentences in the following passage, replacing each first-person pronoun with a third-person pronoun. (Remember that a verb with a third-person singular subject changes its form, usually by adding *s*.)

(1) The freshly unpacked leaves of spring made a comforting roof over my head as I walked along. . . . (2) Nothing I have described here has importance, except to me, and to those few thousands who thanks to chance also live or have lived in Shillington. . . . (3) I had expected to be told who I was, and why, and had not been entirely disappointed. (4) I was "where the people are." I was "out of harm's way." I was "by myself"—a phrase whose meaning could not be deduced by a stranger to the language, even though he knew the meanings of "by" and "myself." (5) A passing car slowed suspiciously, diluting my intense happiness.

After you have rewritten the piece, think about how the change in the point of view of the narrator, from first person to third person, affects the impact of the paragraph.

_____

_____

_____

_____

_____

_____

_____

_____

_____

_____

_____

_____

_____

_____

_____

_____

The Cases of Personal Pronouns

The **case** of a personal pronoun is the form that shows how the pronoun is being used in a sentence. Use the **nominative** case for subjects and predicate nominatives; use the **objective** case for objects of verbs (direct objects and indirect objects) and objects of prepositions. Use the **possessive** case to show ownership.

	Nominative	Objective	Possessive
Singular	I	me	my, mine
	you	you	your, yours
	he, she, it	him, her, it	his, her, hers, its
Plural	we	us	our, ours
	you	you	your, yours
	they	them	their, theirs

A. Identifying the Case of Personal Pronouns

Identify the case of each boldfaced personal pronoun in the following sentences. On the line write **N** for nominative, **O** for objective, or **P** for possessive.

1. Arthur Miller, one of America's foremost playwrights, was born in 1917, in New York; **his** father was a manufacturer and his mother a teacher. _____

2. Miller was a poor student; until his teens **he** had not read many books. _____

3. When his parents suffered financially, he helped **them** by getting a job. _____

4. For something to read on the subway, he bought a copy of Dostoyevsky's *The Brothers Karamazov;* **it** inspired him to beomce a writer. _____

5. His best-known play is *Death of a Salesman;* he won a Pulitzer Prize for **it.** _____

6. Today many writers credit Arthur Miller for inspiring **their** work. _____

B. Using the Correct Case of Personal Pronouns

Fill in the blanks in the following sentences with appropriate personal pronouns. Then, on the lines, identify the case of each pronoun you supply.

1. She urged young people to set _____ goals carefully. _____

2. As the comet passed, we clearly saw _____ tail. _____

3. Lydia, _____ could get more for _____ money at outlet stores. _____

4. Mark refinished the table after Jen showed _____ how to do it. _____

The Cases of Personal Pronouns

A. Using the Correct Case of Personal Pronouns

Underline the pronouns that are in the correct case. On the lines, write the case of each pronoun you choose: **N** for nominative, **O** for objective, or **P** for possessive.

Example: Please save seats for my friend and (I, <u>me</u>).   **O**

1. Recently my grandparents showed (I, me) a small elementary school. _____

2. "(I, Me) was once the shortest first-grader in that school," Granddad said.

   "(You, Your) grandmother was the smartest girl in the building." _____

3. "(We, Us) had a very long school day in the 1940's," Gram said. _____

4. (They, Them) told (I, me) how the country was at war during the 1940's. _____

5. The pupils brought (they, their) dimes to pay for defense stamps. _____

6. The government would give (they, them) a pink stamp for ten cents. _____

7. "As a surprise for (we, us)," Gram said, "a soldier drove up to the school one day

   in an army Jeep." _____

8. He said the Jeep was really (ours, us) because (our, we) stamps had paid for it. _____

9. "Marie," Granddad told her, "(You, Your) memory is even better than (me, mine)." _____

10. He said that it was (she, her) who had suggested a visit to the school. _____

B. Using Pronoun Cases Correctly in Writing

Write a paragraph about a memorable experience in your own past. Use the correct cases of personal pronouns in your sentences.

_____

_____

_____

_____

_____

_____

_____

_____

_____

_____

Reflexive Pronouns and Intensive Pronouns

Reflexive pronouns and **intensive pronouns** are formed by adding *-self* or *-selves* to certain personal pronouns. Reflexive pronouns reflect an action back upon the subject. They add necessary information: *Roald hurt himself.* Intensive pronouns simply emphasize a noun or pronoun: *Roald himself will write the report.* A reflexive or an intensive pronoun must be used with an antecedent.

A. Identifying Reflexive Pronouns and Intensive Pronouns

Underline the reflexive pronoun or intensive pronoun in each sentence below. In the appropriate blank, identify each pronoun as reflexive or intensive.

1. Frank could kick himself for forgetting his lines in the show. _____

2. The show itself was a comedy with some very witty lines. _____

3. During rehearsal, the performers themselves broke up in laughter. _____

4. I was so proud of myself and my crew for designing such unusual sets. _____

5. The two directors prepared themselves for a celebration. _____

6. You yourself did an excellent job with the costumes. _____

7. After the show, we threw ourselves a lavish party. _____

8. The star gave herself a hilarious review. _____

9. Did you know she wrote both the music and the lyrics herself? _____

10. I hope she gives herself credit for her great work. _____

B. Using Reflexive Pronouns and Intensive Pronouns

Complete each sentence, adding a reflexive pronoun or an intensive pronoun.

1. I _____ would like to read the review of the play.

2. The critic considers _____ an authority on this playwright.

3. We _____ are to blame for these terrible seats.

4. I promised _____ I'd check out the seats' location in advance.

5. The director has earned _____ a reputation for being creative.

6. The music _____ was especially inspiring.

7. The director, Ann Ajiro, designed the sets _____.

8. Before we ave, I will get _____ a seating plan.

9. Jon, the understudy, showed _____ to be very competent.

10. Would you say that most people in the audience enjoyed _____?

Reflexive Pronouns and Intensive Pronouns

A. Identifying Reflexive Pronouns and Intensive Pronouns

Write the reflexive or intensive pronoun that correctly completes each sentence. Identify each as **intensive** or **reflexive** in the blank at the right.

1. Mr. Green _____ enjoyed his work as a literacy volunteer. _____

2. "Helping people to help _____ is exciting," Mr. Green said. _____

3. "Ask _____ if you can spare the time to change someone's life," he continued. _____

4. We _____ decided to volunteer. _____

5. Henry _____ was most eager to start the program. _____

6. After the training session, Henry gave _____ a deserved rest. _____

7. The book _____ lay on the shelf, waiting to be read. _____

8. Once-illiterate people will soon be able to read it by _____. _____

9. "I ask _____," Mr. Green stated, "how I would feel in the nonreader's place." _____

10. "Volunteers should remind _____ never to embarrass the people they intend to help." _____

B. Using Reflexive Pronouns and Intensive Pronouns

Imagine that you have written a letter to your cousin describing the ninth-grade camping trip. You notice that what you have written is not grammatically correct or as dramatic as it could be. Rewrite each numbered sentence by using a reflexive pronoun or an intensive pronoun correctly. Make sure all your pronouns have antecedents.

> The ninth-grade class trip to a mountain camp was quite a challenge. Mrs. Critchell, our advisor, told us the trip would be a test of our physical endurance and team spirit. **(1)** Only she had ever been to this camp. **(2)** The teachers had to perform all activities. First, each of us had to climb up a 30-foot wall. **(3)** The climb was not too hard. Going down, however, was frightening. **(4)** We had to rappel down. No one could help us. **(5)** Before rappelling down, I asked why I was so scared. What exactly did I fear? Finally, I started to climb down, cheered on by my teammates. Afterwards, I felt a new sense of self-confidence.

1. _____

2. _____

3. _____

4. _____

5. _____

Orange Level, Copyright © McDougal, Littell & Company

40   Handbook 32   Using Pronouns

Demonstrative Pronouns

The pronouns *this*, *that*, *these*, and *those* are **demonstrative pronouns.** *This* and *these* point out people or things that are near in space or time. *That* and *those* point out people or things that are farther away. The words *this*, *that*, *these*, and *those* may also be used as adjectives.

A. Identifying Demonstrative Pronouns
Underline the demonstrative pronouns(s) in each sentence. Be sure not to underline these words when they are used as adjectives.

1. Isn't that Marie over there waving to us?
2. The cherry trees are those in the distance.
3. Those are very fragile trees.
4. The blossoms on those trees are pink, while the blossoms on these are white.
5. Do you prefer these or those?
6. Those were a gift to the United States from Japan.
7. That is a country I have always wanted to visit.
8. I would rather visit Southeast Asia; I think that is a fascinating region.
9. This is my reason for wanting to change that rule.
10. Are these your photographs, or are those paintings yours?

B. Choosing the Correct Demonstrative Pronoun
Underline the correct demonstrative pronoun in each sentence.

1. (These, Those) are the planes in the distance.
2. (This, That) is a better photograph than that one.
3. (This, That) is a beautiful morning.
4. (These, Those) are members of our team over there.
5. Look out on the lake! (This, That) is Allan in the blue sailboat.
6. (These, Those) are sweeter than the kiwi fruit I ate yesterday.
7. (This, That) is my home, just over the hill.
8. The oranges in this box are expensive, but (these, those) taste better.
9. (This, That) is a thundercloud on the horizon.
10. (These, Those) were the good old days.
11. (This, That) is yours over there.
12. Those are secondhand cars in the lot, but (these, those) nearby in the showroom are new.
13. (These, Those) are the soccer balls over there.
14. These berries are fresher than (these, those) I picked two days ago.
15. That is the more direct route, but (this, that) is the faster.

Demonstrative Pronouns

A. Using Demonstrative Pronouns

Rewrite each of the following sentences. Begin each sentence with a demonstrative pronoun used as the subject.

Example   The rolls aren't as fresh as the bread.
These aren't as fresh as the bread.

1. Washington, D.C., is one of the most interesting cities for sightseeing.

   _____

2. The Washington Monument, in the distance, is the tallest building.

   _____

3. The flags circling the monument are all American flags.

   _____

4. The statue of Abraham Lincoln is especially dramatic at night.

   _____

B. Using Correct Demonstrative Pronouns

Below is a postcard message you received from a friend. The wording is rather confusing because the demonstrative pronouns have been used incorrectly. On the lines below, rewrite each numbered sentence, using the correct demonstrative pronoun.

   (1) That has been such an exciting trip so far! **(2)** I have visited other Scandinavian countries before, but that is my first visit to Norway. Such variety in the scenery: mountains, fjords, lakes, waterfalls. **(3)** These are just some of nature's wonders on the West Coast. My friend Jan and I spent three days in Bergen. **(4)** This is Norway's second-largest city. In Bergen we took the funicular railway to the top of the mountain where there is a restaurant that overlooks the city and harbor. At the restaurant we sampled smoked salmon, goat cheese, and whale meat. **(5)** Do these sound awful? To tell the truth, we enjoyed them. We're heading for Oslo today. Mårn så lenge!

1. _____

2. _____

   _____

3. _____

   _____

4. _____

5. _____

Indefinite Pronouns

Pronouns that do not refer to a definite person or thing are called **indefinite pronouns.** The following indefinite pronouns are singular: *another, anybody, anyone, anything, each, either, everybody, everyone, everything, neither, nobody, no one, one, somebody,* and *someone.* The following indefinite pronouns are plural: *both, many, few,* and *several.* A few indefinite pronouns, such as *all, none,* and *some,* can be either singular or plural, depending on how they are used in sentences.

A. Identifying Indefinite Pronouns

Underline the indefinite pronouns in the following sentences. Ignore all other pronouns.

Example   <u>Several</u> of the applicants came with their parents.

1. One of the backpackers sprained his ankle.
2. The speakers were interesting, but none of them used gestures effectively.
3. Each of the firefighters had to put on an oxygen mask.
4. Few of the stores in our town are open on Sunday.
5. Carmen and Rosemary threw some of their coins into the fountain.
6. Neither of the students could stay after school.
7. Both of the riders were thrown from their saddles.
8. No one in the Pep Club had paid his or her dues yet.
9. None of the gasoline had leaked from its container.
10. Tell everyone that the bus has already arrived.

B. Recognizing Singular and Plural Pronouns

Underline the indefinite pronoun in each of the following sentences. Then write in the blank whether each pronoun is **singular** or **plural.**

1. Everyone has arrived at the station on time. _____

2. Most of my sisters were late for the reunion. _____

3. Anybody who feels like leaving may do so. _____

4. There are only a few of us left to continue the family tradition. _____

5. There is not room for all of us in the back seat of the sports car. _____

6. Somebody sent me a mysterious postcard from Spain. _____

7. Everybody is entitled to his or her own opinion. _____

8. The bargains are gone. I could not find any on the rack. _____

9. There is someone at the door; please see who is there. _____

10. Both passed the exam in economics and will graduate. _____

Orange Level, Copyright © McDougal, Littell & Company

Indefinite Pronouns

A. Choosing Indefinite Pronouns

Underline each sentence by writing an appropriate indefinite pronoun in the blank.

1. _____ who is a natural-born United States citizen, who is at least thirty-five years old, and who has lived in the United States fourteen years can run for President.

2. _____ of the Presidents previously served in Congress.

3. _____ have been governors.

4. Theodore Roosevelt and Lyndon Johnson had similar experiences in one

   respect: _____ had been Vice Presidents.

5. Until recently, _____ of the candidates for Vice President have been men.

6. _____ of the members of the Constitutional Convention feared the executive branch would become too powerful.

7. _____ feared that the President had not received enough powers.

8. _____ realized how much the presidency would change through the years.

B. Using Indefinite Pronouns

Rewrite each of the following sentences, using an indefinite pronoun as the subject. You may need to add, delete, or change some words.

Example   Do they plan to attend summer school?
Do any of them plan to attend summer school?

1. Do the contestants need identification badges?

   _____

2. Not one person thinks Willie has a chance to win.

   _____

3. Almost half of the students in school think Tino will win.

   _____

4. A girl in my physical education class is running for the first time.

   _____

5. Three of the eight competitors in the track meet are already in place.

   _____

Interrogative Pronouns

Interrogative Pronouns are used to ask questions. The interrogative pronouns are *who, whom, whose, which,* and *what.* An interrogative pronoun does not have an antecedent.

A. Using Interrogative Pronouns

Write the interrogative pronoun that correctly completes each sentence.

1. _____ was the Democratic candidate for United States senator?

2. _____ of the candidates received the most votes?

3. _____ are the hours that the polls are open?

4. _____ was the most effective television campaign?

5. _____ is the name of the President's official retreat?

B. Using Interrogative Pronouns

Each sentence below is the answer to a question. Write the question, substituting an interrogative pronoun for the boldfaced word or phrase. You may change other words in the sentence.

Example   *Elena* is the most popular girl in her class.
Who is the most popular girl in her class?

1. *Ted* met Will at the pizzeria yesterday.

_____

_____

2. *The clasp of the bracelet* broke into pieces.

_____

_____

3. *Molly* owns an antique locket.

_____

_____

4. *Those* computers sold well in November.

_____

_____

5. *Beryl's* camera was lost as the girls ran for the bus.

_____

_____

Interrogative Pronouns

A. Using Interrogative Pronouns

Each of the following sentences answers a question. On the line below each sentence, write the question, substituting an interrogative pronoun for the boldfaced word or phrase. You may change or drop other words in the sentence.

Example   *Truman* was President when World War II ended.
Who was President when World War II ended?

1. *Anthony Kennedy* was appointed to the Supreme Court in 1988.

_____

2. The role of the Senate is *confirming presidential nominees to the Court.*

_____

3. In 1986 *William Rehnquist* was appointed Chief Justice.

_____

4. Of the nine justices, *Sandra Day O'Connor* is the only woman.

_____

5. The responsibility for leading the Court is *the Chief Justice's.*

_____

B. Using Interrogative Pronouns

Imagine that in your journalism class, you are studying news and feature articles. You have learned that many news and feature articles answer these questions: *Who? To whom? Which? Whose?* and *What?* Your assignment is to write five questions based on the numbered sentences in the following article. Use the interrogative pronoun indicated on the numbered lines below to form each question.

(1) Governments of the United States and Canada are trying to regenerate flocks of ducks and other migratory birds. (2) Biologists say that the loss of habitats is the main reason for the decreasing number of birds. (3) The governments want to protect the remaining breeding grounds of the ducks, geese, and swans. (4) In the 1980's, the number of ducks fell more than the number of geese. (5) Workers in the program will try to make the remaining habitats more productive.

1. *who* _____

2. *what* _____

3. *whose* _____

4. *which* _____

5. *who* _____

Relative Pronouns

A **relative pronoun** is used to relate, or connect, an adjective clause to the word or words it modifies. An **adjective clause** is a group of words that modifies a noun or pronoun. The clause has a subject and a verb but cannot stand alone as a complete sentence. The noun or pronoun that the adjective clause modifies is the antecedent of the relative pronoun.

The pronouns used as relative pronouns are *who, whom, whose, which,* and *that;* all except *that* can be used as **interrogative pronouns**. Interrogative pronouns are used to ask questions and do not have antecedents.

A. Identifying Relative Pronouns
Underline the relative pronoun in each sentence once. Underline its antecedent twice.

1. Japan, whose lands form an archipelago, lies off the coast of Asia.

2. Honshu, the island that Tokyo is on, is the largest of the Japanese islands.

3. Tokyo, which is the capital of Japan, is one of the world's most populous cities.

4. The samurai, who were a warrior class, arose during Japan's medieval period.

5. The rapid industrial recovery that Japan experienced after World War II is a well-known phenomenon.

B. Distinguishing Relative from Interrogative Pronouns
Underline the relative or interrogative pronoun in each sentence. Then, in the blank, write **REL** if the pronoun is a relative pronoun. Write **INT** if the pronoun is an interrogative pronoun.

| **Examples** | Who is coming to dinner? | **INT** |
| | Hana, who is a pianist, will accompany us. | **REL** |

1. She is the first person who spoke to me. _____

2. What was the answer to that trivia question? _____

3. Which of your friends will make the varsity football team? _____

4. The actor whose part you took is recovering in the hospital. _____

5. The music that you played was very loud and obnoxious. _____

6. Whom did Mr. Scinta choose as co-chairperson? _____

7. I played the video of the person whom I heard play last Saturday night. _____

8. At Cape Canaveral I saw an astronaut who had flown in a space shuttle. _____

9. Who was on the telephone this morning? _____

10. The painting that won the prize is in the art gallery. _____

Relative Pronouns

Using Relative Pronouns

Rewrite each sentence, replacing one part of it with an adjective clause. The adjective clause should contain a relative pronoun that refers to the boldfaced word.

Example A *leech* is a worm; it has been used in medicine. (which)
A leech, which is a worm, has been used in medicine.

1. The *1920's* was an era of prosperity preceding the Great Depression. (which)

_____

2. *F. Scott Fitzgerald* was a gifted American novelist; he immortalized the Jazz Age. (who)

_____

3. Women's *suffrage* was won in 1920 and reflected a changing society. (which)

_____

4. *King Harold of England* is one of the people depicted in the Bayeux Tapestry; William the Conqueror defeated Harold in 1066. (whom)

_____

_____

5. The *accident* took place at the Chernobyl nuclear plant in the Soviet Union on April 25, 1986, and caused families for miles around to evacuate. (that)

_____

_____

6. *Charles Lindbergh* flew alone across the Atlantic and earned instant fame. (who)

_____

7. *Francois Duvalier* was dictator of Haiti; many people feared him. (whom)

_____

8. Charles Babbage designed a *machine*; it was a forerunner of the computer. (that)

_____

9. Dick Francis wrote the novel *Reflex*; he based it on his career as a jockey. (which)

_____

10. *Crocuses* are popular flowers; they bloom early in spring. (that)

_____

Agreement with Antecedents

Pronouns must agree with their antecedents in number, gender, and person. Use a singular pronoun to refer to a singular antecedent. Use a plural pronoun to refer to a plural antecedent. Make sure that third-person singular pronouns agree with their antecedents in gender.

> Visitors can check *their* coats at the entrance.
> Sophia Hawthorne helped *her* husband start a writing career.
> Our old silver tableware has lost *its* shine.

A. Identifying Pronouns and Their Antecedents
In each sentence underline the pronoun once and the antecedent twice.

1. The prospectors led their burros into the California valley.

2. Michelle brought her geode collection to class.

3. Vera said she enjoyed the outdoor concert.

4. Javier went snorkeling in the Bahamas by himself.

5. The chameleon can change its color to match the foliage.

6. José, are those folders yours?

7. Mr. Birdseye revolutionized the frozen-food industry when he patented a quick-freezing process.

8. At the center of the earth is its core, which has temperatures up to 9,000° F.

9. The twins taught themselves dance steps from a book with diagrams.

10. Has Carlos taken his tennis racket home?

B. Agreement with Antecedents
Underline the pronoun that correctly completes each sentence. Then underline the antecedent(s) of the pronoun.

1. Two cardinals make (its, their) home in that tree every spring.

2. Juan and Louis compared (his, their) collections of rare coins.

3. Flower lovers prize the rose for (its, their) delicate scent.

4. George Bernard Shaw didn't become a successful playwright until the publication of a collection of (its, his) plays.

5. Like other gifted child performers, Shirley Temple was known for learning (her, their) lines quickly.

6. Those directors shot (his, their) films on location in Australia.

7. Katie and Abbie are both in (her, their) first year of high school.

8. That mother seal lost (her, their) pup during the ice storm.

9. Brazilians celebrate (its, their) independence day on September 7.

10. The panther is quite beautiful; (its, their) coat is jet black.

Agreement with Antecedents

Making Pronouns and Antecedents Agree

Fill in the correct pronouns in the following sentences.

1. Mystery novels are admired for _____ clever plots and colorful

   characters.

2. Some detective fiction is also praised for _____ vivid description of

   setting.

3. Among the best-loved fictional detectives is Sherlock Holmes, who sometimes

   relied on _____ even smarter brother.

4. Miss Jane Marple, the English detective in many of Agatha Christie's novels,

   did much of _____ sleuthing in the countryside.

5. Donald J. Sobol's mysteries feature as _____ hero a remarkable

   young man named Encyclopedia Brown.

6. I love mysteries, and _____ favorite detective is Robert B. Parker's

   Spenser.

7. A mystery novelist's fans are likely to form a club based on _____

   delight in that writer's work.

8. Jane and I have a club in which _____ share _____

   copies of Agatha Christie's mysteries.

9. You can join the club if you are willing to share _____ mystery

   novels with us.

10. The Baker Street Irregulars is a famous group of Sherlock Holmes fans;

    the club takes _____ name from a fictional group of children who

    sometimes assisted Holmes.

11. The Wolfe Pack is another fan club; _____ is centered on the fictional

    detective Nero Wolfe and _____ cases.

12. Fans of the fictional detective Spenser gather at Kate's Mystery Books,

    where _____ enjoy meetings and other activities.

Indefinite Pronouns as Antecedents

When the antecedent of a pronoun is an indefinite pronoun, the two pronouns must agree in number. Some indefinite pronouns are singular, while others are plural. Still others can be either singular or plural, depending on how they are used.

Singular   *Each* of the doctors explained *his or her* specialty.
All of the manuscript was in *its* original condition.

Plural   *Many* of the bargain-hunters brought *their* own shopping bags.
All of the artifacts were in *their* original condition.

A. Identifying Indefinite Pronouns
Underline the indefinite pronoun in each sentence. Then underline the correct possessive pronoun(s) in parentheses.

1. Several of the containers in the chemistry lab were missing (its, their) labels.

2. Everyone has paid (his or her, their) part of the rental fee.

3. Many of the musicians in the band bought (his or her, their) own instruments.

4. None of the sulfur is in (its, their) flask.

5. All the gymnasts practiced (his or her, their) routines before the tournament.

6. Neither of the girls brought (her, their) swimsuit.

7. If anyone is interested, have (him or her, them) fill out an application.

8. Nobody wanted (his or her, their) lunch after seeing that film.

9. Both the stores raised (its, their) prices.

10. Neither of the scientists completed (his or her, their) experiment.

11. Everything was returned to (its, their) owner.

12. Some of the architects have already sent in (his or her, their) designs.

13. Each of the typewriters comes with (its, their) own carrying case.

14. Everyone helped (his or her, their) neighbors after the flood.

15. Most of the seasoning had lost (its, their) flavor.

B. Using Indefinite Antecedents
Read each of the following incomplete sentences. In the blank, write an appropriate indefinite pronoun as the subject. Then, on the line, write **S** if the pronoun you supply is singular or **P** if it is plural.

1. _____ of the contestants withdrew their entries.   _____

2. _____ in the room seemed to be in its proper place.   _____

3. Will _____ who can run a projector give the principal his or her name?   _____

4. _____ of the musicians tuned her own instrument.   _____

5. Has _____ here lost these proofs of his yearbook photos?   _____

Orange Level, Copyright © McDougal, Littell & Company

Handbook 32   Using Pronouns   **51**

Indefinite Pronouns as Antecedents

A. Identifying the Function of Indefinite Pronouns

Underline the indefinite pronoun in each sentence. Then decide whether the indefinite pronoun functions as the subject of the sentence or as an adjective. On the line, write **S** if it functions as a subject or **A** if it functions as an adjective.

Examples   Many visitors to the Greek islands are Americans.   A

                       Others, of course, are vacationing Europeans.   S

1. Several Greek cruise ships travel the Aegean Sea. _____

2. Everyone on board as a passenger may attend a special talk each night. _____

3. Any sites to be visited the next day are described. _____

4. Some of the guides who give the talks are trilingual. _____

5. All qualified Greek guides pass government examinations. _____

B. Using Indefinite Pronouns in Writing

Complete the following sentences, using the indefinite pronouns shown as subjects. Be sure not to use the pronouns as adjectives.

Examples   Some of the jewelry was in the tan box.

                       Some of the tourists were carrying their luggage.

1. Few _____

2. One _____

3. Both _____

4. Neither _____

5. Several _____

6. All (plural) _____

7. All (singular) _____

8. Everybody _____

9. Most (singular) _____

10. Most (plural) _____

Orange Level. Copyright © McDougal Littell & Company

52   *Handbook 32   Using Pronouns*

Vague Pronoun References

When you write or speak, be sure that each pronoun refers clearly to its antecedent. If a pronoun appears to have more than one antecedent or if there is no apparent antecedent, the pronoun reference is vague. Rewrite or rephrase such sentences.

Vague	Ben told Fred that he was sick.
Clear	Ben admitted his illness to Fred.

A. Identifying Vague Pronoun References

Underline the pronoun in each sentence. In the blank following each sentence, write the antecedent of the pronoun. If the reference is vague or ambiguous, write **vague.** If the reference is missing, write **missing.**

1. Paul called Martin after he bought the materials for the science project. _____

2. Paul and Martin worked all afternoon building their volcano. _____

3. Martin called Paul about his research. _____

4. In one film it showed how volcanic activity formed the Hawaiian Islands. _____

5. During the excavation of Vesuvius, they examined artifacts of ancient Roman life. _____

B. Revising to Eliminate Vague Pronoun References

Underline the vague pronoun in each sentence, and rewrite the sentence to correct the vague pronoun reference.

Example	In my town they have fireworks on the Fourth of July.
	My town has fireworks on the Fourth of July.

1. Mrs. Jackson asked Mrs. Castillo about her voting preferences.

_____

2. In the newspapers it says snow is coming.

_____

3. Before playing a concert, they set up their speakers.

_____

4. When the coach spoke to the referee, he was very calm.

_____

5. When you write a letter to the editor, they never answer.

_____

Vague Pronoun References

A. Correcting Vague Pronoun References

Rewrite each of the following sentences to correct the vague pronoun reference.

1. Amy took the novel *Jane Eyre* from the bag and laid it on the table.

_____

2. In this novel it shows the writing talents of Charlotte Brontë, one of the famous Brontë sisters.

_____

_____

3. In reading Emily Brontë's *Wuthering Heights,* Amy discovered her tragic view of love and the forces of nature.

_____

_____

4. They made *Wuthering Heights* into a movie starring Laurence Olivier.

_____

B. Revising Vague Pronoun References

Rewrite each numbered sentence by correcting the vague pronoun reference.

Appearing in a movie is not as exciting as you may think. **(1)** They recently hired my cousin Theresa as an extra for the filming of *Nightmare in Flight*. **(2)** Theresa expected to see glamorous stars, but it turned out to be a lot of dull waiting in an airport. **(3)** When Theresa did see the leading lady, she looked tired and cranky. **(4)** When they were finally ready, the director made the crew shoot the scene twelve times.

1. _____

_____

2. _____

_____

3. _____

_____

4. _____

_____

Choosing the Correct Pronoun (I)

When you use pronouns in compound constructions, you can tell which pronoun is correct by saying the sentence twice, trying out each part separately.

Problem	Ralph and (I, me) went to the movies.
Correct	*I* went to the movies.
Correct	Ralph and *I* went to the movies.

Because *Ralph and I* is the compound subject of the sentence above, the nominative-case pronoun, *I,* is correct.

Problem	Frank asked (she, her) and (I, me) for our votes.
Correct	Frank asked *her.* Frank asked *me.*
Correct	Frank asked *her* and *me* for our votes.

Because *her and me* is the compound direct object of the sentence above, the objective-case pronouns are correct.

Using Correct Pronouns

Underline the correct pronoun of the two given in parentheses. On the line identify its case. Write **N** for nominative or **O** for objective.

1. My mother and (I, me) want to read *Before the Mayflower* by Lerone Bennett. _____

2. User-friendly computer software has been helpful to John and (I, me). _____

3. Zack and (he, him) visited the reptile exhibit at the zoo. _____

4. Nancy and (she, her) both want to be congressional pages. _____

5. The store owner gave (he, him) and Frances part-time jobs. _____

6. Using sunscreen lotion is a necessary precaution for Laura and (I, me). _____

7. My sister and (I, me) are researching the value of certain American autographs. _____

8. With Hubert and (he, him), there are never any problems in running the pharmacy. _____

9. Without Gus and (I, me), the newspaper's editorial staff will suffer. _____

10. Gloria taught Richard and (I, me) how to waltz. _____

11. Harry and (she, her) are developing a time line of early American history. _____

12. The news brought joy to the hearts of David and (we, us). _____

13. (We, Us) learned that the first female Secretary of Transportation was Elizabeth Dole. _____

14. When we are ready to move, the Rabbs will help Britt and (I, me). _____

15. There is a special bond of friendship between you and (I, me). _____

Choosing the Correct Pronoun (I)

Revising to Eliminate Pronoun Errors

Underline any pronoun that is in the wrong case and rewrite the sentence to correct the mistake. If a sentence has no pronoun error, write **Correct**.

Example Orienteering is new to my sister and *I*.
Orienteering is new to my sister and me.

1. Carl and him are diving to locate the mooring for their boat.

_____

2. Please send invitations to my friend Cherelle and me.

_____

3. Can you and her represent us at the next Junior Achievement meeting?

_____

4. We would advise that polls be taken by you and them at two-week intervals
   during the campaign.

_____

5. Did you and he enjoy the play *Fences?*

_____

6. Those pedestrians and us witnessed the accident, called the police, and offered
   evidence.

_____

7. You and me can get aerobic exercise just by doing some fast walking every day.

_____

8. Nobody had told Yvette and she that they could have bought artistic posters
   in the federal building's bookstore.

_____

9. I probably should have given Dave and him more explicit directions to Southside
   Terminal.

_____

10. Candidates for public office always need the support of citizens like you and I.

_____

Choosing the Correct Pronoun (II)

When two or more antecedents are joined by *or* or *nor,* use a singular pronoun if each antecedent is singular; use a plural pronoun if the antecedents are plural. If one singular and one plural antecedent are joined by *or* or *nor,* the number of the pronoun is governed by the antecedent that is nearer the verb.

Singular	Neither Sam nor Bob has *his* baseball mitt.
Plural	Either the monkeys or the tigers will have *their* cages cleaned.
Plural	Neither Sara nor her friends have *their* sheet music with them.

When a pronoun is part of a comparison using *than* or *as,* use the nominative form.

She is bigger than *I.* (Think: . . . bigger than *I am.*)

A. Identifying Correct Pronouns
Underline the correct pronoun of the two given in parentheses.

1. Neither Sue nor the other finalists could conceal (her, their) nervousness.

2. He is older than (I, me) by twelve years.

3. Either Mary or Elise will perform (her, their) solo in the competition.

4. Neither Todd nor Andy has received a reply to (his, their) job applications.

5. Ms. Barton likes the novels of Charles Dickens as much as (me, I) do.

6. Neither Mr. Buckle nor the singers waited for (his, their) bus.

7. Eileen O'Toole is as lighthearted as (her, she).

8. Either Peter or his brothers brought (his, their) friends to the movie.

9. My friend Kara is a better cook than (me, I).

10. Either she or her sister will read (her, their) speech to the graduating class.

B. Using Pronouns in Comparison
Underline the correct pronoun in the following sentences.

1. I am as interested in that documentary on civil rights as (she, her).

2. They are as eager to go to the Whitney Houston concert as (we, us).

3. Mr. Boone was as brave as (her, she) during the long ordeal.

4. I was later than (her, she) for the guidance meeting.

5. My sister is taller and bolder than (I, me), but people still say I seem older.

6. The bank teller seems to be as tired as (me, I).

7. Do you really think that Marty is as qualified as (he, him)?

8. They are just as excited about the plans for a new city pool as (we, us).

9. Could Janice be more ready for this vacation than (me, I)?

10. Christopher is not more prepared for the test than (me, I) simply because he stayed up late.

Choosing the Correct Pronoun (II)

A. Using Pronouns Correctly

In the blank, write an appropriate pronoun form.

1. Neither the amaryllis nor the poinsettia had lost _____ leaves.

2. My mother is as excited as _____ about my award.

3. Neither the Itos nor their neighbors hid _____ joy when the judge pronounced them citizens of the United States.

4. Donald stayed underwater longer than _____.

5. Ask either Kirk or Allen to bring _____ camera.

6. Either Kristin or one of her sisters bought _____ art supplies.

7. You don't really need a stepladder, Mia; you are as tall as _____.

8. Neither the candidate nor her staff gave me _____ opinions.

9. Neither Maura nor Kimberly had received _____ final grades.

10. After hearing Sharon, we felt no one had ever sung better than _____.

B. Correcting Problems with Pronouns

Some students are blocking out ideas for a short dramatization about a community problem. On the lines below, rewrite and correct any sentences containing pronoun problems. If a sentence contains no errors, write **Correct**.

(1) Either a student or a teacher tells of their impression that our school is going to be closed. (2) At first, neither students nor our teacher could believe her ears. (3) The principal then learns that a high-tech firm wants the building for office space, and no one is more surprised than him. (4) The students realize they could all be sent to different schools, and no one tries harder than them to save the school.

1. _____

_____

2. _____

_____

3. _____

_____

4. _____

_____

Choosing the Correct Pronoun (III)

Do not confuse the possessive pronouns *its, your, their,* and *whose* with the contractions *it's, you're, they're,* and *who's.* **Contractions** are formed by joining two words and omitting one or more letters. An apostrophe shows where letters are left out. There are no apostrophes in possessive pronouns.

Incorrect	The dog hurt it's paw.
Correct	The dog hurt its paw.

Do not confuse *who* and *whom.* Use *who* as the subject of a sentence or clause: *Who is at the door?* Use *whom* as the direct object or the object of a preposition.

Incorrect	Who did you invite?
Correct	Whom did you invite?

Do not use *them* in place of *those. Them* is a pronoun used only as an object: *The prize went to them. Them* is never used as a subject or as any other part of speech. *Those* is a pronoun used sometimes as an adjective.

Incorrect	I don't know them people.
Correct	I don't know those people.

The pronouns *we* and *us* are often used with nouns. Use *we* if the noun is the subject of the sentence: *We bikers finished the race.* Use *us* if the noun is the object of the sentence: *They waited for us bikers to finish the race.*

Using Pronouns Correctly
Underline the correct word in each sentence.

1. (Who's, Whose) in charge of feeding the sharks?

2. May I use (your, you're) terminal to enter the data?

3. (We, Us) swimmers are ready for the meet.

4. Phil and Annie are here; (their, they're) in the kitchen.

5. (It's, Its) almost time for the late late show.

6. Do you like (them, those) hats with the feathers?

7. (Their, They're) compact discs sold several million copies.

8. The owner spoke to (we, us) tenants about the garbage collectors' strike.

9. (Who's, Whose) bracelet is that on the bottom of the pool?

10. The advertising campaign lost (it's, its) appeal after a few short weeks.

11. The interviewer questioned (we, us) applicants about our grades.

12. (Who, Whom) first inhabited North America?

13. To (who, whom) did she report the missing items?

14. These are my sneakers, and (them, those) are Sam's.

15. (Who, Whom) did the teacher call on for the answer?

Choosing the Correct Pronoun (III)

A. Using Pronouns Correctly
Underline the correct pronoun in each sentence.

1. Most of (we, us) Americans know about the signing of the Constitution.

2. If (your, you're) interested in history, study the development of the railroads.

3. The town of Milford plans to celebrate (it's, its) two hundredth anniversary.

4. (Who, Whom) received a perfect score on the biology test?

5. (Who's, Whose) coat is hanging in the closet?

6. (Your, You're) birthday gift is to be a surprise.

7. My favorite apples are (them, those) green Granny Smiths.

8. (Who, Whom) do you imitate when you do impersonations?

9. (Its, It's) been raining steadily for thirty-six hours.

10. The neighbors for (who, whom) Andy shoveled snow rewarded him with a gift.

11. (Us, We) three have been friends since the first grade.

12. In May (their, they're) going to Washington, D.C., on a class trip.

13. (Them, Those) aren't my clothes on the floor.

14. The Emerys called the fire department to rescue (they're, their) kitten from a roof.

15. Who left (them, those) rain boots under the hall stairs?

B. Correcting Problems with Pronouns
You are a member of the student council. You are preparing a poster calling for new fund-raising ideas. You notice that the message on your poster reads poorly because of problems with pronouns. On the lines below, rewrite each numbered sentence by correcting the pronoun problem(s).

> **(1)** Whose got a great plan to raise money for Central High? **(2)** Us members of the student council would like to hear you're ideas for fund-raising activities. **(3)** Anyone who thinks they have an original and creative idea should submit their proposal by Friday to the student council. **(4)** We will consider all of you're proposals.

1. _____

_____

2. _____

_____

3. _____

_____

4. _____

_____

Skills Assessment 1   Handbooks 29–32

Directions One or more of the underlined sections in the following sentences may contain errors of grammar, usage, punctuation, capitalization, or spelling. Write the letter of each incorrect section; then rewrite the item correctly. If there is no error in an item, write *E.* Write your answers on your own paper or an answer sheet, as your teacher directs.

Example   Of all the songs with <u>English lyrics: "Happy Birthday</u>
                                                    A   **B**
<u>to You"</u> is the one <u>sung</u> <u>most frequent.</u>   <u>No error</u>
                      C   **D**   **E**

Answer   A—English lyrics,   D—most frequently

1. Ice hockey <u>began</u> in Canada in the middle of the <u>1800's by</u> about 1900, it
                    A   **B**
   <u>had become</u> <u>Canada's</u> national sport.   <u>No error</u>
        C   **D**   **E**

2. <u>Between</u> <u>Andrew, Carlos, and I,</u> we <u>have won</u> thirteen <u>trophies.</u>   <u>No error</u>
       A   **B**   **C**   **D**   **E**

3. In 1921 polio paralyzed <u>Franklin D. Roosevelt's</u> <u>legs, but</u> he went on to
                                          A   **B**
   become the <u>thirty-sixth</u> <u>President of the United States.</u>   <u>No error</u>
                    C   **D**   **E**

4. According to <u>Greek mythology. The</u> <u>god</u> Apollo <u>drove</u> his fiery chariot across
                          A   **B**   **C**
   the <u>skys</u> each day to light the world.   <u>No error</u>
         D   **E**

5. The <u>people</u> in the audience showed <u>their</u> enthusiasm for the opera singer
            A   **B**
   Luciano <u>Pavarotti by cheering him</u> for more than an <u>hour and by demanding</u>
                        C   **D**
   165 curtain calls.   <u>No error</u>
                              E

6. "Hang <u>them streamers</u> <u>higher!"</u> shouted <u>Saras' brother-in-law</u> to <u>Sara and me.</u>
                A   **B**   **C**   **D**
   <u>No error</u>
        E

7. Among my <u>heroes</u> are <u>musician's</u> <u>who</u> play complicated <u>solos</u>. <u>No error</u>
        A   **B**   **C**   **D**   **E**

8. The <u>Heisman Memorial Trophy, which</u> is awarded annually to the <u>countrys'</u>
            A   **B**   **C**

   outstanding college football player, was named for a coach who revolutionized the

   <u>rules and strategies</u> of football. <u>No error</u>
      D   **E**

9. <u>These here</u> concert tickets are <u>hers;</u> I <u>haven't bought</u> <u>your's</u> yet. <u>No error</u>
       A   **B**   **C**   **D**   **E**

10. Surprisingly, <u>no one</u> <u>except</u> <u>Hugo and myself</u> knew that raw or undercooked eggs
                 A   **B**   **C**

    can contain <u>dangrous</u> bacteria. <u>No error</u>
             D   **E**

11. <u>Who's</u> birthdays do <u>we</u> Americans <u>celebrate</u> on the third Monday in <u>Febuary?</u>
      A   **B**   **C**   **D**
    <u>No error</u>
      E

12. Abraham Lincoln <u>hisself</u> <u>wrote</u> the Gettysburg <u>Address,</u> he delivered the speech
                   A   **B**   **C**

    on <u>November 19,</u> 1863. <u>No error</u>
       D   **E**

13. Anna and <u>I</u> are treating <u>ourself</u> to a Saturday afternoon at the <u>movies;</u> we hope
          A   **B**   **C**

    you can join <u>her and I.</u> <u>No error</u>
            D   **E**

14. Is it accurate to say that <u>Chris's</u> <u>sisters-in-law</u> are his <u>brothers'</u> <u>wives?</u> <u>No error</u>
                           A   **B**   **C**   **D**   **E**

15. <u>Has</u> either of the <u>girls</u> remembered to bring <u>their</u> leotard for <u>gymnastic's</u> class?
      A   **B**   **C**   **D**
    <u>No error</u>
      E

Directions Read the passage and choose the word or group of words that belongs in each numbered space. Write the letter of the correct answer on your own paper or on an answer sheet, as your teacher directs.

Example   In the early ___(1)___ commercial radio was still unknown, and amateurs tinkered with home wireless sets. However, when World War I broke ___(2)___ United States banned all amateur radio transmissions to discourage spying.

1. A. 1900s,
   B. 1900's,
   C. 1900's
   D. 1900s

2. A. out. The
   B. out the
   C. out? The
   D. out, the

Answers   1—B   2—D

"A laser beam shot out of the spaceship and split the oncoming craft in two." This is not a description of a technologically sophisticated 1990's battle in ___(16)___ it is a line taken from a story in the 1920's in a magazine called *Amazing Stories*. This periodical, the first science fiction journal, was created by Hugo Gernsback. What a remarkably creative man he ___(17)___.

Gernsback had always been fascinated by ___(18)___ this interest was reflected in his superbly illustrated magazine. ___(19)___ had to be scientifically accurate, for Gernsback ___(20)___ today's science fiction could inspire tomorrow's technology.

16. A. space
    B. space; instead,
    C. space.
    D. space, instead,

17. A. was?
    B. was!
    C. was.
    D. was;

18. A. technology. And
    B. technology and
    C. technology,
    D. technology, and

19. A. Its storys
    B. It's stories
    C. Its stories
    D. It's storys

20. A. believed, that
    B. believed, which
    C. believed. That
    D. believed that

Few people were ___(21)___ at predicting than Gernsback himself. He foretold the development of radar, microfilm, fax machines, aluminum foil, medical diagnostic machines, computer dating ___(22)___ countless other developments.

Because Gernsback carefully kept up with the work of scientists, ___(23)___ had great respect for one another. For example, he managed to meet Thomas ___(24)___ spend a memorable day in the great ___(25)___ laboratory.

21. A. better
    B. more better
    C. good
    D. more good

22. A. services,
    B. services and
    C. services, and
    D. services

23. A. him and them
    B. he and they
    C. him and they
    D. them and him

24. A. Edison, and
    B. Edison.
    C. Edison and
    D. Edison;

25. A. inventor
    B. inventors
    C. inventors'
    D. inventor's

Transitive and Intransitive Verbs

Verbs that have direct objects are called **transitive verbs.** Verbs that do not have direct objects are called **intransitive**.

The secretary *took* notes.
Sue *waited* at the art gallery.

Some action verbs may be transitive in one sentence and intransitive in another. Linking verbs are always intransitive.

Identifying Transitive and Intransitive Verbs

Underline the verb in each of the following sentences. Then, in the blank, identify the verb as **transitive** or **intransitive.** If the verb is transitive, circle the direct object.

1. The network canceled the show. _____

2. The pomegranate originated in Persia or Afghanistan. _____

3. Dogs have keen senses of hearing and smell. _____

4. The Egyptians used a uniform system of measurement. _____

5. Luckily, hard ice forms quickly over the lake. _____

6. Bees make 80,000 trips for a single pound of honey. _____

7. Of course, Hollywood attracts job seekers by the thousands. _____

8. In the fall, salmon spawn in the Sacramento River of California. _____

9. The classical music was coming from the next room. _____

10. Put mustard on the hot dog, please. _____

11. Sandra felt overwhelmed during her first computer class. _____

12. Do you have an extra ticket to the Monet exhibit? _____

13. He has always played percussion in the band. _____

14. Can you actually understand the logic in his argument? _____

15. I have never heard a live performance of Beethoven's Ninth Symphony. _____

16. The leaves look yellow and somewhat limp. _____

17. We broke the long loaf of bread in half. _____

18. Unfortunately, the glass broke into tiny fragments. _____

19. Tighten the tiny strap between the lenses of your goggles. _____

20. State Senator Inada seemed the better choice for governor. _____

Transitive and Intransitive Verbs

Using Transitive and Intransitive Verbs

In the blank, tell whether the boldfaced verb in each sentence is **transitive** or **intransitive.** Then, if the verb is transitive, write a new sentence using it as an intransitive verb. If the verb is intransitive, write a new sentence using it as a transitive verb.

> **Example**   Judy *moved* quickly. **intransitive**
> **Judy moved the chair to the window.**

1. The ice sculptures *melted* in the morning sun.

   _____

2. The string quartet *entertained* for an hour.

   _____

3. The crew *sailed* the cutter around the Cape of Good Hope.

   _____

4. Mattie and Louise *ate* most of the hors d'oeuvres.

   _____

5. We *drove* from here to Los Angeles in two days.

   _____

6. In the second part of our experiment, we *increased* the concentration of sodium chloride by fifty percent.

   _____

7. Jennifer and John *danced* brilliantly in the new production of Tchaikovsky's *Swan Lake.*

   _____

8. During the last semester our chorus *expanded* its repertoire from a few well-known songs to a wide variety of classical and popular works.

   _____

9. As a biology project, we *studied* the life cycle of the osprey.

   _____

10. In Henrik Ibsen's play *A Doll's House,* Nora's perspective on a woman's role *changes* dramatically.

    _____

Active and Passive Voice

A verb is in the **active voice** when the subject of a sentence performs the action.

Denise *prepared* her speech.

A verb is in the **passive voice** when the subject receives the action. The passive voice is made by using some form of the helping verb *be* with the past participle. The receiver of the action comes before the verb; it is the subject of the sentence.

The speech *will be prepared* by Denise.

Identifying Active and Passive Voice Verbs

Underline the complete verb in each sentence. Label the active verbs **A** and the passive verbs **P.**

1. In the 1984 Olympics, Valerie Briscoe-Hooks raced to three gold medals.

2. Conwy Castle in Wales was built by King Edward I.

3. Ninety-five percent of the land in Alaska is owned by the federal government.

4. The *Iliad* and the *Odyssey* were composed by the Greek poet Homer.

5. Usually street performers attract a great deal of attention.

6. George Gershwin wrote the piano concerto *An American in Paris.*

7. The word *poet* is derived from a Greek word meaning "to create."

8. Last year my favorite team won the World Series.

9. In her speech the candidate thanked her family and friends for their help.

10. This exhibit includes paintings by Samuel Morse, the inventor of the telegraph.

11. Toni Morrison's novels are written in a compelling and lyrical style.

12. Many foreign correspondents accompanied the diplomatic mission.

13. This photograph has been enlarged several times.

14. The actors were evidently overwhelmed by the enthusiasm of their audience.

15. John Maynard Keynes has contributed much to our understanding of economics.

16. Many of Leonardo da Vinci's works were never completed.

17. The thesis was not clearly expressed in the opening paragraph.

18. The Italian writer Italo Calvino observes life with the curiosity of a scientist.

19. The Colorado River never reaches the sea.

20. Most of the show cats were being groomed as the judges arrived.

Active and Passive Voice

A. Using Active and Passive Voice Verbs

Complete each of the following sentences by adding a verb in the voice given in parentheses.

1. Ricardo and Angela _____ several pieces of furniture for their first home. (active voice)

2. All these pots and pans _____ by my sisters at a garage sale. (passive voice)

3. Our animal clinic _____ pets physical examinations, immunization shots, booster shots, and certain other types of treatment. (active voice)

4. Laura _____ several sweaters for her trip to the White Mountains. (active voice)

5. The lasagna, the steamed vegetables, and the whole-wheat rolls _____ on the menu. (passive voice)

B. Changing Passive Voice Verbs to Active Voice Verbs

Rewrite the following sentences, changing verbs in the passive voice to active voice verbs. You may add, subtract, or change words as necessary.

Examples That small, one-story house *has been rented* by Jake's parents.
Jake's parents have rented that small, one-story house.

1. Joanne was rushed by ambulance to the nearest community hospital.

_____

_____

2. Clare was elected chairperson of the outing committee by a vote of 10 to 8.

_____

_____

3. The Pulitzer Prize-winning volume *Lord Weary's Castle* was written by poet Robert Lowell.

_____

_____

4. "Blue Winds Dancing," an essay about his Native American heritage, was written by Dr. Thomas Whitecloud.

_____

_____

5. After dark, homeless persons are offered a ride to a shelter by search-van drivers.

_____

_____

Principal Parts of Regular Verbs

A verb has four **principal parts.** These basic forms are the *present*, the *present participle,* the *past,* and the *past participle*. All verbs add *-ing* to the present to make the present participle. The **present participle** is used as a main verb with a form of the helping verb *be.*

    Regular verbs form the past tense and the past participle by adding *-d* or *-ed* to the present form. Some change their spelling when the *-d* or *-ed* is added. The **past participle** is used with a form of the helping verb *be* or *have.*

Present	Present Participle	Past	Past Participle
act	(is) acting	acted	(have) acted
cry	(is) crying	cried	(have) cried

A. Forming the Principal Parts of Verbs

Write the principal parts of the following verbs.

Present	Present Participle	Past	Past Participle
1. continue	(is) _____	_____	(have) _____
2. hope	(is) _____	_____	(have) _____
3. walk	(is) _____	_____	(have) _____
4. purchase	(is) _____	_____	(have) _____
5. wander	(is) _____	_____	(have) _____

B. Using the Principal Parts of Verbs

Complete each sentence by using the form of the verb indicated in parentheses.

1. (present of *enjoy*) Many hikers also _____ mountain climbing.

2. (past participle of *love*) Since childhood I have _____ to read in bed.

3. (present participle of *play*) He is _____ the French horn.

4. (past participle of *receive*) Joanne and Dave have _____ many wedding gifts.

5. (present of *cook*) Both Uncle Burt and Dad _____ wonderful omelets.

6. (past participle of *finish*) Have you _____ the book?

7. (past participle of *develop*) Has the photo lab _____ the film?

8. (present participle of *fry*) I am _____ the fish in vegetable oil.

9. (past of *earn*) Luis soon _____ an increase in pay.

10. (past participle of *carry*) Arlene has _____ her puppy out to the car.

Principal Parts of Regular Verbs

A. Using the Principal Parts of Verbs

Complete each sentence by using the form of the verb indicated in parentheses.

1. (present of *taste*) I can't _____ the seasoning in this meatloaf.

2. (past participle of *deny*) The Senator has _____ the charges.

3. (past of *slither*) The snake _____ under a rock.

4. (present of *reply*) Please _____ to this invitation before Friday.

5. (past of *remove*) The dentist _____ the broken tooth.

6. (past participle of *draft*) The two nations have _____ a treaty.

7. (present of *prove*) _____ your theory if you can.

8. (present of *telephone*) During the telethon, many contributors _____ the station.

9. (past participle of *rescue*) The Coast Guard has _____ the survivors.

10. (present of *exercise*) I _____ almost every day.

B. Using Regular Verbs

For the new "How-To" column in the school newspaper, you volunteer to write about how cartoons are made. You notice problems with some verbs in your first draft. On the lines below, rewrite each numbered sentence correctly by changing the past participle to the present participle. Remember to use a form of the helping verb *be* with the present participle.

      Making comic art is hard work. **(1)** Cartoonists have always looked for fresh ideas. They want to be funny but thought-provoking, too. For a comic strip, the cartoonist begins by drawing the action of the story in several boxes. **(2)** At this point, she or he has used a pencil. In this first draft, the figures and the dialogue are drawn in. The next step is to draw in the details of the background and make the pencil lines firmer. **(3)** The cartoonist has approached a crucial stage. The artist inks in the pencil lines with a pen or a brush dipped in India ink. Then the comic strip is ready for the newspaper editor. Next morning, you open the newspaper. **(4)** On the comics page, your favorite comic strip has waited for you.

1. _____

2. _____

3. _____

4. _____

    _____

Principal Parts of Irregular Verbs (I)

Irregular verbs do not add *-d* or *-ed* to form the past tense and past participle. Three groups of irregular verbs are shown below.

Group 1 The present, the past, and the past participle have the same form.

Present	Present Participle	Past	Past Participle
burst	(is) bursting	burst	(have) burst
cost	(is) costing	cost	(have) cost
let	(is) letting	let	(have) let
put	(is) putting	put	(have) put
set	(is) setting	set	(have) set

Group 2 The past and the past participle have the same form.

Present	Present Participle	Past	Past Participle
bring	(is) bringing	brought	(have) brought
lead	(is) leading	led	(have) led
lose	(is) losing	lost	(have) lost
sit	(is) sitting	sat	(have) sat
teach	(is) teaching	taught	(have) taught

Group 3 Add *-n* or *-en* to the past to form the past participle.

Present	Present Participle	Past	Past Participle
break	(is) breaking	broke	(have) broken
choose	(is) choosing	chose	(have) chosen
freeze	(is) freezing	froze	(have) frozen
speak	(is) speaking	spoke	(have) spoken
wear	(is) wearing	wore	(have) worn

Using Correct Forms of Irregular Verbs

Complete each sentence by adding the appropriate form of the verb given in parentheses.

1. Laney finally _____ the lens cover back on her camera. (put)

2. Mr. Dufour has _____ French for many years. (teach)

3. Marco Polo _____ the Europeans many innovative ideas from China. (bring)

4. Our kitten just _____ a fragile vase on the windowsill. (break)

5. The projection TV would have _____ more than we could afford. (cost)

6. Ted was startled yesterday when André _____ into the room. (burst)

7. Last year our float _____ the New Year's Day parade. (lead)

8. Empress Josephine, wife of Napoleon, _____ gowns with an empire waistline. (wear)

9. The house plants near the window have _____. (freeze)

10. On February 4, 1991, Congressman Joseph P. Kennedy _____ at the John F. Kennedy Library. (speak)

Principal Parts of Irregular Verbs (I)

A. Using the Correct Forms of Irregular Verbs

Write the present participle, the past, or the past participle of each verb in parentheses.

> **Example** The explorers have (lose) their way. **lost**

1. Who has (lead) the discussion at previous meetings? _____

2. The audience (burst) out laughing during the opening scene. _____

3. Jennifer's volleyball team (lose) the championship game. _____

4. Steve was (sit) in his favorite chair, reading *The Mayor of Casterbridge*. _____

5. Some young men in Boston (wear) hats with felt antlers in the summer of 1979. _____

6. My cousin is (choose) a pet at the animal shelter today. _____

7. I have (set) two extra places for dinner tonight. _____

8. What has that documentary (teach) you about Stonehenge? _____

9. Ellen has just (break) her sunglasses again. _____

10. Last year my friends (bring) a comedy album to my birthday party. _____

B. Using the Correct Forms of Irregular Verbs

Underline the correct verb form of the two in parentheses. Write whether the part of the verb is the **present participle,** the **past,** or the **past participle.**

> **Example** My sister has (setted, *set*) the table. **past participle**

1. They have (brought, brung) me a reward. _____

2. The Senator has (spoke, spoken) to the committee about budget limitations. _____

3. Has Wilma (wore, worn) her new ski boots yet? _____

4. So far this season the first baseman has (hit, hitted) six home runs. _____

5. Ms. Compton (teached, taught) us algebra. _____

6. Have you (losed, lost) your house keys again? _____

7. Disloyalty has (cost, costed) him a valued friend. _____

8. We were (sat, sitting) in the shade. _____

9. Polly (set, setted) high career goals. _____

10. I am (taught, teaching) my friend to play tennis. _____

Principal Parts of Irregular Verbs (II)

Group 4 The verbs in this group change their final vowels. The vowel changes from *i* in the present to *a* in the past and *u* in the past participle.

Present	Present Participle	Past	Past Participle
begin	(is) beginning	began	(have) begun
drink	(is) drinking	drank	(have) drunk
ring	(is) ringing	rang	(have) rung
shrink	(is) shrinking	shrank	(have) shrunk
sing	(is) singing	sang	(have) sung
sink	(is) sinking	sank	(have) sunk
swim	(is) swimming	swam	(have) swum

Identifying Correct Forms of Irregular Verbs

Underline the correct form of the verb.

1. Troy (drank, drunk) five glasses of cider after the softball game.
2. Vanessa has (swum, swam) across the lake to the cottage.
3. Felice and I (sung, sang) in the choir last year.
4. The phone has not (rung, rang) at all for days.
5. We (began, begun) the yearbook meeting without you.
6. Jody has (sang, sung) in school musicals for the past two years.
7. The rugby shirt (shrank, shrunk) when it was washed.
8. We have not yet (began, begun) to fight.
9. The fire alarm (rang, rung) during homeroom.
10. The wedding music had already (began, begun) when the bride arrived.
11. A Japanese freighter (sank, sunk) during the hurricane.
12. Kurt has usually (drank, drunk) only water with meals.
13. The *Monitor* had (sank, sunk) to the ocean floor off Cape Hatteras.
14. A piranha (swum, swam) alone in the huge tank.
15. Alicia's sweater had (shrank, shrunk) in the dryer.
16. Who wrote the book *I Never (Sang, Sung) for My Father*?
17. Has the bell for assembly already (ring, rung)?
18. Have you ever (drank, drunk) coconut milk?
19. James has never (sang, sung) all the verses of the national anthem.
20. Has any continent actually (sank, sunk) beneath the sea?
21. What kind of juice are you (drank, drinking)?
22. I think that boat is (sank, sinking).
23. The child (shrank, shrunk) back in fear as the dog growled.
24. My friends have (swam, swum) out to the island.
25. Why are those bells (ringing, rang) so loud?

Principal Parts of Irregular Verbs (II)

A. Using the Correct Forms of Irregular Verbs

Underline the correct verb of the two in parentheses. In the blank, identify this part of the verb as the **present participle,** the **past,** or the **past participle.**

1. She has not (sang, sung) professionally in years. _____

2. Ralph is (drink, drinking) freshly made limeade. _____

3. Two concerned-looking neighbors (rung, rang) our doorbell. _____

4. Have they (begun, began) negotiating for peace yet? _____

5. The tenor (sang, sung) the aria with great expression. _____

6. Julie has always (drank, drunk) a glass of milk at breakfast. _____

7. My feet were (sinking, sanking) into the spongy turf. _____

8. Janet has never (swam, swum) in salt water before. _____

9. The wool blanket (shrank, shrunk) because we washed it in hot water. _____

10. The *Andrea Doria* (sank, sunk) to the bottom of the Atlantic Ocean. _____

B. Correcting Errors in Irregular Verbs

Most of the following sentences have an error in the verb forms. Underline the incorrect verbs and write the correct form in the blank. If a sentence has no error, write **Correct.**

1. The school choir sung *The Battle Hymn of the Republic*. _____

2. My friends and I begun the jigsaw puzzle this morning. _____

3. Have you ever swum in the Pacific Ocean? _____

4. The people shrunk away from the boa constrictor exhibit. _____

5. Who rung the Liberty Bell before it cracked? _____

6. We have sung together for years. _____

7. Unknowingly, Tristan and Isolde drunk the love potion. _____

8. Our canoe sunk while we were crossing Lake Seneca. _____

9. No one has even began to solve that problem. _____

10. The heavy gold ring apparently had sank below the sand. _____

Principal Parts of Irregular Verbs (III)

Group 5 For these verbs, the past participle is formed from the present tense, often by adding *-n* or *-en*.

Present	Present Participle	Past	Past Participle
come	(is) coming	came	(have) come
do	(is) doing	did	(have) done
drive	(is) driving	drove	(have) driven
eat	(is) eating	ate	(have) eaten
fall	(is) falling	fell	(have) fallen
give	(is) giving	gave	(have) given
go	(is) going	went	(have) gone
grow	(is) growing	grew	(have) grown
know	(is) knowing	knew	(have) known
ride	(is) riding	rode	(have) ridden
rise	(is) rising	rose	(have) risen
run	(is) running	ran	(have) run
see	(is) seeing	saw	(have) seen
take	(is) taking	took	(have) taken
throw	(is) throwing	threw	(have) thrown
write	(is) writing	wrote	(have) written

Identifying the Correct Forms of Irregular Verbs

Underline the correct form of each verb.

1. I (seen, saw) your newspaper article and am (given, giving) your suggestion some thought.

2. Pete (fell, fallen) from his bike near the beginning of the race, but no one (done, did) anything to help him.

3. Jenny had already (threw, thrown) the receipt away.

4. Our neighbors have (went, gone) on a trip to the Black Hills of South Dakota.

5. Have you (seen, saw) the exhibit of Eskimo art?

6. My brother (wrote, written) me that he has (grown, grew) two inches this summer.

7. I (knew, known) right away that he must have (ate, eaten) the entire turkey himself.

8. The bikeathon participants (rode, rid) their bikes in the specially marked bike lanes.

9. Donna has (took, taken) courses in business, math, and accounting.

10. Who (did, done) the illustrations for the yearbook?

11. Bill Rodgers has (ran, run) in many marathons.

12. Has the mail (came, come) yet?

13. Tammy and Pam have (knowed, known) each other for ten years.

14. Ms. Jackson has (written, wrote) me a recommendation for the part-time job.

15. The temperature (rised, rose) ten degrees in the last two hours and nearly (driven, drove) me indoors.

Principal Parts of Irregular Verbs (III)

A. Recognizing Errors in Irregular Verbs

Underline the incorrect verbs in the following sentences. Write the correct form of the verb in the blank. If there is no error, write **Correct.**

1. They have saw the film classic *Citizen Kane* four times. _____

2. Has Mr. Marshall gave you that amethyst ring? _____

3. Martha may not have knew that you were on the team. _____

4. Fred seen his older brother Henry only once last year. _____

5. Has the lacrosse goalie threw the ball to midfield? _____

6. The equestrian champion has rode in the horse show before. _____

7. Has Lisa really grown those tomato plants from seeds? _____

8. Sergeant Combs knowed who was on leave. _____

9. They come to see the Egyptian exhibit last summer. _____

10. Have they wrote their senator on this matter? _____

B. Using Irregular Verbs

You are given an assignment to write about Sherlock Holmes. In rereading your paragraph, you realize you have used some verbs incorrectly. On the lines below, rewrite each numbered sentence, correcting the verb.

"Elementary, my dear Watson." Is there anyone who does not recognize that familiar phrase? **(1)** Sherlock Holmes has brung fame to his author, Sir Arthur Conan Doyle. **(2)** Holmes's cases begun as newspaper stories in the 1880's. When the author tried to end the series, the public was outraged. Sherlock Holmes was too popular to die!

(3) Conan Doyle writed about Sherlock Holmes in fifty-six short stories and four novels. Holmes, who was based on an actual Scottish physician, had a sharp eye for detail and an amazing knowledge of science. **(4)** In fact, Holmes could have teached science. His deductive skills have never been surpassed by any other fictional detective.

1. _____

_____

2. _____

3. _____

_____

4. _____

Verb Tense

Changes in verb form are called **tenses.** Every verb has six tenses: the **present tense** (she *studies*), the **past tense** (she *studied*), the **future** (she *will study*), the **present perfect** (she *has studied*), the **past perfect** (she *had studied*), and the **future perfect** (she *will have studied*).

A. Recognizing Verb Tenses

Underline the verb in each sentence. In the blank, write the tense of each verb.

1. From the airplane window, they saw the sunset. _____

2. When will Teresa begin her new after-school job? _____

3. Kira had designed a perfect logo for the school newspaper. _____

4. Woodchucks hibernate during the winter months. _____

5. The firefighters have extinguished the trash-can fire. _____

6. By Monday, Barry will have been a club member for two years. _____

7. Marcie has taken three years of Spanish. _____

8. Mr. Eliot will answer your questions after the lecture. _____

9. The paramedics had saved Harry's life. _____

10. We were not at home during the storm. _____

B. Using Verb Tenses

Complete each sentence by writing the form of the verb indicated in parentheses.

1. (past of *seem*) The music _____ to be coming from the next floor.

2. (past perfect of *move*) The Olneys _____ from Alaska last year.

3. (present of *score*) Rodney _____ most of our goals.

4. (future perfect of *sell*) We hope we _____ our house by next summer.

5. (future of *go*) I _____ surfing at the north beach.

6. (present of *cook*) Mom always _____ our dinner at night.

7. (past perfect of *be*) Sandy _____ the best tennis player.

8. (past of *take*) The calf-roping contestant _____ a big chance.

9. (future of *help*) Detective work _____ in this case.

10. (present perfect of *have*) My brother _____ a good time at camp.

Verb Tense

Form B

A. Identifying Verb Tenses

Underline the verb in each sentence. Then write the tense of each verb on the line.

1. In May we will have owned our house for five years. __________
2. The Fair Labor Standards Act of 1938 set the minimum wage at twenty-five cents per hour. __________
3. I like the combination of textures in this painting. __________
4. By the end of the week, the hikers will need more supplies. __________
5. We have won two free tickets to the boat show. __________
6. For a long time our neighbors had wanted a larger house. __________
7. Many modern poets have written about their personal lives. __________
8. When will Congress finish its debate on acid rain? __________
9. We had always had fun at our cousin's summer cottage. __________
10. In *Paradise Lost* Milton extended the epic tradition of Homer and Virgil. __________

B. Using Verb Tenses

Write a sentence containing each of the following verbs. Use the verb tense indicated in parentheses.

1. *travel* (future) ____

   ____

2. *learn* (present perfect) ____________________________________

   ____

3. *change* (past) ____

   ____

4. *found* (future perfect) _____________________________________

   ____

5. *hope* (past perfect) ______________________________________

   ____

6. *write* (present) ____

   ____

Progressive Verb Forms

Each of the simple and perfect tenses has a **progressive form** that shows continuing action. The progressive form is made by using a form of the helping verb *be* with the present participle.

Present Progressive	Margaret is hurrying.
Past Progressive	Margaret was hurrying.
Future Progressive	Margaret will be hurrying.
Present Perfect Progressive	Margaret has been hurrying.
Past Perfect Progressive	Margaret had been hurrying.
Future Perfect Progressive	Margaret will have been hurrying.

Identifying Progressive Verb Forms

Underline the entire verb in each of the sentences below. On the line identify the form as **present progressive, past progressive, future progressive, present perfect progressive, past perfect progressive,** or **future perfect progressive.**

1. My history teacher will be visiting Italy next summer. _____

2. He is telling us about the destruction of Pompeii. _____

3. The ancient city of Pompeii had been sitting on volcanic rock. _____

4. Mount Vesuvius, the volcano, had been rumbling ominously. _____

5. Suddenly, Mount Vesuvius was erupting. _____

6. Poisonous gas and fumes were filling the air. _____

7. Those people left in their homes were dying from the hot ashes. _____

8. Many people had been fleeing with their families and possessions. _____

9. After the eruption of the volcano, some citizens were looking for valuable

   objects under the ashes. _____

10. Archaeologists have been uncovering and restoring Pompeii for over two

    hundred years. _____

11. At first they had been removing artifacts from the site. _____

12. Then they were losing track of many treasures. _____

13. Archaeologists are now keeping the items in their original settings. _____

14. These items will have been lying intact for nearly two thousand years. _____

15. Historians have been learning much from the ruins. _____

Progressive Verb Forms

A. Using Progressive Verb Forms

Complete each sentence by using the form of the verb indicated in parentheses.

1. The backhoe _____ a load of dirt.
   (present progressive of *lift*)

2. I _____ the lecture at the observatory.
   (present perfect progressive of *attend*)

3. This month, she _____ with us two years.
   (future perfect progressive of *work*)

4. We _____ just last weekend.
   (past progressive of *ski*)

5. We _____ a cottage in the mountains this summer.
   (future progressive of *rent*)

6. Josh _____ Olympic stamps and medallions.
   (past perfect progressive of *collect*)

7. You _____ too hasty with your decision.
   (present progressive of *be*)

8. George _____ for two hours.
   (future perfect progressive of *jog*)

9. Isabel _____ a savings account at the Citizens' Bank.
   (past progressive of *open*)

10. During the winter, Toni _____ ice-skating lessons.
    (future progressive of *give*)

B. Using Progressive Verb Forms

Below are notes for an article on the city of tomorrow. Write a paragraph based on the notes. Change at least three of the verbs to the future progressive form.

> people live in a controlled climate . . . fans enjoy favorite sports out-of-doors all year long . . . robots cooking food and cleaning homes . . . most people shop by television . . . decline of physical illnesses . . . people living in safer but very controlled environments

_____

_____

_____

_____

_____

_____

Orange Level, Copyright © McDougal, Littell & Company

84 *Handbook 33 Using Verbs*

Avoiding Shifts in Tense

When two actions occur at the same time, use the same tense for both.

> Kay *danced* and I *sang.* Coretta *played* the guitar.

Avoid unnecessary shifts in tense between sentences or within paragraphs.

A. Identifying Shifts in Tense

Underline the verbs in each of the sentences below. If the tenses of the verbs agree, write **A** in the blank. If there is a shift in tense, write **S** in the blank.

> **Example**   Alberto <u>was laughing</u> while Pat <u>tells</u> a funny story.   **S**

1. The class was studying *Julius Caesar*. Everyone was reading a part.   _____

2. Chico is enjoying the part of Marc Antony, but Cal had complained about his role as Brutus.   _____

3. Cal coaxes Chico. Finally, Chico will exchange roles with Cal.   _____

4. Now, Cal is playing the heroic Antony, and Chico is acting the part of Brutus.   _____

5. The school principal came to a rehearsal. She likes Cal as Antony, but she raves about the part of Brutus.   _____

B. Correcting Shifts in Tense

Rewrite each of the following sentences, changing the tense of the boldfaced verb to correct the shift in tenses.

> **Example**   Debra took woodworking and ***makes*** toys for her sister.
> **Debra took woodworking and made toys for her sister.**

1. Charlie likes tennis and ***practiced*** his backhand stroke for many hours.

_____

2. Marita will draw the still life, and I ***am painting*** a self-portrait.

_____

3. We will play charades now, and we ***are having*** a snack later.

_____ _____

4. Matt ***had been*** late as usual, but Eva was prompt.

_____

5. We won the first-place trophy, and Joy ***will win*** an honorary medal.

_____

Avoiding Shifts in Tense

A. Avoiding Shifts in Tense

You are writing an article on cave paintings. As you read your first draft, you notice that four of your sentences have unnecessary shifts in tense. On the lines below, rewrite each of those numbered sentences so that verb tenses are consistent.

> **(1)** Today, artists will admire cave paintings and have marveled at their beauty. A discovery made in 1940 was met with great interest. Young boys discovered paintings on the upper walls of a cave depicting bison and hunters. **(2)** When these paintings were first found, they had been called fakes. **(3)** Today, scientists have instruments that tested the age of objects such as paintings. It is now agreed that the Stone Age paintings are genuine and are over 20,000 years old. **(4)** Experts believe that the ancient artists probably perched on ledges as they paint.

1. _____

   _____

2. _____

3. _____

   _____

4. _____

   _____

B. Avoiding Shifts in Tense in Writing

Imagine that you have found an old coin. You believe it is valuable, but a coin dealer tells you it is a fake. Write a paragraph telling how you feel. Use at least four sentences that contain two verbs, both of which use the same tense. Draft your paragraph on a separate sheet of paper, and write the final version on the lines below. Underline the verbs that agree in tense.

_____

_____

_____

_____

_____

_____

_____

_____

Using the Right Verb (I)

The following verbs are often confused.

Bring refers to movement toward the speaker. *(bring, brought, brought)*
Take refers to movement away from the speaker. *(take, took, taken)*

Learn means "to gain knowledge or skill." *(learn, learned, learned)*
Teach means "to help someone learn." *(teach, taught, taught)*

Let means "to allow or to permit." *(let let, let)*
Leave means "to go away from." *(leave, left, left)*

Choosing the Correct Verb

Underline the correct verb in each of the following sentences.

1. Danielle (learned, taught) her sister how to French-braid her hair.

2. Please (leave, let) me help you carry those groceries.

3. When you go to the library, please (bring, take) these books with you.

4. Yesterday the class (taught, learned) how to use the library computer.

5. The waiter (brought, took) us menus and glasses of water.

6. Mrs. Noe, the math teacher, tried to (learn, teach) me the algebraic formula.

7. When you go to the gymnasium for practice, (bring, take) your sneakers.

8. Will the guards (let, leave) us into the building early?

9. (Learn, Teach) a child to look both ways before crossing a street.

10. Who (lets, leaves) the house without locking the door?

11. Gram's cat always (took, brought) her any mouse he caught.

12. Surely we can (learn, teach) some Spanish by listening to tapes.

13. The coach told us to (bring, take) our equipment home today.

14. Joan and Kerry are (leaving, letting) their hair grow.

15. Has anyone (left, let) the dog in yet?

16. Mom just (brought, took) the car downtown for its inspection.

17. Those two women are (teaching, learning) the younger campers to float.

18. Our exchange students (took, brought) us gifts from their homelands.

19. Frances, (bring, take) an umbrella as you leave for school.

20. My parents are (letting, leaving) my brother cook several meals each week.

21. I can (teach, learn) basic hand sewing to anyone willing to try it.

22. Judy (brought, took) a zippered, soft-sided suitcase when she left for Maine.

23. Please (take, bring) me fruit salad and whole-wheat rolls from the buffet.

24. Hasn't anyone ever (learned, taught) those students to cheer for a guest team?

25. Just (leave, let) me rest a few minutes and I'll feel fine.

Using the Right Verb (I)

A. Correcting Troublesome Verbs

Study the boldfaced verb in each of the following sentences. If the verb is not correct, write the proper form on the line. If there is no error, write **Correct.**

1. Hasn't experience *taught* us a great deal? _____

2. Will you *take* these suits to the cleaners across the street? _____

3. Clara *learned* me how to tie-dye a shirt. _____

4. Did Marcella *teach* you how to pronounce some French words? _____

5. Please *leave* me finish this private telephone conversation. _____

6. The school bus *left* Jeffrey behind this afternoon. _____

7. Robyn is *bringing* her sister to our meeting today. _____

8. During his nightmare Jack kept shouting, "*Leave* me go!" _____

9. Al picked up his sisters at my house and then *brought* them to the mall. _____

10. During clear weather, we *left* the lawn chairs out all night. _____

B. Correcting Troublesome Verbs

Your family is moving, and you decide to make a list of the last-minute things you have to do. After writing the list, you notice that you have confused the use of certain verbs. Rewrite each sentence, using the correct verb. One or more sentences may already be correct.

1. Take the *Wild Nature* magazines that are setting on the sofa back to the library.
2. Bring the masks that I made for the Chinese play to Jenny and Alex Po.
3. Learn Jeffrey to use the school's public address system.
4. Leave Consuelo Paz have my collection of baseball cards.

1. _____

_____

2. _____

_____

3. _____

4. _____

Using the Right Verb (II)

The following verbs are often confused.

> **Lie** means "to rest in a flat position" or "to be in a certain place." It does not take a direct object. *(lie, lay, lain)*
> **Lay** means "to place." It takes a direct object. *(lay, laid, laid)*
>
> **Rise** means "to go upward." It does not take a direct object. *(rise, rose, risen)*
> **Raise** means "to lift" or "to make something go up." It does take a direct object. *(raise, raised, raised)*
>
> **Sit** means "to occupy a seat." It does not take a direct object. *(sit, sat, sat)*
> **Set** means "to place." It usually takes a direct object. *(set, set, set)*

Choosing the Correct Verb

Underline the correct verb in each of the following sentences.

1. Descending toward City Hall, the helicopter (set, sat) a huge box on the roof.

2. Several obstacles (lay, laid) in the path of the athlete's success.

3. On which chair will you (sit, set) at the table?

4. The hesitant member of the audience (raised, rose) his hand.

5. The unemployment figures have (raised, risen) again this month.

6. The sun in Whittier's poem "Snowbound" sank from sight before it (sat, set).

7. The hens had been (laying, lying) their eggs somewhere outside the barn.

8. My ice skates have (lain, laid) in the hall closet all winter.

9. I (lay, laid) my book bag on the table only moments ago.

10. The curtain (rose, raised) and the show began.

11. The evergreen's branches could not (raise, rise) under the weighty snow.

12. John (sat, set) down and started to complain.

13. There at last was our missing pet, (laying, lying) asleep in the sun.

14. As we walked toward the parade ground, the flag was (risen, raised).

15. Why exactly does yeast make bread dough (raise, rise)?

16. Long before the sun had (raised, risen), we started on our journey.

17. Yes, there was a book titled *Don't (Rise, Raise) the Bridge, Boys; Lower the River.*

18. Do you think we have (set, sat) our goals too low?

19. Tremont Street (lays, lies) near one of Boston's three major hills.

20. We had (set, sat) under the tree for hours, talking about the future.

21. When the band members finished playing, they (lay, laid) down their instruments.

22. The speaker (rose, raised) some important issues.

23. "Still (sets, sits) the schoolhouse by the road," wrote James Whitcomb Riley.

24. What state (lies, lays) across the river from Cincinnati?

25. A tired student (set, sat) in the library, staring into space.

Using the Right Verb (II)

A. Correcting Troublesome Verbs

Study the boldfaced verb in each of the following sentences. If the verb is not correct, write the proper form on the line. If the verb is correct, write **Correct.**

1. A python *laid* in the tall grass.

2. The mail carrier often *sits* packages inside the screen door.

3. A postal worker *laid* the package on the counter.

4. Last summer we *set* on the porch after dinner.

5. The croquet wickets had *lain* outdoors all winter and were rusted.

6. *Rising* your spirits through laughter benefits your health.

7. *Set* right where you are until the picture has been taken.

8. Don't *lay* down if you feel faint; sit with your head between your knees.

9. At a signal from the conductor, the tenor *rised* from his seat.

10. Someone left his or her helmet *sitting* on the shelf.

B. Correcting Troublesome Verbs

Five of the following sentences contain incorrectly used verbs. Rewrite those five sentences correctly on the lines below.

(1) Sally first tried to lay in a hammock at camp during free times one day. (2) She had taken a magazine outdoors and set on the grass to relax. (3) She rose from that position at once, though; the ground was still wet with dew. (4) Then she noticed an old net hammock strung between two trees.

(5) Setting her magazine on the hammock, Sally scrambled in and laid down. (6) The sides of the hammock instantly rose, closing over her like a bag. (7) The startled girl cautiously rose her head and pushed outward and down with her palms. (8) Then she began carefully climbing over the side. (9) The aging rope at one end of the hammock suddenly gave way. (10) "I seem to be back where I started!" Sally muttered, rising herself from the ground.

Nouns and Pronouns as Adjectives

Nouns may sometimes function as adjectives in sentences: *leather* purse.

Possessive nouns always function as adjectives. They show possession by adding -'s or -s' to the singular form of the noun: *girl's, girls'*.

The following kinds of pronouns may also function as adjectives: possessive pronouns *(my, your, his, her, its, our their)*; indefinite pronouns *(some, any, many, few, several)*; demonstrative pronouns *(this, that, these, those)*; and interrogative pronouns *(what, which, whose)*.

A. Identifying Nouns and Pronouns Used as Adjectives

In the following sentences, underline once the nouns and pronouns used as adjectives. Underline twice the words that are being modified.

1. Medieval churches had thick stone walls to support their heavy vaults.

2. Whose oil paintings did we see in the gallery?

3. Some newspapers offer internships to students interested in journalism.

4. The new office building downtown is impressive.

5. There is a sculpture exhibit opening at the art museum next week.

6. The car door was badly damaged in the accident, but no one was hurt.

7. These two books are interesting. Which one do you prefer?

8. She walked into the house, put her bags on the kitchen table, and went upstairs.

9. Which television program was about domestic cats and their earliest ancestors?

10. Some of the mirrors have metal frames, while others have none at all.

B. Using Nouns and Pronouns as Adjectives

Write an adjective in the blank that fits the category given in parentheses and that also makes sense in the sentence. Be sure to capitalize the first word in the sentence.

Example (interrogative pronoun) child was injured? **Which**

1. Katy has spent a lot of time preparing (possessive pronoun) report. _____

2. (indefinite pronoun) people attended this year's Rose Bowl. _____

3. If you plan to go hiking this weekend, you should bring a (noun) sweater. _____

4. Where are (possessive noun) binoculars? _____

5. We'll need some (noun) towels to clean up this mess. _____

6. (demonstrative pronoun) women are outstanding musicians. _____

7. We saw (indefinite pronoun) stars leaving the Academy Awards ceremony. _____

8. I think I saw (possessive noun) brother at the game last week. _____

9. (interrogative pronoun) position do you play on the soccer team? _____

10. Lauren worked in a (noun) shop all last summer. _____

Nouns and Pronouns as Adjectives

A. Using Pronouns as Adjectives
Fill in the blanks with appropriate pronouns used as adjectives.

(1) In 1921, a jury in Massachusetts handed down _____

historic guilty verdict in the Sacco–Vanzetti murder case. (2) People throughout

the country, however, believed that the two men were innocent. (3) What was the

real issue in _____ case? (4) Sacco and Vanzetti were

Italian immigrants who were charged with killing two men during a robbery, but

_____ people believed they were really being tried for

political beliefs. (5) Sacco and Vanzetti were professed anarchists (anarchists are

against any form of government), and the jury made _____

decision of guilty even though the trial evidence was very weak.

B. Using Nouns and Pronouns in Writing
Think of the things you do in school and after school. Do you play on a team? What
kind of team? Chess team? Basketball team? Track team? Listed below are some
words that are frequently modified by nouns. Write a sentence for each word, using
one or more nouns to modify it. You may use pronouns as well as nouns.

1. test _____

_____

2. project _____

_____

3. club _____

_____

4. textbook _____

_____

5. report _____

_____

Using the Correct Modifier

To decide whether to use an adjective or an adverb in a sentence, determine what kind of word in the sentence is being modified. If the modified word is a noun or pronoun, use an adjective. If the modified word is an action verb, adjective, or adverb, use an adverb. Remember that predicate adjectives are used after linking verbs.

A. Using the Correct Modifier
Underline the correct word in each of the following sentences.

1. The blue jay clung (tenacious, tenaciously) to the branch throughout the storm.

2. The sun rose (real, really) early this morning.

3. Clara exercises (vigorous, vigorously) for thirty minutes every day.

4. Auto racing can be an (awful, awfully) dangerous sport.

5. The witness's story sounded (suspicious, suspiciously) to me.

6. It seems (obvious, obviously) that Kim has been studying more.

7. Joellen looked (hilariously, hilarious) in her clown makeup.

8. The rain poured down (steady, steadily) all day.

9. Larry felt (bad, badly) about leaving his brother home alone.

10. The toddler looked (wistful, wistfully) at the toys on the shelf.

B. Using the Correct Modifier
Underline once the correct word in parentheses in each sentence. Then underline twice the word it modifies.

> **Example** The nurse <u>spoke</u> (pleasant, <u>pleasantly</u>) to us.

1. Marian Anderson sang (beautiful, beautifully).

2. Tanya is a (thoughtful, thoughtfully) person.

3. Transmission fluid dripped (steady, steadily) from beneath the car.

4. The elevator stopped (sudden, suddenly) between floors.

5. This machine produces copies (quick, quickly).

6. The vault opened (easy, easily), but there was nothing inside.

7. Paul's description of the suspect was (accurate, accurately).

8. Most people think quinine water tastes (bitter, bitterly).

9. Ice cream feels (soothing, soothingly) to a person with a sore throat.

10. The defendant paced the floor (nervous, nervously).

11. Marge reclined (lazy, lazily) on the beach towel.

12. The laboratory technician checked the sample (careful, carefully).

13. Dinner smells (wonderful, wonderfully) tonight.

14. Nancy laughed (loud, loudly) throughout the movie.

15. You seem (terrible, terribly) upset about the election.

Using the Correct Modifier

A. Identifying Adjectives and Adverbs

Label each boldfaced word **ADJ** for adjective or **ADV** for adverb. Then underline the word modified by the boldfaced word. Finally, in the blank, write the part of speech of the word modified by the adjective or adverb.

ADJ
Example   Egrets have *silky* <u>plumes</u>.   **N**

1. Warm yourself *well* before going out into the cold.   _____

2. A huge grizzly bear emerged from the *shadowy* forest.   _____

3. She was *extremely* happy about the results of her experiment. _____

4. The bell rang *so* loudly that I nearly jumped out of my seat.   _____

5. Cats are *naturally* curious creatures.   _____

6. We were pleased that our play was *favorably* reviewed.   _____

7. An odyssey is another name for a *long* journey.   _____

8. Oranges grow *wonderfully* in a hot climate.   _____

9. We found a shaggy stray dog; it seemed *hungry.*   _____

10. Have you *ever* run in a marathon?   _____

B. Using Adjectives and Adverbs Correctly

Write sentences in which you use correctly the adjectives and adverbs given. Try to use verbs other than forms of *be*. Use action verbs or linking verbs such as *feel, seem, appear, become, taste, smell,* and *look.*

1. beautiful _____

2. beautifully _____

3. careful _____

4. carefully _____

5. gentle _____

6. gently _____

7. honest _____

8. honestly _____

9. thankful _____

10. thankfully _____

Using Modifiers in Comparisons

A modifier in the **comparative degree** compares two persons, places, things, ideas, or actions. A modifier in the **superlative degree** compares three or more. Most modifiers form the comparative by adding -er and the superlative by adding -est. Modifiers of three syllables or more and modifiers that sound clumsy with -er and -est use more and most. Some modifiers are irregular in their comparisons: good, better, best; bad, worse, worst; and little, less, least.

A. Identifying Comparative and Superlative Modifiers

In the blank, label the italicized modifier **C** for comparative or **S** for superlative.

1. The **most picturesque** town I have ever seen is in Vermont. _____

2. The bus ride was the **longest** I've ever taken. _____

3. Robert thinks he can run **faster** than I can. _____

4. Ethiopia has some of the **most magnificent** scenery in the world. _____

5. Small, sporty cars sell **better** than large, luxury models. _____

6. Mitsuko practices her violin **more diligently** than her sister Hideko does. _____

7. Sonya is the **quietest** person I know. _____

8. Gretchen threw the javelin the **farthest** in the mock-Olympic competition. _____

9. The route Aunt Shana takes to the beach seems **more direct** than Mom's. _____

10. The film was **worse** than we expected, so we left. _____

B. Using Modifiers in Comparisons

Study the boldfaced modifier in each of the following sentences. If the comparison is correct, write **Correct** on the line. If the comparison is incorrect, rewrite it correctly.

1. Who in our class is **more likely** to succeed? _____

2. Charmaine dances **more gracefully** than I do. _____

3. Who worked **hardest,** Roy or Jerome? _____

4. Of the three techniques, Molly enjoys using watercolors **more.** _____

5. The lake water is **muddier** than it was ten years ago. _____

6. Which of your daughters is **oldest,** Francine or Jennifer? _____

7. Which is **biggest,** Canada or the Soviet Union? _____

8. This book was **the least helpful** of the two. _____

9. Of all the flutists, Suzanne was the **better.** _____

10. This painting is **the more beautiful** of the three. _____

Using Modifiers in Comparisons

A. Using Adjectives and Adverbs in Comparisons

Underline the comparatives and superlatives in the following sentences. If the comparative or superlative is correct, write **Correct** in the blank. If it is incorrect, rewrite it correctly.

1. Janice dived the most gracefully of all the swimmers. _____

2. Karen is the tallest of the twins. _____

3. That was the worse meal I've ever eaten. _____

4. This new drill can dig more deeply than the old one. _____

5. The sequoia is more tall than any other tree. _____

6. William was more happy than Sara. _____

7. Rhode Island is the smallest state. _____

8. Of the three friends, Rita likes traveling more. _____

9. My Frisbee sailed the farther of the three. _____

10. Charles makes pasta best than anyone else. _____

B. Using Comparisons in Writing

Write sentences comparing the following items by using the comparative or superlative form of the word given in parentheses.

> **Example**　　one group of oranges compared with another group
> of oranges (juicy)
> **These oranges are juicier than those oranges.**

1. one movie compared with two others (funny)

_____

2. one piano player compared with another (good)

_____

3. one book compared with two others (interesting)

_____

4. how one person drives compared with how another person drives (slowly)

_____

5. one sister compared with the other (old)

_____

Using Correct Comparisons

Do not use double comparisons. These occur when *-er* or *-est* is used with *more* or *most*.

Incorrect	sunny, more sunnier, most sunniest
Correct	sunny, sunnier, sunniest

Avoid illogical comparisons. Illogical comparisons do not make sense because words are missing.

Unclear	Tim talks with Jane more than Richie.
Clear	Tim talks with Jane more than Richie does.

A. Identifying Double Comparisons and Illogical Comparisons

The following sentences contain errors in comparisons. In the blank, write **DC** if the error is a double comparison and **IC** if the error is an illogical comparison.

1. Last winter was one of the most coldest winters I remember. _____

2. The lake she saw in Canada was prettier than any lake she'd seen. _____

3. That book I read last week was more interesting than any book. _____

4. I like ice skating better than my sister. _____

5. That word processor was more easier to use than this one is. _____

B. Correcting Double Comparisons and Illogical Comparisons

The following sentences may contain comparison errors. If you find a comparison error, write the sentence correctly on the line below it. If the sentence has no comparison error, write **Correct.**

1. In this day and age, we have many more labor-saving machines than earlier generations.

   _____

2. Today, people can sew more faster with a sewing machine than by hand.

   _____

3. Typewriters enable us to write more quickly than our ancestors could.

   _____

4. Computers can perform many tasks more faster than people can.

   _____

5. A microwave oven now cooks faster than any oven used at home.

   _____

Using Correct Comparisons

A. Finding Comparison Errors

Rewrite the following sentences, correcting all comparison errors.

1. The day we took the training wheels off my sister Kristen's bike was one of the most happiest days in her life.

_____

_____

2. The old bike with the missing fender was more rickety, but she loved that battered heap.

_____

_____

3. When I saw her trying to balance, I thought she looked cuter than any child I'd seen.

_____

_____

4. The first turn Kristen tried was most difficult than any turn she'd tried.

_____

_____

5. That photo of her is more funnier than the photo of you in your clown costume.

_____

_____

B. Using Correct Comparisons in Writing

Imagine that you are making a decision about joining a school club. Write a paragraph about some of the comparisons you made before making your selection. Draft your paragraph on a separate sheet of paper, and then write the final version on the lines below.

_____

_____

_____

_____

_____

Problems with Modifiers (I)

Here are some guidelines for you to follow to avoid using modifiers incorrectly.

1. Do not use double negatives (two negative words used together).
2. Do not use negative words after negative contractions (couldn't, hardly).

A. Identifying the Correct Modifier
Underline the correct word in parentheses in each of the following sentences.

1. Beth never wrote to (any, none) of us this summer.

2. Since he didn't hear (any, no) bell, Jeff kept on working.

3. Ed wasn't (never, ever) on a farm before.

4. Jorge doesn't want (any, no) onions in his omelet.

5. Sam (can, can't) barely breathe when he has an asthma attack.

6. There (are, aren't) no safety checks required for mopeds.

7. Nothing (could, couldn't) stop the rising flood waters.

8. Lisa (has, hasn't) asked no one for references yet.

9. Eileen (had, hadn't) scarcely begun working when Doris arrived.

10. Please don't serve me (any, none) of the pickled herring.

11. Mandy hasn't (never, ever) taken the subway at night.

12. When she heard my plan, Sabrina (could, couldn't) hardly stop laughing.

13. Ms. Nicolette hasn't told (anybody, nobody) about her promotion.

14. We haven't heard (anything, nothing) from Ron in nearly a month.

15. Phil said he didn't have (any, no) homework tonight.

B. Identifying Errors with Modifiers
Underline all of the problems with modifiers that you find in the sentences below. Then rewrite the incorrect word or words on the line.

1. We couldn't hardly see the road because of the dense fog. _____

2. I can't never hear the teacher when I sit in the back of the room. _____

3. You're not supposed to eat nothing between meals. _____

4. We couldn't scarcely believe the good news. _____

5. You shouldn't never mix ammonia and bleach. _____

6. Didn't nobody give you the math assignment? _____

7. Suki says she doesn't want none of her older sister's clothes. _____

8. Stan hasn't told me nothing about his new job at the pizza parlor. _____

9. Please don't give the baby no more of the salty crackers. _____

10. Harry just didn't want nobody to know he was injured. _____

Problems with Modifiers (I)

A. Correcting Problems with Modifiers

Rewrite each sentence below that contains an error in the use of modifiers. If a sentence does not contain any errors, write **Correct.**

1. I don't hardly know what to do about this broken television set.

_____

2. Joshua could barely control his temper when Sue told him he couldn't come along.

_____

_____

3. That teacher never gives no homework for weekends or vacations.

_____

4. I don't know anyone who has seen that movie.

_____

5. Since she's always lived in the Midwest, Melinda hasn't never seen the ocean.

_____

_____

B. Using the Correct Modifier in Writing

Rewrite the paragraph below, correcting all errors in the use of modifiers.

Last summer my family went on a camping trip in the mountains. We had camping equipment, but we didn't have no room to carry extra food or supplies. I hadn't never been fishing before, but there was no choice—we had to fish to eat. I couldn't hardly believe it when I caught a huge trout!

_____

_____

_____

_____

_____

_____

_____

Problems with Modifiers (II)

Here are some further guidelines to follow to avoid using modifiers incorrectly.

1. Never use the word *them* as an adjective. Use *those* instead.
2. Do not use the expressions *this here* and *that there*.
3. Use *this* and *that* to modify the singular nouns *kind* and *sort*. Use *these* and *those* to modify the plural nouns *kinds* and *sorts*.
4. The word *good* is always an adjective modifying a noun or a pronoun. *Well* is usually an adverb, but it can also be used as a predicate adjective meaning *in good health*.

A. Identifying the Correct Modifier

Underline the correct word in parentheses in each of the following sentences.

1. The plans for the new auditorium sounded (good, well).

2. Our agency specializes in (this, these) kinds of cases.

3. (That, That there) scaffold was built by the construction crew.

4. Nancy never makes (that, those) kinds of mistakes.

5. Neil gave Amy (this, this here) hand-crafted bracelet.

6. Cheddar cheese tastes (good, well) on rye bread.

7. Annie uses (that, those) kind of tennis racket.

8. The band from Ireland plays (good, well).

9. Use (these, these here) disks for that computer.

10. Mr. Otsuka carved (them, those) intricate figures from sandalwood.

11. That leather belt goes (good, well) with those jeans.

12. (That, Those) sort of book usually has no index.

13. May I borrow (this, this here) ski magazine?

14. Bob went home because he didn't feel (good, well); he probably has the flu.

15. Polish the car (good, well) so it will really shine.

B. Using the Correct Modifier

Underline all of the problems with modifiers that you find in the sentences below.

1. This here story about travels in space is really intriguing.

2. That sorts of magazines are popular.

3. These kind of car uses less gas but is not as reliable.

4. I went to the doctor today for a check-up because I wasn't feeling good.

5. Hot salsa sauce tastes really well with tacos.

6. These kind of electrical adapter works best.

7. Hand me that there wrench so I can loosen this bolt.

8. This sorts of records are valuable.

9. My grandfather doesn't hear too good anymore.

10. Children don't look well in adult clothing.

Problems with Modifiers (II)

A. Correcting Problems with Modifiers

Rewrite each sentence below that contains errors in the use of modifiers. If a sentence contains no errors, write **Correct**.

1. I can't sleep because that there baby is crying so much.

_____

2. The letter I got from my pen pal in India made me feel good.

_____

3. Those kind of movies are too childish; I prefer mysteries.

_____

4. Do you like them miniature televisions?

_____

5. Teresa reads very well for her age, but she needs to work on her writing.

_____

B. Using the Correct Modifier in Writing

Below is a descriptive paragraph showing incorrect use of modifiers. Rewrite the paragraph, correcting the errors in the use of modifiers.

> Last month I attended that there benefit concert for the homeless. I couldn't see the stage very well, but I did hear some bands that played really good. I think these kind of fundraisers are very important. Supporting them makes me feel well.

_____

_____

_____

_____

_____

_____

_____

Directions One or more of the underlined sections in the following sentences may contain errors of grammar, usage, capitalization, punctuation, or spelling. Write the letter of each incorrect section; then rewrite the item correctly. If there is no error in an item, write **E.** Write your answers on your own paper or on an answer sheet, as your teacher directs.

Example   Of all the <u>caracters</u> in <u>Shakespeare's</u> plays, Hamlet, with over
                                A   **B**

                11,000 <u>words.</u> has <u>the most longest</u> part. <u>No error</u>
                   C   **D**   **E**

Answer   A—characters   D—the longest

1. Of all <u>American</u> horse races, the Kentucky Derby, <u>which</u> <u>is held</u> each year at
      A   **B**   **C**

   Churchill Downs racetrack, is the <u>more famous.</u> <u>No error</u>
                           D   **E**

2. Most of the chorus members <u>did sing</u> <u>better than</u> Lorenzo, but no one <u>sang</u>
                            A   **B**   **C**

   <u>more louder.</u> <u>No error</u>
    D   **E**

3. To increase profits, the store owner <u>rose</u> prices on her <u>best-selling</u> <u>jewelry,</u> but
                                A   **B**   **C**

   within a month sales <u>had fell</u> by ten percent. <u>No error</u>
                 D   **E**

4. <u>Them</u> seats <u>were</u> <u>further</u> from the stage than I <u>thought.</u> <u>No error</u>
  A   **B**   **C**   **D**   **E**

5. Although the leftover fish <u>didn't</u> look or smell <u>bad.</u> Rachel <u>chose</u> to eat just the
                       A   **B**   **C**

   <u>vegetables.</u> <u>No error</u>
     D   **E**

6. Since <u>your</u> last poem <u>was wrote</u> in free verse, why <u>don't</u> you try a poem with
      A   **B**   **C**

   <u>ryhme</u> and meter this time? <u>No error</u>
    D   **E**

7. George is <u>real familiar</u> with the book *A Tale of Two Cities* by Charles <u>Dickens, but</u>
          A   **B**

    he <u>never seen</u> <u>any</u> of the movie versions. <u>No error</u>
        C   **D**   **E**

8. Although <u>its fur</u> was <u>long, thick and warm,</u> the dog shivered when <u>Dad</u> <u>took</u> the
           A   **B**   **C** **D**

    animal outside in the snow. <u>No error</u>
                          E

9. Because construction and traffic <u>have made</u> cities <u>noisyer,</u> some officials
                                 A   **B**

    <u>are considering</u> imposing stricter limits on <u>these kind</u> of noise. <u>No error</u>
      C   **D**   **E**

10. When she starts coughing and <u>don't</u> feel <u>good,</u> Bonnie, the <u>youngest</u> of my three
                                 A   **B**   **C**

    sisters, <u>goes</u> straight to bed. <u>No error</u>
         D   **E**

11. Michael Dukakis <u>losted</u> the 1988 presidential election to George Bush, <u>who</u> <u>ran</u> a
                   A   **B** **C**

    <u>more aggressive</u> campaign. <u>No error</u>
         D   **E**

12. In the period prior to and during <u>World War II,</u> Eleanor Roosevelt <u>served</u> as a
                              A   **B**

    powerful role model for American <u>women</u> and <u>provides</u> leadership in causes such
                                     C   **D**

    as civil rights. <u>No error</u>
                E

13. Credit card users hardly <u>never</u> stop to <u>calculate</u> how much <u>their</u> use of credit
                       A   **B**   **C**

    <u>has cost</u> them over the years. <u>No error</u>
      D   **E**

14. Michael Jordan <u>has scored</u> more points in a game than <u>any</u> professional
                 A   **B**

    basketball <u>player;</u> he <u>wins</u> the NBA Most Valuable Player award in 1988. <u>No error</u>
           C   **D**   **E**

15. If you drive <u>careful,</u> <u>your</u> car insurance rates will be <u>more lower</u> than <u>those</u> of
            A   **B**   **C**   **D**

    drivers who have many accidents. <u>No error</u>
                          E

Directions Read the passage and choose the word or group of words that belongs in each numbered space. Write the letter of the correct answer on your own paper or on an answer sheet, as your teacher directs.

Example Samuel admires the writer Jane Austen even more than __(1)__ In fact, yesterday he __(2)__ his own copy of her novel *Pride and Prejudice*.

1. A. his friend Leon.
    B. his friend Leon does.
    C. his friend Leon's.
    D. his friend, Leon.

2. A. buyed
    B. is buying
    C. buys
    D. bought

Answers 1—B   2—D

The planet Neptune is much __(16)__ than the earth, but it __(17)__ so far away that it cannot be seen with the naked eye. In fact, Neptune is more distant from the earth than __(18)__ planet, with one exception. Only the planet Pluto is __(19)__ away.

16. A. more larger
     B. more large
     C. large
     D. larger

17. A. lay
     B. lies
     C. lays
     D. laid

18. A. any
     B. no other
     C. any other
     D. no

19. A. farther
     B. further
     C. more far
     D. more farther

The existence of Neptune was determined by mathematics before the planet __(20)__ by telescope. Astronomers, noticing that the planet Uranus did not move predictably, __(21)__ that it was being influenced by the force of an unknown planet. The skies were so vast, however, that even trained observers __(22)__ expect to find such a __(23)__ knowing just where to look.

Then, in 1843, a __(24)__ astronomer and mathematician named Adams calculated the likely position of the unknown planet. Three years later, a telescope was trained on the area, and Neptune was __(25)__ to where Adams had predicted.

20. A. is observing
     B. is observed
     C. has been observed
     D. was observed

21. A. felt certainly
     B. feel certain
     C. felt certain
     D. feeled certain

22. A. could hardly
     B. couldn't hardly
     C. can hardly
     D. can't hardly

23. A. planet. Without
     B. planet; without
     C. planet without
     D. planet without not

24. A. young, English
     B. young English
     C. young English,
     D. young, English,

25. A. discovering close
     B. discovered closely
     C. being discovered, close
     D. discovered close

Prepositional Phrases as Modifiers

A prepositional phrase modifies some other word or group of words in a sentence.

An **adjective phrase** is a prepositional phrase that modifies a noun or a pronoun and tells *which one* or *what kind*.

> The desk *in the corner* is mine.
> Some *of the players* were injured.
> The cause *of the power failure* is still unknown.

An **adverb phrase** is a prepositional phrase that modifies a verb, an adjective, or an adverb and tells *how, when, where,* or *to what extent* something occurred.

> We worked *without a break.*
> *In June* Mrs. Lee will retire.
> The small cat's eyes gleamed green *as bottle-glass.*

Identifying Prepositional Phrases

Underline each prepositional phrase once, and underline the word or words modified by the prepositional phrase twice. Then, in the blank, write **ADJ** or **ADV** to tell what kind of phrase it is.

Example   Bob <u>has run</u> <u>in the marathon</u> before.   **ADV**

1. Can you pronounce the name of the country?   _____

2. The soprano sang one of my favorite songs.   _____

3. In the cave an ancient artist had painted a hunting scene.   _____

4. Along the path we planted pink, lavender, and yellow tulips.   _____

5. Can you see well in the dark?   _____

6. The baseball flew over the fence.   _____

7. Can you see that mountain in the distance?   _____

8. The band played a song from 1954.   _____

9. One of the hockey players was seriously injured.   _____

10. The fans shouted with enthusiasm.   _____

11. The tour bus will leave at 8:30 A.M.   _____

12. Reuben is planning a career in scientific research.   _____

13. The basketball dropped through the net.   _____

14. During the storm all traffic stopped.   _____

15. Do you know the girl in the red dress?   _____

Prepositional Phrases as Modifiers

A. Identifying Prepositional Phrases

Underline the prepositional phrase in each sentence once, and underline the word it modifies twice. Then, in the blank, write **ADJ** or **ADV** to identify what kind of prepositional phrase it is.

> **Example** The <u>desk</u> <u>in the corner</u> is mine. **ADJ**

1. The line stretched around the theater.

2. Two of the silver rings are quite valuable.

3. The album contains a medley of hit tunes.

4. Mechanics worked on the plane.

5. The toboggan raced down the hill.

6. I don't understand the end of the joke.

7. We all jumped into the pool.

8. The voice on the tape sounds familiar.

9. Turn at the next corner.

10. Mr. Powell trimmed the roots of the plant.

B. Using Prepositional Phrases as Modifiers

Revise the sentences below, adding prepositional phrases to modify the words in boldface type.

> **Example** Thomas *studied.*
> Thomas **studied in the library with Brendan.**

1. The *woman* gave me the information.

_____

2. I *looked,* but I couldn't find the photo album.

_____

3. I am now reading a *book.*

_____

4. Mother and Dad *went.*

_____

5. Dolores was *happy.*

_____

Conjunctions

A **conjunction** connects words or groups of words. A **coordinating conjunction,** such as *and, but, for, nor, or, so,* or *yet,* connects ideas of equal importance. **Correlative conjunctions,** such as *both . . . and, either . . . or, neither . . . nor, not only . . . but also, whether . . . or,* also join similar words or groups of words. Correlative conjunctions are always used in pairs.

A. Identifying Conjunctions

Underline the conjunctions in the following sentences.

> **Example**   Tennyson <u>and</u> Kipling were English poets.

1. Smog is a combination of smoke and fog.

2. A body in orbit around a planet may be called a satellite or a moon.

3. Neither José nor I can be at practice on Wednesday.

4. The teacher asked whether dew falls or simply condenses.

5. Leonard Cohen is both a poet and a musician.

6. Sandy will either shellac or varnish the table.

7. Leave the room quietly but quickly.

8. I cannot eat cucumbers, for I am allergic to them.

9. A guardrail was installed there, yet accidents still occur.

10. Millie is not only a photographer but also a graphic artist.

B. Identifying Coordinating and Correlative Conjunctions

Underline the conjunctions in the following sentences. Then label each conjunction **CD** for coordinating conjunction or **CR** for correlative conjunction.

> **Example**   Snowflakes <u>and</u> frost are two forms of frozen water.
>   **CD**

1. Painting is not only fun but also relaxation.

2. The wind quieted somewhat, but it still whistled occasionally.

3. My knees ache in both rainy and humid weather.

4. Play aggressively but fairly.

5. You can join the swim team or the gymnastics team.

6. Becoming both a lawyer and a doctor is Mary's goal.

7. It does not matter whether you print or use cursive.

8. Neither carrots nor lettuce has many calories.

9. Whether we go or stay is entirely up to you.

10. Graphite and iron ore are on display in the science lab.

Orange Level, Copyright © McDougal, Littell & Company

Handbook 35   Using Prepositions, Conjunctions, Interjections   **115**

Conjunctions

A. Identifying Coordinating and Correlative Conjunctions

Within each sentence, fill in the blank(s) with a conjunction or with a pair of conjunctions. Then, in the blank at the right, tell what kind of conjunction each one is. Use **CD** for coordinating conjunction and **CR** for correlative conjunction.

1. Gregory enjoys basketball _____ track.

2. Debby planned the meeting _____ could not attend.

3. _____ soup _____ salad comes with the meal.

4. May I borrow your book for a week _____ two?

5. _____ lettuce _____ mushrooms are low in calories.

B. Using Coordinating and Correlative Conjunctions

You have written a report about Helen Keller. Your first draft seems choppy and repetitive. On the lines below, rewrite each numbered sentence by combining it with the next one or two sentences, using coordinating and correlative conjunctions.

> **(1)** At the age of nineteen months, Helen Keller was stricken with an illness that left her deaf. It also left her blind. **(2)** Her mother did not know what to do with such a child. Neither did her father. When Helen was seven, her parents hired Anne Sullivan to teach her. Miss Sullivan used her fingers to spell words on Helen's palm. **(3)** Within two years Helen had learned the manual alphabet. She had also learned braille. **(4)** Helen learned to speak. She was hard to understand. She required an interpreter. As an adult she gave many speeches and wrote many books. **(5)** Helen Keller deserves much credit for what she accomplished. So does Anne Sullivan.

1. _____

   _____

2. _____

   _____

3. _____

   _____

4. _____

   _____

5. _____

   _____

Subordinating Conjunctions

A **subordinating conjunction** begins a clause that cannot stand alone and joins it to a clause that can stand alone. Commonly used subordinating conjunctions are *after, although, as, as if, as though, because, before, if, in order that, provided, since, so that, than, till, unless, until, when, where, whereas,* and *while.*

> *Although* I prefer short stories, I also like novels.
> She bought five tickets to the movie *so that* everyone could go.

A **conjunctive adverb** can join two sentences. It is usually preceded by a semicolon and followed by a comma. Conjunctive adverbs clarify the relationship between two parts of a sentence. Commonly used conjunctive adverbs are *accordingly, also, besides, consequently, finally, furthermore, hence, however, instead, nevertheless, otherwise, similarly, still, therefore,* and *thus.*

> The plot was unbelievable; *thus,* I didn't enjoy the play.

Identifying Subordinating Conjunctions and Conjunctive Adverbs

In each sentence underline the subordinating conjunction or the conjunctive adverb. Then write above the underlined word(s) **SC** for subordinating conjunction or **CA** for conjunctive adverb.

1. In 1929, when Frank Laubach went to the island of Mindanao, in the Philippines, he found many illiterate people; furthermore, no one had ever written down the Maranaw language.

2. Written language requires letters or symbols so that people can "see" the sounds.

3. Laubach listened carefully to the language; thus, he could write symbols for all of its sounds.

4. He used only one letter or combination of letters for each sound; consequently, learning to read was easy.

5. English would be much easier to read if it were written that way!

6. After Frank Laubach taught the people in the Philippines to read, he went to other countries to start literacy campaigns.

7. He made learning easy in order that more people could learn to read.

8. He used pictures with letters so that people could associate shapes with sounds.

9. In English, the word *snake* begins with an *s;* therefore, he might make the letter *s* into a picture of a snake.

10. Because he made reading easy, many people around the world learned to read.

Subordinating Conjunctions

A. Writing to Show Relationships
Rewrite each pair of sentences as one sentence by using the word in parentheses.

1. I didn't realize that the lake was so close to the city. I would have gone there

   sooner. (otherwise) _____

   _____

2. It is raining. The game will probably be canceled. (since) _____

   _____

3. Prague, the capital of Czechoslovakia, has many churches. It has been called the

   "City of a Hundred Spires." (because) _____

   _____

4. The car overheated. Jan did not arrive in time for the first act. (therefore) _____

   _____

B. Using Subordinating Conjunctions and Conjunctive Adverbs
In the paragraph below, combine each numbered sentence with the sentence following it. Use a subordinating conjunction or a conjunctive adverb. Above each subordinating conjunction, write **SC**; above each conjunctive adverb, write **CA**.

> **(1)** Many adults in the United States do not know how to read. These people live under a terrible handicap. **(2)** They have difficulty finding jobs. They are unable to fill out application forms. **(3)** Illiterate adults cannot read directions. They have to ask people for help. However, there is a way in which they can overcome their handicap. **(4)** They can go to adult education centers. Adults can learn to read.

1. _____

   _____

2. _____

   _____

3. _____

   _____

4. _____

   _____

Gerunds

A **gerund** is a verb form ending in *-ing* that functions as a noun. For example, a gerund may be used as a subject, a direct object, an object of a preposition, or a predicate nominative.

> *Jogging* is very popular. (subject)
> Jackie enjoys *fishing*. (direct object)
> He is tired of *practicing*. (object of preposition)
> One major industry is *mining*. (predicate nominative)

A **gerund phrase,** consisting of a gerund plus its modifiers and complements, also functions as a noun.

> *Throwing curve balls frequently* can damage the arm of a young athlete.

A. Identifying Gerunds and Gerund Phrases
Underline each gerund phrase once and the gerund twice in the following sentences.

1. A catamaran is a sailboat made by joining two separate hulls together.

2. Leaving a little space between the two hulls is important.

3. Natives of the South Seas invented the "cat" by tying two logs together.

4. Using paddles and sometimes sails made the "cats" go very fast.

5. People who ride on a "cat" enjoy skimming over the water and attracting the attention of curious onlookers.

B. Identifying Gerunds and Gerund Phrases
Underline each gerund or gerund phrase. In the blank, write how it is used: **S** for subject, **DO** for direct object, **OP** for object of a preposition, or **PN** for predicate nominative.

1. Elephants have excellent hearing. _____

2. Washing cars is the club's main fund-raising project. _____

3. Speaking another language is an advantage. _____

4. Thank you for listening to my explanation. _____

5. An act that requires considerable self-discipline is dieting. _____

6. Flying a glider must be difficult. _____

7. Kristin is good at solving math problems. _____

8. One good form of exercise is roller skating. _____

9. Stella enjoys planning parties. _____

10. Leonardo da Vinci invented shoes for walking on water. _____

Gerunds

A. Identifying Gerund Phrases

Underline each gerund phrase. In the blank, write how it is used: **S** for subject, **DO** for direct object, **OP** for object of a preposition, or **PN** for predicate nominative.

1. Eating tomatoes hardly seems a daring act today, but tomatoes were once thought to be poisonous. _____

2. Thomas Jefferson could count growing the first tomato in the United States among his accomplishments. _____

3. Many people, by believing the tomato poisonous, slowed its acceptance until 1990. _____

4. People eventually started appreciating the tomato's value. _____

5. Although the tomato is no longer considered harmful, some doubt still exists about classifying it as a fruit or a vegetable. _____

6. Labeling it as a fruit seemed logical to botanists. _____

7. Yet using a fruit in soups and sauces seemed strange to nonscientists. _____

8. The controversy continued, and eventually the Supreme Court was faced with deciding the issue. _____

9. The Court's problem was satisfying both the scientific and nonscientific worlds. _____

10. In 1893 the Court solved the problem by classifying the tomato as a vegetable for purposes of trade only. _____

B. Gerund Phrases

Rewrite each sentence. Change the boldfaced words to a gerund phrase, and underline the phrase. You may need to alter some other words in the sentence.

1. A popular modern sport is *to parachute from the sky.*

   _____

2. To *jump from an airplane* and *to fall freely at a speed in excess of one*

   hundred miles per hour are the sky-diver's challenges.

   _____

   _____

3. The pilot's task is *to fly the plane at a height of up to fifteen thousand feet.*

   _____

4. *To perform stunts with other divers during the free-fall* is part of the sport.

   _____

Participles

A **participle** is a verb form that functions as an adjective. The **past participle** of a regular verb is formed by adding *-d* or *-ed* to the present tense: *call, called.* The past participle of an irregular verb is formed differently and must be learned separately: *sing, sung; catch,* caught. The **present participle** is formed by adding *-ing* to the present tense: *fish, fishing.* A **participial phrase** consists of a participle plus its modifiers and complements. The entire participial phrase functions as an adjective.

Identifying Participles and Participial Phrases

Underline the participle or participial phrase in each sentence. In the blank at the right, write the word that the participle or participial phrase modifies.

1. A baked potato comes with every meal. _____

2. Soothed by the music, Linda fell asleep in her chair. _____

3. Packing hurriedly, Tara forgot her shoes. _____

4. In the film about endangered species, I saw a bald eagle. _____

5. The doctor examining me ordered a blood test. _____

6. We frantically bailed water from the flooded basement. _____

7. David Letterman bowed to the laughing audience. _____

8. Tired after the long practice, the athlete stumbled. _____

9. The tailor repaired my ripped jacket in just a few minutes. _____

10. A motorist driving recklessly through the town was arrested. _____

11. Andrea, leaping several feet into the air, caught the softball. _____

12. The book told about actual buried treasure in the United States. _____

13. The Founding Fathers of our nation showed great foresight. _____

14. Using combinations of leaves and stems, the Japanese make artful arrangements. _____

15. Increased demand for food is the result of the growth in the world's population. _____

16. That extravagantly bound book is a first edition of *Treasure Island.* _____

17. James finally found his gym socks, stuffed into a corner of his dresser drawer. _____

18. The Cullinan is the world's largest diamond, having weighed 3,024 carats in its

    rough state. _____

19. Fred, observing Florida law, switched on the car headlights as the rain began. _____

20. The scraping sound from outdoors was being made by a snowplow. _____

Participles

A. Using Participles and Participial Phrases

Write sentences using the following participles and participial phrases. Use a comma after each participial phrase that begins a sentence. Then underline the words the participles and participial phrases modify.

1. hearing the music _____

_____

2. written _____

_____

3. running down the street _____

_____

4. finding no one at home _____

_____

5. exhausted _____

_____

B. Using Participial Phrases in Writing

Combine the following pairs of sentences, using the boldfaced word to form a participial phrase. Use a comma after each participial phrase that begins a sentence.

1. Japanese paper folding is **known** as *origami*. Japanese paper folding is of two kinds: traditional and creative.

_____

_____

2. Traditional origami **calls** for folding colored paper into simple figures such as a butterfly or frog. It has the greatest appeal for children.

_____

_____

3. Creative origami is used to make original, complex figures. Creative origami **requires** cutting, combining, and pasting.

_____

_____

Infinitives

An **infinitive** is a verb form that usually begins with the word *to* and functions as a noun, adjective, or adverb. An **infinitive phrase** consists of the infinitive plus its modifiers and complements. Infinitive phrases function in the same way as infinitives.

To be a successful artist takes years of work. (noun)
I need someone *to help me lift this box*. (adjective)
The horses are eager *to race*. (adverb)

A. Identifying Infinitives
Underline the infinitive in each sentence.

1. Laura's goal is to become a psychologist someday.

2. The patriots decided to throw the tea into the harbor.

3. Who wants to go with me to the game?

4. Paramedics arrived and tried to revive the victim.

5. Tony worked to earn money for a bicycle.

6. Paula would like to learn some Spanish before her trip to Mexico.

7. The umpire stopped to clean home plate.

8. To save time, George Bernard Shaw learned shorthand.

9. To listen well is an important skill.

10. The manager of the team didn't want to miss the kickoff.

B. Identifying Infinitive Phrases
Underline the infinitive phrases in the following sentences. In the blank, label the phrase **N** for noun, **ADJ** for adjective, or **ADV** for adverb.

Example   Hal tried <u>to convert the fraction to a decimal</u>.   **N**

1. To understand the difference between a democracy and a republic is important.   _____

2. The class approved the decision to offer tutoring services to younger children.   _____

3. Kara's plan is to take a trip to Australia next year.   _____

4. The captain struggled to regain control of the foundering ship.   _____

5. The political prisoner refused to denounce his principles.   _____

6. Magellan's ship was the first to circumnavigate the globe.   _____

7. To win an Olympic medal is the dream of many athletes.   _____

8. The hill above the town is the best place to watch the fireworks.   _____

9. Exercise regularly to stay physically fit.   _____

10. Prospective team members must promise to attend regular practice sessions.   _____

Infinitives

A. Using Infinitive Phrases

Underline the infinitive phrase in each of the following sentences. In the blank, label the phrase **N** for noun, **ADJ** for adjective, or **ADV** for adverb.

1. When gold was discovered in Montana in 1862, many people rushed to Montana

   to strike it rich.   _____

2. Such hardwoods as mahogany, ebony, walnut, and rosewood are

   used to make furniture.   _____

3. To take karate lessons is my fondest wish.   _____

4. A charming place to visit is the medieval walled town of Carcassonne. _____

5. Christopher Columbus tried to find a new route to India.   _____

B. Using Infinitive Phrases

Use each of the following infinitive phrases in a sentence.

1. to revive the victim speedily

   _____

2. to arrange flowers attractively

   _____

3. to provide a good target for the baseball pitcher

   _____

4. to swim in the Olympics

   _____

5. to explore the depths of the ocean

   _____

6. to become fluent in French

   _____

7. to recall the year of the blizzard

   _____

8. to write a best seller

   _____

Misplaced and Dangling Modifiers

Form A

A verbal or verbal phrase should be placed as close as possible to the word it modifies. If a verbal or verbal phrase is misplaced, it may appear to modify the wrong word and can confuse the reader. A word that modifies the wrong word or group of words is called a **misplaced modifier.** A **dangling modifier** occurs when there is no word in the sentence that the verbal phrase can logically modify.

A. Identifying Misplaced and Dangling Modifiers
Underline the misplaced or dangling modifier in each of the following sentences.

> **Example** Squirming furiously, the farmer pulled the pig from the pit.

1. Having traveled over three thousand miles from coast to coast, his house was a welcome sight.
2. While mowing the lawn, a nest of wasps was spotted in the hemlock tree by Jennifer.
3. To win friends and influence people, a course in self-improvement was taken by Jonathan.
4. Having learned to say the alphabet and to count to twenty, Elise's enthusiasm for school was sparked.
5. I read David a humorous story laughing a good deal.
6. The new pediatric unit accepted all patients built with the aid of an anonymous donor.
7. To study effectively, distractions should be avoided.
8. Opening the front door, snow was falling at a rapid rate.
9. Eating half a grapefruit, toast, and cereal for breakfast, Fred's day was off to a good start.
10. Jogging along the woodland path, a moose was spied by Andy.

B. Identifying Misplaced and Dangling Modifiers
Underline the misplaced or dangling modifier in each of the following sentences.

1. Used as paddles or flippers, pinnipeds are fin-footed mammals with limbs.
2. Living in the oceans, the cold water of the Arctic and Antarctic is home for about thirty different kinds of pinnipeds, including seals and walruses.
3. Tapered and streamlined, a thick layer of blubber gives the pinnipeds added buoyancy in the water and helps keep them warm.
4. Diving as experts, the bottom of the ocean is a good place for pinnipeds to find food.
5. Returning to land or a cake of ice, the young pinnipeds are born with their eyes open and with full coats of hair or fur.

Handbook 37 Using Verbals and Appositives   **129**

Misplaced and Dangling Modifiers

Correcting Misplaced and Dangling Modifiers

Revise each of the following sentences to make the intended meaning clear.

Example   Working in the hot sun, Tony's thirst became acute.
Working in the hot sun, Tony became extremely thirsty.

1. We heard the sound of thunder sitting on the front porch

_____

2. To carry bulky packages on the bus, they should be tied together.

_____

3. Liking the color red, Arthur's new car is a brilliant flamingo.

_____

4. The program was beneficial to all students pointing out good methods of study.

_____

5. Riding in the country in the early spring, the air was so refreshing.

_____

6. Chasing a car down the street, Stan saw the runaway dog.

_____

7. Shattered beyond repair, Jonathan swept up the pieces of the lamp.

_____

8. Ellie was driven to the clinic by a teammate holding ice to her forehead.

_____

9. Living on land and in the sea, prehistoric times had gigantic creatures that were larger than any animal alive today.

_____

_____

10. Weighing over 125 tons and having a length of over 100 feet, the head of the whale constitutes about one third of the whale's total mass.

_____

_____

Appositives

An **appositive** is a noun or pronoun that usually follows another noun or pronoun and identifies or explains it.

> The Smooth Dogfish, *a shark,* is commonly found along the Atlantic coast.

An **appositive phrase** consists of the appositive and its modifiers.

> Billy Wilder, *the famous Hollywood director,* was born in Vienna, Austria.

Identifying Appositive and Appositive Phrases

Underline the appositive or appositive phrase in each of the following sentences.

1. Richard the Lion-Hearted ruled England from 1189 to 1199.

2. Marilyn Monroe, the motion picture actress, made her film debut in 1948.

3. The llama, a member of the camel family, has no hump.

4. Ludwig Mies van der Rohe, the famed architect, designed skyscrapers with steel frames and thin metal and glass walls.

5. The pink and white lady's-slipper, an orchid, is the state flower of Minnesota.

6. Two English painters, John Constable and Joseph M. W. Turner, added significantly to the Romantic Movement.

7. Mt. McKinley, the highest peak in North America, is in Alaska.

8. The American composer Aaron Copland wrote several books about modern music.

9. The Indianapolis 500, an automobile race, is 805 kilometers long.

10. Copenhagen, the capital of Denmark, is located on two islands in the Baltic Sea.

11. Harvard University is named for John Harvard, an English clergyman.

12. *Murder in the Cathedral*, a drama in verse by T. S. Eliot, is based on the death of Thomas à Becket.

13. Henry the Eighth had six wives.

14. Isabel has two nice qualities, honesty and kindness.

15. Al eats lunch every day with Walter the crane operator.

16. Truman Capote called his most successful work, *In Cold Blood,* a "nonfiction novel."

17. Early this morning I phoned my friend Jennie in California.

18. One kind of English toy spaniel, a dog that came from China or Japan, is called the *Prince Charles.*

19. Each year thousands of tourists visit Kenya, a land that offers a marvelous variety of wild animals.

20. On her archaeological dig in New Mexico, Jane had one objective, to find projectile points.

Appositives

A. Using Appositives and Appositive Phrases

Combine each of the following sentences by using an appositive or appositive phrase. Use commas or other punctuation marks as they are needed.

1. *Mustelids* is the name of the group of animals to which otters belong. The word *mustelids* means "weasels."

   _____

   _____

2. Otters love water. Water is an environment well suited to them because of their webbed feet, thick tails, and dense fur.

   _____

   _____

3. Two kinds of otters are found in North America. Both the freshwater otter and the sea otter live in North America.

   _____

   _____

4. The sea otter is large and has white whiskers. The white whiskers are a feature that give the otter its nickname of "old man of the sea."

   _____

   _____

B. Using Appositives and Appositive Phrases

Imagine that you have organized a neighborhood cleanup campaign. Write a short paragraph, describing the jobs that need to be done and the persons who should do them. Use a variety of appositives and appositive phrases in your sentences. Draft your paragraph on a separate sheet of paper and write the final version on the lines below. Underline the appositives and appositive phrases in your paragraph.

_____

_____

_____

_____

_____

_____

Agreement in Number

A verb must agree in number with its subject. If a subject is singular, its verb must be singular. If a subject is plural, then its verb must be plural.

Phrases beginning with words such as *with, together with, including, as well as,* and *in addition to* are not part of the subject. Any prepositional phrase separating the subject and verb should also be disregarded.

> *Integrity,* as well as diligence, *is* desirable in business.
> A bouquet of flowers *stands* on the piano.

A. Making Subjects and Verbs Agree

Underline the verb that agrees with the subject.

1. The term "quarter horse" (identify, identifies) a special American breed of horse.

2. Quarter horses (is, are) so named because they are the fastest horses in the quarter-mile race.

3. These horses (was, were) first bred over two hundred years ago.

4. In those days, the track for races (was, were) cut through dense forests and rarely ran more than a quarter mile long.

5. Today people in the American West (uses, use) this horse for work that requires quick starts and fast turns.

B. Using Agreement in Number

Correct the errors in subject-verb agreement in these sentences by writing the correct verbs in the blanks. If the sentence contains no error, write **Correct** after it.

1. The national forests belong to all citizens of the United States. _____

2. This kind of forest, as well as national grasslands, are protected by the Forest Service. _____

3. The United States Department of Agriculture oversee the Forest Service. _____

4. The national forests in this country is the home of big game animals. _____

5. Many national forests is named for Indian tribes. _____

6. The total area maintained are large enough for almost three hundred thousand people to camp. _____

7. The Forest Service, with its many responsibilities, offer the public beautiful ski areas and miles of streams for fishing. _____

8 The first national forest was established in 1907, in Wyoming. _____

9. A natural, ecological reason for forest fires was discovered in 1990. _____

10. Still, many people is disturbed by the idea of letting a forest fire burn itself out. _____

Agreement in Number

A. Using Agreement in Number

Locate the subject and verb of each numbered sentence. If there is an agreement error, write the subject and the correct form of the verb on the lines below. If the subject and verb agree, write **Correct**.

(1) Jade, as well as other precious stones, have been valued for many years. Jade is usually white in its pure state. (2) Mineral impurities in the jade makes the stone turn bright yellow, red, or various shades of green. The most desired shade of jade is emerald green, known as "Imperial" jade. (3) This type of jade come from Burma. Jade is so tough that it is very difficult to carve. Steel chisels will not work. (4) Therefore, grit is rubbed over the surface until the jade wears away. Making a simple bowl can take two or three years. (5) Carved pieces of jade, estimated to be thirty-five hundred years old, has been found in Mexico.

1. _____

2. _____

   _____

3. _____

4. _____

   _____

5. _____

   _____

B. Using Correct Subject-Verb Agreement

Write a short paragraph to encourage contributions and support for a pair of ice skaters who have been selected to take part in the Winter Olympics. You should mention the need for a fund-rasing event, donations, and volunteers. Use both singular and plural subjects and ensure agreement in number. Draft your work on a separate page, and then write the final version below. Underline the subjects and verbs.

_____

_____

_____

_____

_____

_____

_____

Compound Subjects

A **compound subject** whose parts are joined by *and* is plural. Therefore, it requires a plural verb. When the parts of a compound subject are joined by *or* or *nor,* the verb should agree with the subject nearer to the verb.

A. Using the Correct Verb with Compound Subjects
Underline the correct form of each verb below.

1. Neither a tornado nor a hurricane (has, have) hit this small Texas town.

2. Meteorologists and forecasters (is, are) ready to cope with impending twisters.

3. Enormous property loss and damage last year (has, have) made everyone aware that an early warning system is necessary.

4. Both the local police force and the state police force (is, are) expected to help if an emergency arises.

5. Either plywood or heavy cardboard (is, are) put over windows during tornadoes.

6. Today's barometric pressure and temperature (promise, promises) a storm.

7. Tornadoes and hurricanes both (has, have) violent winds.

8. The Midwest and the South (experience, experiences) most of the tornadoes.

9. Cold, dry air and hot, humid air (meet, meets) and (form, forms) these storms.

10. "Typhoon" or "cyclone" (is, are) another name for hurricane.

B. Correcting Agreement Errors
Write the correct form of the verb in the blank. If there is no error, write **Correct.**

1. The Metrobus and Metrorail provides public transport in Washington, D.C. _____

2. Neither the yellow line nor the green line are complete. _____

3. The blue line and the yellow line goes to National Airport. _____

4. Either tokens or passes are available at most stations. _____

5. Rush-hour fares and nonrush-hour fares are based on the time of day and the distance traveled. _____

6. Color-coded maps and signs helps Metro passengers find their way. _____

7. Coins and paper money is accepted in the fare-card vending machines found at every station entrance. _____

8. Any senior citizen or handicapped person are eligible for reduced fares. _____

9. Elevators, lifts, and ramps is essential for the mobility-impaired. _____

10. Like other citizens, people with disabilities are entitled to safe, convenient, and affordable public transportation. _____

Compound Subjects

A. Using Compound Subjects

Write the correct form of the verb in the blank. If a sentence contains no error, write **Correct.**

1. The police and the zookeeper seeks a missing elephant.   _____

2. Fame and fortune is fleeting.   _____

3. Groucho, Harpo, and Chico Marx is seen in many movies.   _____

4. Time and tide wait for no one.   _____

5. My mother and father dislikes any kind of yogurt, plain or flavored.   _____

6. The Mayor and the Council favors a curfew for teenagers.   _____

7. Sucre and La Paz are the capitals of Bolivia.   _____

8. Poured concrete and steel is used in the framework of many modern buildings.   _____

9. Herrings and sardines is small bony fish.   _____

10. In many ceremonies masks and costumes conceals the wearer.   _____

B. Correcting Agreement Errors

Locate the subject and verb of each numbered sentence. If there is an agreement error, write the subject and the correct form of the verb on the lines below. If the subject and verb agree, write **Correct.**

   Quarrying is one process used to remove minerals from the ground. A pit quarry is actually a huge hole in the ground. **(1)** Solid rocks or slabs is quarried from the pit. **(2)** Crushed stone and broken stone is also quarried. **(3)** Quarried gravel and sand provides essential material for the building trade. **(4)** Crushed rock or broken stone are used to make roadbeds for paved surfaces. Some rock is quarried above ground from a shelf quarry. **(5)** Neither a pit quarry nor a shelf quarry are established until geologists have run tests.

1. _____

2. _____

3. _____

4. _____

5. _____

Indefinite Pronouns

When **indefinite pronouns** are used as subjects, you must determine their number and make sure the verbs agree. A singular indefinite pronoun requires a singular verb; a plural indefinite pronoun takes a plural verb.

Singular			**Plural**
another	either	nobody	both
anybody	everybody	no one	few
anyone	everyone	one	many
anything	everything	somebody	several
each	neither	someone	

The following indefinite pronouns may be singular or plural: *all, any, most, none,* and *some.*

Using the Correct Verb with Indefinite Pronouns

Underline the verb that agrees with the subject in each of the following sentences.

1. All of the student council candidates (write, writes) their own speeches.

2. None of the speeches (is, are) going to be heard until next Thursday.

3. No one (posts, post) a campaign notice on the board until it has been approved.

4. Some of the candidates (speak, speaks) with more confidence than others.

5. Everyone (votes, vote) secretly in a voting booth.

6. Several of the teachers (is, are) helping with the voting machines.

7. Anyone not present on election day (loses, lose) the opportunity to vote.

8. Someone outside our school (tally, tallies) the votes and (give, gives) the result.

9. Each of the steps in voting (follow, follows) the national election process.

10. Neither of those boys (is, are) running for student council.

11. Each of the horses (is, are) being groomed for the horse show.

12. Many of the owners (is, are) quite nervous about the show.

13. Most of the judges (appear, appears) extremely relaxed.

14. One of the field stewards (signal, signals) for the judging to begin.

15. Each of the judges (eye, eyes) every animal from mane to fetlock.

16. None of the show horses (seem, seems) restless or skittish.

17. All of them (behave, behaves) in a stately manner.

18. Few of the spectators (understand, understands) the complicated system of judging.

19. Everybody (is, are) simply interested in the final results.

20. Somebody (request, requests) silence so the blue ribbon winner can be announced.

Indefinite Pronouns

A. Identifying and Using Verbs with Indefinite Pronouns

Read the following sentences. If the verb agrees with the subject, write **Correct** in the blank. If it does not agree with the subject, write the correct verb in the blank.

1. All of the flaws in the programming have been corrected. _____

2. Each of the horses are beautifully groomed. _____

3. Both of the chickens on the grill looks ready to serve. _____

4. One of the toughest events are the high jump. _____

5. Several of the tornado victims have lost their homes. _____

6. Nobody in the class know her very well. _____

7. Either of those outfits look fine to wear to the concert. _____

8. Few of the senators approves of the bill. _____

9. Neither of them complains much about working such long hours. _____

10. Most of the delegates tries their best to attend all the meetings. _____

B. Using Verbs with Indefinite Pronouns

Write each numbered sentence on the appropriate line, using the correct form of each verb.

The gymnastic exhibition begins with a roll on a drum. **(1)** Each of the gymnasts (prance) to the center of the arena. **(2)** All of the coaches (stand) nervously at the edge of the large mat. **(3)** One of the gymnasts (leap) onto the high beam and (balance) on one foot. **(4)** Another (jump) to grab the bar over the pit. Then he hangs from the bar by his knees. **(5)** Several of the athletes (head) for the mat and (begin) their floor exercises. There is so much to watch!

1. _____

2. _____

_____

3. _____

_____

4. _____

5. _____

_____

Other Agreement Problems

There are several situations that cause problems in subject-verb agreement.

Doesn't is singular and is used with the subjects *she, he,* and *it. Don't* is plural and is used with all other personal pronouns.

In an **inverted sentence** the verb (or part of the verb) comes before the subject. Such sentences may be questions or may begin with *there, here, where,* or a phrase. In such sentences, first find the subject; then make sure the verb is in agreement with it.

> There *are* nine players on a baseball team.

Certain words that end in -*s,* such as *news, molasses,* and *mumps,* are nouns that look plural in form but that have a singular meaning. Use a singular verb with such words.

When **collective nouns** such as *team, class,* and *committee* refer to a group as a single unit, use a singular verb. When they refer to individual members of a group, use a plural verb.

> The finance committee *were* arguing over the school budget.
> The class *has* been given a community service award.

Words of amount and time are usually considered to be single units and are used with singular verbs.

> Thirty minutes *is* a long time to wait.

The title of a work of art is considered singular even if it contains plural words.

> *Roots* is a book by Alex Haley.

Making Subjects and Verbs Agree

Find the subject of each sentence. If the verb agrees, write **Correct** on the line. If there is an agreement error, write the correct form of the verb.

1. An orchestra consist of a large group of musicians. _____

2. There is at least seventy-five players in a symphony orchestra. _____

3. Over one-half of the orchestra play stringed instruments. _____

4. *Romeo and Juliet* is a favorite among members of a symphony orchestra. _____

5. The audience loudly expresses its appreciation for a great performance. _____

6. News of celebrity guest conductors travel quickly from one music-lover to another. _____

7. My cousin don't attend the concerts because he don't recognize any of the music. _____

8. Doesn't Gershwin's tunes always draw a good crowd? _____

9. Three hours are a long time to wait in line for tickets. _____

10. However, there is still season tickets available. _____

Other Agreement Problems

A. Choosing the Correct Verb

Underline the verb that agrees with the subject.

1. *War and Peace* (is, are) by the Russian writer Tolstoy.

2. Physics (is, are) an exciting college major.

3. Susanna (don't, doesn't) believe in astrology or palmistry.

4. The jury (has, have) finally returned to the courtroom.

5. There (are, is) usually two players on each side.

6. *Hard Times* (are, is) my favorite novel by Dickens.

7. The pride of lions (were, was) resting near a stream.

8. (Do, Does) your soccer team play during the fall and spring season?

9. Ten dollars (is, are) too high a price for that.

10. The majority of the students (prefers, prefer) take-home exams.

B. Making Subjects and Verbs Agree

Write each numbered sentence on the appropriate line, using the correct form of each verb.

    (1) Where does bush pilots usually fly? They fly to places where very few people live, such as mountains, jungles, and near the North and South poles. **(2)** Two hundred miles are a short distance to fly to deliver supplies, food, and medicine. **(3)** A bush pilot don't have access to many weather stations. **(4)** Therefore, news with accurate weather details are not available. **(5)** Since isolated areas are decreasing today, this group of heroes are fast disappearing.

1. _____

2. _____

   _____

3. _____

4. _____

   _____

5. _____

Skills Assessment 3   Handbooks 35–38

Directions One or more of the underlined sections in the following sentences may contain errors of grammar, usage, capitalization, punctuation, or spelling. Write the letter of each incorrect section; then rewrite the item correctly. If there is no error in an item, write *E.* Write your answers on your own paper or on an answer sheet, as your teacher directs.

Example   Yes Nicholas II and his wife, Alexandria, was the
_____   _____   _____
A   B   C
last monarchs to rule Russia. No error
                        _____   _____
                          D   E

Answer   A—Yes,   C—were

1. Neither Caracas nor Lima are in Ecuador, but both of the cities
   _____ ___
             A   B
   are located in South America. No error
   _____   _____ _____
       C   D   E

2. Since World War I, people in other countries has used the term, Yankee, to refer to
                                               _____ _____
                                                  A   B
   someone from anywhere in the United States, not just the North. No error
   _____   _____   _____
      C   D   E

3. Freedom of assembly, along with freedom of the press and several other

   freedoms, are garanteed by the Bill of Rights. No error
   _____ ___ _____   _____   _____
      A   B   C   D   E

4. Objects look blurred to nearsighted people because light rays entering
                _____   _____   _____
                   A   B   C
   the eye focus in front of the retina rather than on it. No error
          _____   _____
            D   E

5. Has'nt anyone accept us received permission to go? No error
   _____   _____ __ _____   _____
      A   B   C   D   E

6. "Wow The size of those statues is amazeing." No error
    ____   _____ __ _____   _____
     A   B   C   D   E

7. Ralph Waldo Emerson, <u>which</u> was a nineteenth-century <u>American author,</u>
                        A   **B**

    believed that everyone <u>does have</u> the inner <u>strenth</u> to be self-reliant. <u>No error</u>
                        C   **D**   **E**

8. <u>Because</u> the <u>stadium</u> is a long way from the school, everyone on <u>South High's</u>
   A   **B**   **C**

    football team <u>are taking</u> the bus. <u>No error</u>
                D   **E**

9. The hammer and <u>sickle,</u> the two <u>tools depicted</u> on the Soviet <u>flag</u>
                  A   **B**   **C**

    <u>represents</u> industrial and agricultural workers. <u>No error</u>
      D   **E**

10. <u>Opened</u> in <u>1863,</u> <u>London's</u> subway system is the <u>most oldest</u> in the world.
     A   **B**   **C**   **D**
    <u>No error</u>
     E

11. Dominating the skyline of <u>New York City</u> <u>is</u> the <u>Empire State Building</u> and the twin
                              A   **B**   **C**

    towers of the <u>World Trade Center.</u> <u>No error</u>
                  D   **E**

12. All of the rules <u>are</u> posted on the <u>wall; however,</u> hardly <u>anyone obeys</u> <u>them.</u>
               A   **B**   **C**   **D**
    <u>No error</u>
     E

13. <u>Wow!</u> Fifty dollars <u>is</u> <u>defanitely</u> <u>to much</u> money to charge for tickets to that play.
    A   **B**   **C**   **D**
    <u>No error</u>
     E

14. Neither the state nor the federal <u>government</u> <u>want</u> to pay for the new
                                  A   **B**

    <u>program, nevertheless,</u> the funds <u>are</u> a necessity. <u>No error</u>
            C   **D**   **E**

15. A movie about the American <u>fronteir,</u> <u>Dances with Wolves,</u> <u>were</u> the winner of the
                              A   **B**   **C**

    1990 <u>Academy Award</u> for Best Picture. <u>No error</u>
        D   **E**

Directions Some part or all of each sentence is underlined. Choose the best way to rewrite the underlined section. If the underlined section needs no change, choose answer **A.** Write your answers on your own paper or on an answer sheet, as your teacher directs.

Example The escalators in the subway station <u>has been broken</u> for months.

A. has been broken
B. has been broke
C. have been broken
D. have been broke

Answer C

16. Harold felt embarrassed when he realized that everyone except him <u>is wearing a tie.</u>
A. is wearing a tie.
B. was wearing a tie.
C. were wearing a tie.
D. worn a tie.

17. <u>Because</u> Smith was founded as a women's college in 1871, it did not have a woman president until 1975.
A. Because
B. If
C. Although
D. As long as

18. <u>Have all of the ponds frozen</u> yet, or hasn't the weather been cold enough?
A. Have all of the ponds frozen
B. Have all of the ponds froze
C. Has all of the ponds frozen
D. Has all of the ponds freezed

19. <u>Jessama took twenty pictures of her dog using a high-speed camera.</u>
A. Jessama took twenty pictures of her dog using a high-speed camera.
B. Jessama took twenty pictures of her dog. Using a high-speed camera.
C. Using a high-speed camera; Jessama took twenty pictures of her dog.
D. Using a high-speed camera, Jessama took twenty pictures of her dog.

20. <u>Deliberating for six stormy hours, the problem was finally resolved.</u>
A. Deliberating for six stormy hours, the problem was finally resolved.
B. The problem was finally resolved, deliberating for six stormy hours.
C. Deliberating for six stormy hours, the problem was finally resolved by the committee.
D. Deliberating for six stormy hours, the committee finally resolved the problem.

What Is a Clause?

Be careful to distinguish between clauses and phrases. A **clause** is a group of words that contains both a subject and a predicate. A **phrase** does not have a subject and a predicate. There are two kinds of clauses: independent clauses and subordinate clauses. An **independent,** or main, **clause** is a clause that can stand alone as a sentence. A **subordinate,** or dependent, **clause** cannot stand alone as a sentence.

A. Identifying Independent and Subordinate Clauses

Identify the boldfaced clauses in the following sentences as independent or subordinate. Write **IND** for independent and **SUB** for subordinate in the blanks.

1. The fans felt *that their team's victory was impressive.* _____

2. *Robin planted a diverse mixture of flowers in her garden.* _____

3. Chip's grandfather recalls *that during the winter months he often saw ice cutters at work on a nearby pond.* _____

4. Pam arrived at the party early and stayed late, *but Frank arrived late and left early.* _____

5. Melanie, *who has a very winsome personality,* has many friends. _____

6. *When Medea attends the theater with Kevin,* she looks elegant. _____

7. Suzanne can't play basketball *because she sprained her wrist.* _____

8. After Scott had seen the movie, *he decided not to read the book.* _____

9. Linda and Becca will travel to Alaska *when the weather becomes a little warmer.* _____

10. *If you decide to go,* call me. _____

B. Identifying Independent and Subordinate Clauses

Each sentence contains two clauses. In the blanks provided, identify each clause as independent or subordinate by writing **IND + IND, SUB + IND,** or **IND + SUB.**

1. The female sea turtle lays her eggs in the sand, and she does not bury them. _____

2. Because the eggs are easily found, different types of predators are able to eat many of them before they hatch. _____

3. Conservationists have moved the eggs to cooler spots, and they have reburied them in hidden spots. _____

4. The hidden eggs produced no females because eggs incubated in a cool temperature produce only males. _____

5. Although conservationists were trying to help, they unintentionally further endangered the species by reducing the number of females that hatch. _____

What Is a Clause?

A. Identifying Independent and Subordinate Clauses

Each sentence contains two clauses. In the blanks provided, identify each clause as independent or subordinate by writing **IND + IND, SUB + IND,** or **IND + SUB.**

1. Because Rina wanted to earn some extra money, she applied for a part-time job in a local hardware store.

2. Rina described her previous jobs when the interviewer asked about her sales experience.

3. If Rina would work at least twenty hours a week, the owner would give her a job.

4. After she finished her interview at the hardware store, Rina called her mother.

5. The receptionist was the one who gave Rina directions to the bus stop.

B. Using Independent and Subordinate Clauses

Revise the following dull and choppy paragraph. Use the words indicated on the lines below to combine each numbered sentence with the sentence that follows it. Underline each subordinate clause you create. You will need to delete or change words to create new sentences.

(1) Are you considering the purchase of a home computer? You should do some careful research about what computer is right for you. (2) Cost is a major factor. You must also consider your needs. (3) Certain types of computers and software are appropriate only for specific needs. You should decide exactly what your needs are. (4) Your parents may want to use the computer for their financial planning. You may want to use it for school reports, graphics, and games. (5) Remember, even the best computer can be worth nothing to you. You need to know how to use it.

1. *if* _____

_____

2. *but* _____

_____

3. *since* _____

_____

4. *and* _____

_____

5. *if* _____

_____

Adjective Clauses (I)

An **adjective clause** is a subordinate clause that is used as an adjective to modify a noun or a pronoun. Adjective clauses tell *what kind* or *which one* about a noun or a pronoun. Most adjective clauses are introduced by a relative pronoun: *who, whom, whose, that, which.* Some adjective clauses are introduced by relative adverbs such as *where* and *when.* Sometimes the introductory word is omitted.

A. Identifying Adjective Clauses
Underline the adjective clause(s) in each sentence once. Underline twice the word (or words) that the adjective clause modifies.

1. The horse and the cow are probably the best-known members of the *Ungulate* order, which consists of more than two hundred species of hoofed animals.

2. In Central Asia, where the horse was first domesticated about five thousand years ago, stirrups were introduced about A.D. 750.

3. Modern horse breeds are of two classes: the light horse, which is used for riding, driving, and racing; and the draft horse, which is a strong work animal.

4. Draft horses' ancestors were the work horses that knights rode into battle.

B. Using Adjective Clauses
On the lines below, combine each numbered sentence with the one that follows to make one sentence that contains an adjective clause. Underline each adjective clause.

(1) Jacques Cousteau is an ocean scientist. He makes underwater nature films. He and his partner Emile Gagnan invented modern scuba equipment. (2) Cousteau was an ocean diver. He had been diving with the French Navy. (3) Gagnan was an engineer. He knew a great deal about all kinds of valves. Old-fashioned equipment was extremely unsafe. Cousteau knew that a new kind of valve was needed to control the amount of air that was emitted from divers' tanks. (4) Gagnan was able to make the valve. It was just what Cousteau had in mind.

1. _____

_____

2. _____

_____

3. _____

_____

4. _____

_____

Adjective Clauses (I)

Identifying Adjective Clauses and Introductory Words

Underline each adjective clause once. Underline twice the noun or pronoun the clause modifies. In the blank write the relative pronoun or relative adverb that introduces the adjective clause. Write **none** in the blank if the introductory word has been omitted.

1. Mary Ellen Chase, who wrote a number of successful novels set in Maine, also became a writing instructor at Smith College.   _____

2. The TV special was a study of domestic cats, whose habits are clearly similar to those of lions in the wild.   _____

3. The people I most admire know how to balance work and play in their lives.   _____

4. Laser beams have replaced the surgical knives that were once used for delicate operations such as eye surgery.   _____

5. What is the name of the Massachusetts town where President Jimmy Carter spent a night with an average American family?   _____

6. The Nobel Prizes, which are given annually, reward achievements in physics, chemistry, medicine, literature, economics, and peace.   _____

7. The Outdoor Girls series, the Automobile Girls series, and the Nancy Drew mysteries were books young female readers enjoyed years ago.   _____

8. Richie had no interest in music until the day he first saw a concert grand piano and a big double-bass violin.   _____

9. My grandmother's interest in fitness is one reason why she exercises, watches her weight, and eats healthful foods.   _____

10. Carol's brother is a professional proofreader, whose sharp eyes spot typographical errors in materials about to be published.   _____

11. Bring your application to any Registry of Motor Vehicles clerk you find on the first floor of the State Office Building.   _____

12. The lines beginning "Give me your tired, your poor, . . . " which appear at the foot of the Statue of Liberty, are often quoted.   _____

13. Thomas A. Edison's mother withdrew him from a primary school class where he had been pronounced incapable of learning.   _____

14. The Renaissance was a time when the arts flourished in Western Europe.   _____

15. At the city banquet, our school will be represented by Shana Trotter and Douglas Mason, students whose achievements were outstanding this year.   _____

Adjective Clauses (II)

An **essential adjective clause** is a clause that is essential to the meaning of a sentence. If an essential clause is omitted, the meaning of the sentence changes or is incomplete. Essential clauses are not set off with commas.

The frozen yogurt flavor *that I like best* is strawberry.

A **nonessential adjective clause** merely adds extra information. These clauses are set off with commas.

Katarina Witt and Brian Boitano, *who won Olympic gold medals,* have brought their figure skating routines to ice shows in major cities.

Identifying Essential and Nonessential Clauses

Underline the adjective clause in each of the following sentences. Write **ESS** in the blank if the clause is an essential adjective clause; write **NON** if it is a nonessential clause. Insert commas where they are needed.

1. Clarence Birdseye is the inventor who developed the modern quick-freezing process. _____

2. Stromboli which is considered one of the Lipari Islands is actually the tip of an active volcano. _____

3. The word *wuthering* which is a Yorkshire word means "blowing fiercely." _____

4. The African violet which is a very popular house plant is also called *Saintpaulia.* _____

5. The kind of plain yogurt that is most nutritious contains live bacteria. _____

6. The cardinal which is the state bird of Kentucky belongs to the finch family. _____

7. Charles which is a popular name among European royalty was the name of ten kings of France. _____

8. Alice Liddell was the little girl who inspired *Alice's Adventures in Wonderland.* _____

9. English Nigeria's official language is not the language that is most commonly used. _____

10. The word *philistine* refers to a person who is indifferent or hostile to the arts. _____

11. Mark Twain whose real name was Samuel Clemens is one of my favorite authors. _____

12. I gave the brownies to my mother who loves chocolate. _____

13. The woman who wrote the book lives nearby. _____

14. Thoreau's *Walden* which was published in 1854 has inspired generations of idealists. _____

15. Athens is the city where the first modern Olympic Games were held. _____

Adjective Clauses (II)

Using Essential and Nonessential Adjective Clauses in Writing

Combine each numbered pair of sentences below to form one sentence containing an adjective clause that modifies the boldfaced word. If the clause is nonessential, add commas. If the clause is essential, do not add commas.

> **Example** I just punctured my new bicycle *tires.* They were very expensive.
>
> **I just punctured my new bicycle tires, which were very expensive.**

1. There go the ***workers.*** The workers are resurfacing our street.

_____

2. I found the ***page.*** The page was missing from my notebook.

_____

3. Let me show you my best piece of ***writing.*** I plan to enter it in a short-story contest.

_____

4. ***Yolanda*** finally found our house. She hates to use a street map.

_____

5. Our ***director*** distributed the new band uniforms. He thinks we deserve the best.

_____

6. The ***curb*** has not been repaired. I tripped over the curb yesterday.

_____

7. A Boston ***artist*** attracts many onlookers. He draws in chalk on pavements.

_____

8. My favorite piece of ***needlework*** has been damaged. It took me months to complete.

_____

9. Not ***everything*** is necessarily true. You may hear everything.

_____

10. The ***fire alarm*** went off accidentally. It awakened us last night.

_____

Adverb Clauses

An **adverb clause** is a subordinate clause that is used as an adverb to modify a verb, an adjective, or another adverb. An adverb clause tells *how, when, where,* or *to what extent.* It can also tell *why, how much,* and *under what condition.* Most adverb clauses start with subordinating conjunctions.

A. Identifying Adverb Clauses
Choose the adverb clause in each of the following sentences.

1. Although early zippers were not very reliable, Whitcomb L. Judson took out a patent on the first "slide fastener" in 1893.

2. Because this early slide fastener might pop open by itself, people felt it was much safer and much less embarrassing to use buttons.

3. Sometimes the slide fastener would jam so that it could not be opened or closed.

4. In 1913 things changed when Gideon Sundback of Sweden invented a new, more reliable slide fastener.

5. Since the slide fastener had been unreliable, it remained unpopular.

6. The trade name *Zipper* was officially introduced in 1922 when the B. F. Goodrich Company used the name to describe galoshes with slide fasteners.

7. As leading fashion designers of the 1930's began to use zippers extensively, the popularity of the device grew.

8. Today zippers are used widely where there is a need to fasten and unfasten two adjoining edges of material.

9. Nevertheless, a problem still existed, since some disabled people cannot grasp a zipper's metal tab.

10. After Velcro® was invented, clothing could be fastened just by pressing together two tapes with tiny interlocking loops.

B. Identifying Adverb Clauses
Underline each adverb clause once, and underline the word that it modifies twice.

1. If the weather is inclement, the baseball game may be canceled.

2. Fergus read the play before he attended the stage performance.

3. Bob's soufflé came out better than he had expected.

4. If Christina has a good crop of vegetables this year, she will sell the surplus.

5. I shall never be able to type as fast as George does.

6. Because Marina could not sleep, she got up and read for a couple of hours.

7. Andy felt as though he had a chance to win the decathlon.

8. The coach placed the trophy where everyone could see it.

9. Some lakeshore floods occur when water moves suddenly from side to side.

10. Mark likes his new job, although the hours are long.

Adverb Clauses

A. Using Adverb Clauses

Rewrite each of the following sentences, adding an adverb clause that begins with the word in parentheses. If the clause comes at the beginning or the middle of the sentence, set it off with commas. If it comes at the end of the sentence, do not use a comma.

1. Stanley plans to visit his grandparents in Florida. (Use *when*.)

_____

_____

2. Grandfather Perkins likes to go fishing every morning. (Use *while*.)

_____

_____

3. Stan hopes to spend time at Epcot Center's exhibits of the future. (Use *because*.)

_____

_____

4. Grandmother Perkins will tour the World Showcase. (Use *even though*.)

_____

_____

B. Using Adverb Clauses

Read each of the following sentence pairs. Combine the sentences by using an adverb clause. Use commas correctly in your sentences.

1. Mary found an apartment. She went to a downtown department store to shop for furniture.

_____

2. She didn't have much money. She still wanted to create a comfortable home.

_____

3. A Bentwood rocker looked very comfortable. She headed straight for it.

_____

4. She couldn't buy the chair. She didn't have enough money.

_____

Noun Clauses

A **noun clause** is a subordinate clause that is used in a sentence as a noun. Noun clauses may be used in any way a noun is used. Noun clauses are introduced by pronouns and by subordinating conjunctions.

Subject	*Whoever wants the last piece of cheese* can have it.
Direct Object	We don't know *where the rehearsal is.*
Indirect Object	I'll give *whoever finds my dog* a reward.
Object of Preposition	He was pleased by *how well the ceremony went.*
Predicate Nominative	The decision was *that the defendant was guilty.*

Many noun clauses begin with *that* or *what.* Others begin with these words: *whatever, who, whoever, whomever, where, when, how,* and *why.*

Identifying Noun Clauses and Their Uses

Underline the noun clause in each sentence. In the blank, indicate how the noun clause is used: write **S** for subject, **DO** for direct object, **IO** for indirect object, **PN** for predicate nominative, and **OP** for object of a preposition.

1. Where the treasure is buried has been a mystery for centuries. _____

2. Mr. Robins is worried about how he will cross the Australian Desert in a car with

   no air conditioning. _____

3. We are rarely delighted with what we hear on the news. _____

4. Whomever the principal hires for the teaching position must be able to speak

   French and German. _____

5. No one understands why Jesse did not win the history award. _____

6. Ms. Guffy gave whoever crossed her path a cheerful greeting. _____

7. The weather affects whatever grows in the ground. _____

8. Whoever attempts to climb a mountain should first read a book about

   mountaineering. _____

9. Arnold wondered why the coach chose him as the lead-off batter. _____

10. Whoever sells the most tickets to the class carnival will receive a prize. _____

11. The most embarrassing moment was when Gretchen spilled her soup. _____

12. Greg promised that he would pick up the package at the post office later today. _____

13. Tell whoever answers the phone the reason for our delay. _____

14. How Amanda ever managed to stay upright on those skis is a mystery. _____

15. They argued for over an hour about which one was to blame. _____

Noun Clauses

A. Identifying Noun Clauses

Underline the noun clause(s) in each of the following sentences. Then identify its function in the sentence by writing **S** for subject, **DO** for direct object, **IO** for indirect object, **PN** for predicate nominative, or **OP** for object of a preposition, in the blank.

1. Jeff's opinion is that we should apologize. _____

2. No one could understand why Penny became so angry. _____

3. The author gave a description of what life was like in the Middle Ages. _____

4. The employer gave a generous bonus to whoever had been with the company for over one year. _____

5. Looking at the night sky, Isabel wondered when the next full moon would be. _____

6. Jeannie didn't know how she could break the bad news to the yearbook staff. _____

7. What pleased Alex most was that he would be at a beach for his vacation. _____

8. I don't know whether I'll be able to make it to the meeting next week. _____

9. How global warming affects our planet is a matter of great concern. _____

10. We can offer whoever answers our ad a choice of interview dates. _____

B. Using Noun Clauses

Rewrite each numbered sentence by including a noun clause used as shown in parentheses. Underline the noun clause in each new sentence.

> Like most shortcuts, it was an ill-chosen route. The moon had difficulty shooting its rays through the thick trees. **(1)** The owls hooted at any noise that dared disturb the peace and quiet of their wooded home (OP). The path grew narrower and darker. **(2)** I continued my journey, but I don't know why. (DO). **(3)** I could hear my heart pounding, and it was distressing (S). **(4)** I had determination to make it home, and it helped me (PN).

1. _____

   _____

2. _____

   _____

3. _____

   _____

4. _____

   _____

Sentence Structure (I)

A **simple sentence** contains one independent clause only. (The parts of a simple sentence may, however, be compound.)

      The Mayor and the Governor met today. (compound subject)

A **compound sentence** contains two or more independent clauses joined together.

      Randy is small, but he is an excellent guard.

Identifying Different Types of Sentences

In the blanks provided, label each sentence: **S** for simple or **CP** for compound.

1. Michelle raises and sells African violets and gardenias. _____

2. Did you read the book, or did you see the movie? _____

3. World leaders discussed energy problems and analyzed possible solutions. _____

4. I sent in the application, but I forgot to sign it. _____

5. No doubt, yearbook pictures will be taken tomorrow. _____

6. The 1940's-style radio is on sale, but it still seems too expensive. _____

7. Maureen typed her report and then proofread it for errors. _____

8. The fog lifted, and we could see the mountains. _____

9. Eve likes using our pool at night because of its underwater lights. _____

10. With money from his summer job, Arlo will buy a bookcase or a desk. _____

11. Prepare an outline for your paper; start by listing the main points. _____

12. I did hospital work but only as a volunteer, not for pay. _____

13. Harry and his girlfriend often play chess, yet they like soccer too. _____

14. Jan checks on an elderly neighbor's safety daily and does his errands. _____

15. Both Mom and Gram bake their own bread and make fresh orange juice. _____

16. I have four photos of myself, but none of them look like me. _____

17. I can order your ticket, or you can do it yourself. _____

18. Our PTA is presenting the band and the chorus with tickets to a Broadway show. _____

19. The snow turned to slush, but it froze later in the day. _____

20. Our former neighbors neither mowed their lawn nor kept their hedges trimmed. _____

Sentence Structure (I)

A. Recognizing Types of Sentences
In the blanks provided, label each sentence: **S** for simple or **CP** for compound.

1. For her art project, a high school girl named Kim redecorated a room. _____

2. It was a small, dark den in her home; it was used for watching TV. _____

3. Interior decorating, though, is not easy to carry out! _____

4. Kim wanted to be creative, yet she proceeded carefully. _____

5. At a flea market, she was able to find a colorful braided rug. _____

6. Someone told her about antiquing kits, and she painted all the den's wooden
   furniture an attractive off-white shade. _____

7. The walls of the room were beige, but Kim painted them light blue. _____

8. She unrolled the paper window shades, dusted and washed them, and later
   painted them pale blue. _____

9. She then hung a wide but inexpensive mirror opposite a window view. _____

10. New white "fishnet" curtains provided the final touch, and Kim brought her
    before-and-after photos of the den to school. _____

B. Using Different Types of Sentences
Combine each numbered sentence with the sentence that follows to make a simple or compound sentence. Write the new sentence on the lines provided. Label in parentheses the sentence type: **S** for simple or **CP** for compound.

A balloon is the simplest form of aircraft. **(1)** It is a light spherical bag. It is made of paper, rubber, silk, or a rubberized fabric. **(2)** The balloon is filled with a light gas. A basket may be attached to the bag. As long as the balloon and everything attached to it weigh less than the volume of air it is displacing, the balloon will rise. **(3)** A balloon may lose some of its gas. It will begin to sink. **(4)** The gas in the balloon may be hot air. Another possible gas to use is helium.

1. _____

   _____

2. _____

   _____

3. _____

4. _____

   _____

Sentence Structure (II)

A **complex sentence** contains one independent clause and one or more subordinate clauses. The subordinate clause may be an adverb clause, an adjective clause, or a noun clause.

SUB	IND		IND	SUB
If you need help,	just ask me.		I like the sweater	that you chose.

A. Identifying Different Kinds of Sentences

In the blanks, label each sentence **S** for simple, **CP** for compound, or **CX** for complex.

1. A problem will seem worse if you think about it constantly. _____

2. Try to limit your worrying time to a short period each day. _____

3. The problem that you have been worrying about may not seem so overwhelming then. _____

4. You may experience a sense of relief, and your energy level may rise. _____

5. Meanwhile, your subconscious mind will continue to process whatever information is available to it. _____

6. Your subconscious mind keeps working on problems even during sleep. _____

7. Because the brain continues to process information while you sleep, you may wake one morning with an unexpected insight. _____

8. Artists and writers understand this process, and they often keep notepads next to their beds. _____

9. If they wake up with a fresh solution to a problem, they write down the idea immediately. _____

10. Otherwise, bright ideas from the subconscious often fade away and are forgotten. _____

B. Using Complex Sentences in Writing

Read each of the following sentence pairs. Combine the sentences to form a complex sentence. Use commas where they are needed.

1. President Franklin Roosevelt used leg braces. His legs were paralyzed.

   _____

2. The disease had left him paralyzed. It was polio.

   _____

3. His mother felt he should live like an invalid. Eleanor, his wife, insisted on his using his talents.

   _____

4. Roosevelt was a very courageous man. That is the point.

   _____

Sentence Structure (II)

A. Using Complex Sentences in Writing

Read each pair of sentences. Combine them into a complex sentence by using a subordinate clause. Add or omit words as necessary and use commas where they are needed.

1. Freezing rain was falling yesterday. Roads quickly became icy.

_____

2. The storm occurred at rush hour. That was the problem.

_____

3. Driving became even more hazardous. Motorists found visibility very poor.

_____

4. Workers became anxious. They were people who wanted to get home safely.

_____

B. Using Complex Sentences in Writing

Rewrite each sentence, adding a subordinate clause. Follow the directions given in parentheses. Use commas where they are needed.

Example   My oldest sister has wanted a dog. (Tell how long.)
Since she was three, my oldest sister has wanted a dog.

1. We helped Mom buy a freezer at the warehouse sale. (Tell when.)

_____

_____

2. We were shopping for food several times a week. (Tell a reason or condition.)

_____

_____

3. Our family can now stock up on frozen foods. (Tell which frozen foods.)

_____

_____

4. My parents are very pleased with their purchase. (Describe the parents.)

_____

_____

Sentence Structure (III)

Form A

A **compound-complex sentence** contains two or more independent clauses and one or more subordinate clauses.

      IND   **SUB**   **IND**
    Gina knew that she would have to wait, but she didn't mind.

      SUB   **IND**   **IND**   **SUB**
    When you get home, give me a call, and I'll tell you the news that I heard.

Identifying Different Types of Sentences

Underline each independent clause once and each subordinate clause twice. In the blanks provided, label each sentence: **CP** for compound, **CX** for complex, or **CP-CX** for compound-complex.

1. Monopoly® is a game of strategy, but it has an element of chance.   _____

2. Hangman is a word game that both children and adults enjoy.   _____

3. Chinese checkers is played with marbles; it is an easy game to learn.   _____

4. Chess, which probably originated in India in the 600's, is still played throughout the world.   _____

5. A game that is played on a checkerboard of sixty-four squares is called checkers in the United States, but it is called draughts in Great Britain.   _____

6. Checker-type games were played by the ancient Egyptians, Greeks, and Romans, but checkers as it is played in the United States dates back only to the 1500's.   _____

7. In chess, international rules govern the playing of the game, but in checkers, each nation has its own rules.   _____

8. Horseshoe pitching is a game that may be traced to Roman soldiers of about A.D. 100.   _____

9. Ninepins must be at least several hundred years old, since the story "Rip Van Winkle" depicts colonial settlers playing it.   _____

10. Children are still playing ring-around-a-rosy, and this is a game that dates back to medieval times.   _____

Sentence Structure (III)

A. Identifying Different Types of Sentences

In the blanks, label each sentence: **CP** for compound, **CX** for complex, or **CP-CX** for compound-complex.

1. Have you had any new ideas about a summer job that I could apply for? _____

2. I heard that Jaymie is applying for jobs at health clubs and public recreational facilities. _____

3. She has restaurant experience, which is useful for facilities with snack bars. _____

4. She has been trained as a lifeguard, and she has learned CPR. _____

5. Anyone who can teach swimming is a welcome job candidate. _____

6. Jaymie was aware of opportunities offered by public parks and pools, but her swim coach also suggested health club jobs. _____

7. The coach said that she should apply as early as March. _____

8. Jaymie will approach a club manager in person; she will ask if she may fill out an application form. _____

9. She will mention her child-care experience, as that could be useful at a wading pool. _____

10. She knows that there is competition for jobs at health clubs and public facilities, so she will list all experience that may be relevant. _____

B. Using Different Types of Sentences

Combine each numbered sentence with the sentence that follows to make a compound, complex, or compound-complex sentence. Write the new sentence on the lines provided. Label in parentheses the sentence type: **CP, CX,** or **CP-CX.**

> **(1)** In the 1940's, a phone was always black. It had a straight cord.
> **(2)** The phone had no dial. Operators placed all calls. **(3)** A caller lifted the receiver and waited. The operator said, "Number, please." **(4)** There were no call-forwarding or call-waiting features, and there were no answering machines. There was little automation in those days.

1. _____

2. _____

3. _____

    _____

4. _____

    _____

Orange Level Copyright © McDougal Littell & Company

Using Clauses Correctly (I)

Although a subordinate clause has a subject and a verb, it cannot stand alone as a sentence because it does not express a complete thought. Treating a subordinate clause as a sentence causes a fragment. You can correct the type of sentence fragment by making the clause part of a sentence.

A. Identifying Clause Fragments

For each complete sentence, write **S** in the blank. For each sentence fragment, write **F** in the blank.

1. If Sully plays tonight, we are likely to win. _____

2. Who was born before the discovery of penicillin. _____

3. Although there probably won't be enough time. _____

4. That can't be the only explanation. _____

5. Whether or not the rain begins tonight. _____

6. Which took several weeks to heal. _____

7. Unless her father drives her, she'll walk. _____

8. While I was writing a brief résumé. _____

9. Why in the world is Phil unhappy now? _____

10. Provided that you pass a physical exam. _____

B. Identifying Sentence Errors

Add the necessary words to make each fragment a complete sentence. Use appropriate capitalization and punctuation. If a numbered item is a sentence, write **Correct**.

1. Since the entire cast had spent so much time making the scenery.

_____

_____

2. The actors, to whom the audience responded enthusiastically.

_____

_____

3. All who were in the play were asked to sell tickets.

_____

_____

4. Because the play was a musical.

_____

Using Clauses Correctly (I)

Eliminating Clause Fragments in Writing

None of the following numbered clauses express a complete thought. Rewrite each clause fragment, adding a main clause by following the directions in parentheses. Use commas where they are needed.

1. than they used to (Add a main clause about buying from catalogs.)

_____

2. who enjoy the catalogs' colorful pages (Add a main clause about catalogs' appeal.)

_____

_____

3. since so many people would rather shop at home (Add a main clause about catalogs' success.)

_____

_____

4. when most customers have fewer hours free (Add a main clause about time saved.)

_____

5. while others come from specialty stores (Add a main clause about catalogs from department stores.)

_____

_____

6. whether you want books, quilts, tools, gadgets, cassettes, or clothes (Add a main clause about catalog merchandise.)

_____

_____

7. although some catalog items are expensive (Add a main clause about catalogs of close-outs or other special values.)

_____

_____

8. which are directories of other catalogs (Add a main clause about catalog guides.)

_____

9. so that merchandise can be exchanged (Add a main clause about instructions for customers.)

_____

10. because people's lives keep getting busier (Add a main clause about the future of catalog shopping.)

_____

Using Clauses Correctly (II)

Place adjective clauses and adverb clauses as close as possible to the words they modify. Otherwise the meaning of the sentence may be unclear, inaccurate, or unintentionally humorous.

Unclear   The card was thrown into the garbage that you wanted to save.

Clear   The card that you wanted to save was thrown into the garbage.

Identifying Misplaced Clauses

Underline each misplaced clause in the following sentences. In the blank write the word the clause should modify. If a sentence has no misplaced clause, write **Correct**.

1. I asked Granddad about old-time radio serials that used to be popular when he visited us last Sunday. _____

2. As a small boy, Granddad prized the bedside radio given him by an uncle that was manufactured by Philco. _____

3. Adventure, justice, love, and patriotism were some of the values that radio serials promoted. _____

4. The sound of an airplane opened each *Captain Midnight* episode as it roared into the night sky. _____

5. When they pooled their wits and kept one another's courage up, the daring captain and his assistants were an unbeatable combination against the menacing Ivan Shark. _____

6. Granddad could easily picture the heroic Lone Ranger as he listened to each dramatic adventure. _____

7. That deep-voiced masked rider of the plains frequently praised his great horse Silver who brought outlaws to justice. _____

8. The dog King was another valiant animal of radio days when *The Challenge of the Yukon* was a favorite family program. _____

9. During each episode, King showed himself eager to follow Sergeant Preston of the Mounties when he began barking. _____

10. Granddad felt a sense of companionship with the radio-serial announcer when he was at home alone in the daytime, sick and bored. _____

11. He was too young, however, to respond to romance serials that were directed at adult listeners. _____

12. These shows pleased his parents when they came on the air. _____

13. The serial was on after dinner that Granddad most wanted to hear. _____

14. Granddad's eyes sparkle when he remembers these programs from his youth. _____

15. When I grow older, I hope I have such vivid memories of the past. _____

Using Clauses Correctly (II)

A. Using Clauses Correctly
Rewrite each sentence, correcting any misplaced clauses.

1. The child pleaded for a toy whose parents had gone out for the evening.

_____

2. She went to buy some paper at the store that she could use for typing.

_____

3. I browsed through a book at the library that was about American folk art.

_____

4. The car stalled on the expressway that we had owned for many years.

_____

5. I went to see the statue of David in Florence, which was sculpted by Michelangelo.

_____

B. Using Subordinate Clauses Correctly in Writing
Rewrite the following paragraph, correcting each misplaced clause. Not every
sentence is incorrect.

> **(1)** Katarina Witt and Brian Boitano starred in an ice show in Boston's
> North End that demonstrated their athletic skills. **(2)** The show, "Skating II,"
> which was on tour, proudly featured these Olympic gold medalists. **(3)** Their
> daring jumps and spins won bursts of applause, which are figure skaters'
> unique trademarks. **(4)** Other routines that the audience liked included
> those of the Russians and Germans who were appearing in the show.

_____

_____

_____

_____

_____

_____

_____

_____

_____

_____

Using Clauses Correctly (III)

Who is a subject form. *Whom* is an object form. The use of *who* or *whom* in a subordinate clause depends on whether the pronoun is used in the clause as a subject, a predicate nominative, or an object.

Subject	Those cheerleaders who are turning cartwheels are amazing.
Predicate Nominative	No one has said who our math teacher will be.
Direct Object	The volunteer whom I met was my age.
Object of a Preposition	The person to whom this belongs has left.

A. Identifying How Pronouns Are Used

Identify the boldfaced pronoun in each underlined clause as **S** if it is used as a subject, as **DO** if it is used as a direct object, as **OP** if it is used as the object of a preposition, or as **PN** if it is used as a predicate nominative.

1. The mice in the fable were wondering **who** would put the bell on the cat. _____

2. Remind anyone to **whom** you are giving a kitten that it needs water to drink. _____

3. An Emily Dickinson poem asks **who** has seen the wind. _____

4. Can you tell us **who** the best runner was? _____

5. "I shall marry **whom** I please," Meg March in *Little Women* calmly told her aunt. _____

6. Coach Johnson wants to know **who** was in charge of equipment last season. _____

7. I couldn't see the person **who** was talking. _____

8. Would you mind telling me **whom** you voted for? _____

9. We haven't any idea **who** those two girls are. _____

10. The goddess of wisdom, **whom** the Greeks knew as Athena, was called Minerva by the Romans. _____

B. Using the Correct Pronoun Form

Underline the pronoun that correctly completes each of the following sentences. On the line identify the use of the pronoun you choose. Write **S** for subject, **DO** for direct object, **OP** for object of a preposition, or **PN** for predicate nominative.

1. There has been some dispute about (who, whom) discovered ether: William Morton or Crawford Long. _____

2. "Never send to know for (who, whom) the bell tolls," wrote a poet named John Donne; "it tolls for thee." _____

3. Please invite (whoever, whomever) will enjoy our play. _____

4. It was Arthur Gordon (who, whom) wrote the short story "The Sea Devil." _____

5. The bronze charioteer (who, whom) has been placed in a Delphi museum is said to have "living eyes." _____

Using Clauses Correctly (III)

A. Using Who and Whom
In the blank write an appropriate pronoun form.

1. Someone _____ I had hoped to meet wasn't at the party after all.

2. A meter maid was writing up a violation notice for a driver _____

   had ignored a NO PARKING sign.

3. The friend to _____ I lent my sweater has never returned it.

4. I hoped my father wasn't one of the people _____ were aboard the

   train that broke down.

5. I can't remember _____ the fourth President of the United States was.

B. Using Who and Whom in Writing
Write a short paragraph about the ideal friend. Use *who* and *whom* correctly in
subordinate clauses in at least two sentences. Remember to avoid using sentence
fragments or misplaced clauses. Draft your paragraph on a separate sheet of paper.
Write the final version on the lines below.

_____

_____

_____

_____

_____

_____

_____

_____

_____

_____

_____

_____

_____

_____

Proper Nouns and Proper Adjectives

Capitalize proper nouns and adjectives. Follow these rules: Capitalize people's names and the initials that stand for people's names. Capitalize titles used before people's names and abbreviations that stand for those titles.

Mayor Janet Gray Hayes   Gov. Edmund G. Brown, Jr.

Do not capitalize titles used without names as common nouns: He is a general. Capitalize titles of very high importance, even when used without names.

the President of the United States   the Secretary of State

Capitalize such words as *mother* and *uncle* when they are used as names or as parts of names. If the noun is preceded by a possessive adjective or by *a, an,* or *the*, it is not capitalized.

Uncle Bob is my father's brother.

Capitalize all words referring to God, to the Holy Family, and to religious scriptures.

the Almighty   the Old Testament   the Holy Spirit

Capitalize personal pronouns referring to God.

They gave thanks to God for His bounty.

Capitalizing Proper Nouns and Proper Adjectives

Underline the letters that should be capitals in each of the following sentences. If the sentence is already correct, write **Correct.**

1. Prime Minister Winston Churchill was both a statesman and a writer. _____

2. A book in the old testament tells of jonah's experience with a sea creature. _____

3. Did general dwight d. eisenhower lead the United States forces in Korea? _____

4. Both dad and aunt polly will be attending the variety show. _____

5. The bible contains the words of god and of his prophets. _____

6. The secretary of the treasury decides when currency should be printed. _____

7. According to dr. purzansky, Phyllis may need to get braces on her teeth. _____

8. Did mr. simon appear on the talk show? _____

9. My grandfather knew Dr. Martin Luther King, Jr., the famous civil right leader. _____

10. Rudolf diesel invented the famous engine that was named after him. _____

11. Some characters in one walt disney film are sneezy, grumpy, and bashful. _____

12. My lawyer's formal title is william j. smithers, esq. _____

13. Kevin and his dad traveled to Ireland to visit Uncle Sean. _____

14. Our teacher, professor silverstein, often quotes shakespeare. _____

15. My mother says that Reverend Howard is her favorite speaker. _____

Proper Nouns and Proper Adjectives

A. Using Proper Nouns and Proper Adjectives
Underline the letters that should be capitalized in each of the following sentences. If the sentence is correct, write **Correct.**

1. What position did miss harriet lane hold when buchanan was president? _____

2. Did you know that pope john paul I served for only thirty-four days? _____

3. We enjoyed talking with grandmother about the 1940's. _____

4. Prince william of england will probably be king william someday. _____

5. Mr. and mrs. mullin are traveling with my mother and aunt. _____

6. The chief justice of the supreme court reviewed the case. _____

7. Have you read any poems by langston hughes? _____

8. The president of the senior class is Marilyn J. Taylor. _____

9. Staff sgt. daniel g. hernandez spoke to the platoon. _____

10. Mr. agube read a hymn from the koran, the sacred book of the moslems. _____

11. My favorite uncle sent me a microscope for my fourteenth birthday. _____

12. The artist michelangelo painted frescoes that depict god creating the world. _____

13. gerald casazza was once the mayor of our town. _____

14. Last month aunt josie celebrated her ninety-fifth birthday. _____

15. A young american woman, lisa halaby, became queen noor of jordan. _____

B. Capitalizing Proper Nouns and Proper Adjectives Correctly
Underline each letter that should be capitalized in the following paragraph.

Many people do not know that America's favorite uncle, uncle sam, was a real person. Until a quarter of a century ago, most people believed that uncle sam was a mythical figure. Then evidence was found in an 1830 newspaper showing that uncle sam was a man named samuel wilson, who was born in 1766. Interestingly enough, sam wilson was a childhood playmate of another figure from both history and legend—john chapman, better known as johnny appleseed. johnny appleseed traveled across America preaching scripture and planting apple orchards.

Orange Level, Copyright © McDougal, Littell & Company

Geographical Names

In **geographical names**, such as the names of continents, bodies of water, landforms, world regions, political units, public areas, and roads and highways, capitalize the first letter of each word except articles and prepositions.

Capitalize names of **sections of the country** or the world and proper adjectives derived from these names.

Do not capitalize **directions of the compass** or adjectives that merely indicate direction or general location.

Capitalize the names of planets and other **objects in the universe,** but do not capitalize *sun* and *moon*.

Capitalizing Geographical Names

Underline the letters that should be capitals in each of the following sentences. If the sentence is already correct, write **Correct.**

1. The southwest has hotter summers than new england does. _____

2. Red beans and rice is a traditional louisiana dish. _____

3. Some dangerous mudslides have occurred along the pacific coast highway in

   california. _____

4. Jeanette, who is from atlanta, georgia, has a lovely southern accent. _____

5. If you drive west on interstate 30, you will reach dallas, texas. _____

6. The rocky mountain goat is really an antelope. _____

7. The wind is traveling northwest at sixty miles per hour. _____

8. The most photographed mountain in the far east is mt. fujiyama near tokyo, japan. _____

9. The danube is the second longest river in europe. _____

10. The southern cross is a constellation visible from the southern hemisphere. _____

11. Carlsbad caverns in new mexico is one of the southwest's most impressive

    tourist attractions. _____

12. Mercury and Venus are the only planets without at least one moon. _____

13. The name of sixth avenue was changed to avenue of the americas. _____

14. Two of hawaii's beautiful islands are maui and kauai. _____

15. As you might guess, the finger lakes in new york are long and narrow. _____

Geographical Names

A. Using Geographical Names

Underline each letter that should be capitalized in the following sentences. If the sentence is correct, write **Correct.**

1. Parts of the ohio river sometimes freeze over.

2. The black hills of south dakota contain countless fossils.

3. Interstate Highway 90 runs east and west from coast to coast.

4. The atlantic washes east coast beaches; the pacific washes west coast ones.

5. Do you know that chicago is the largest city in the midwest?

6. Jupiter, saturn, and uranus are gaseous planets circling the sun.

7. The himalayas are a mountain system in southern asia.

8. The union of soviet socialist republics is the official name of the soviet union.

9. Reservations are required for camping at yellowstone national park.

10. The Gulf of Mexico is the largest gulf in the world.

11. All of Australia is located in the southern hemisphere.

12. The big dipper is part of the constellation ursa major.

13. Lake michigan is the only one of the great lakes entirely within the united states.

14. Bermuda, a group of 150 small islands, lies 575 miles east of Cape Hatteras.

15. In cold weather deer from the Rocky mountains seek food in cities.

B. Capitalizing Geographical Names Correctly

Underline each letter that should be capitalized in the following paragraph.

The capital of the united states is washington, d.c. It is also known as the district and d.c. The potomac river separates the district of columbia from its neighbors, virginia and maryland. Historic georgetown lies on the banks of the potomac. Since d.c. has a height limit for buildings, crystal city has sprung up in arlington, virginia. From this high-rise complex there is a view of landmarks such as the capitol, the jefferson memorial, and the towering washington monument. This obelisk is set in the national mall, a parklike area that stretches from capitol hill. Tourists know this area well, and many visit the smithsonian institution buildings there.

Organizations, Events, and Other Subjects

Use capital letters for the following:

> the names or organizations and institutions
> the names of races, languages, nationalities, and religions; and proper
>   adjectives that come from these names
> the names of historical events, documents, and periods of time
> the names of months, days, and holidays but not seasons
> the time abbreviations B.C., A.D., A.M., and P.M.
> the names of specific school courses that are followed by a number
> the names of language courses
> the names of specific ships, trains, airplanes, and spacecraft
> the names of monuments, bridges, and buildings
> the names of awards and special events
> brand names but not common nouns that follow brand names

Identifying Proper Capitalization

Underline the letters that should be capitals in each of the following sentences. If the sentence is correct, write **Correct**.

1. Most of the french people are roman catholic. _____

2. Lyndon Johnson guided the civil rights act through congress in 1964. _____

3. Pedro loves art from the renaissance and the middle ages. _____

4. Ernest Hemingway served as an ambulance driver during world war I. _____

5. The first olympic games were held in 776 b.c. _____

6. The society for the prevention of cruelty to animals was formed in 1866. _____

7. One of the most important jewish holidays is rosh hashana. _____

8. Are you taking algebra 2, chemistry, and french? _____

9. The *mayflower* carried the first pilgrims to America. _____

10. The holiday known as thanksgiving is celebrated on a designated thursday

    in november. _____

11. All flavors of Kitty Kwizeen cat food are on sale this week. _____

12. A member of the international red cross spoke at mayfield high school. _____

13. The luncheon menu included german potato salad and swedish meatballs. _____

14. Many people regard memorial day as the beginning of summer. _____

15. Pulitzer prizes are awarded annually by columbia university. _____

Organizations, Events, and Other Subjects

A. Capitalizing Organizations, Events, and Other Subjects

Underline each letter that should be capitalized in the following sentences.

1. The hospital volunteers of america has an active chapter at rock county hospital; the chapter holds a blood drive every spring.

2. Several cambodian and vietnamese refugees live in our apartment building.

3. The battle of concord was fought during the revolutionary war.

4. Two holidays in may are mother's day and memorial day.

5. Will the twenty-first century begin at 12:01 a.m. in a.d. 2000 or 2001?

6. The *amtrak limited* will take us to the stadium for the first world series game.

7. In history class we studied the construction of the golden gate bridge.

8. The TV ad for berry-good granola bars features animated talking strawberries.

9. The canadians celebrate thanksgiving in october.

10. The ancient greek civilization existed from about 900 to 200 b.c.

B. Using Capital Letters Correctly

Imagine that you are the publicity chairperson for a school club. Write a newspaper notice about your club's next meeting, inviting others to attend. Include at least one of each of the following:

the name of an organization	the name of a building
a time abbreviation	an award or special event
a person's name	a date (day and month)

_____

_____

_____

_____

_____

_____

_____

_____

_____

_____

_____

First Words and the Pronoun I

Use capital letters for the following:

> the first word of every sentence and every line of poetry
> the first word of a direct quotation
> the first word of the greeting and complimentary close of a letter
> the name or title of the person addressed in a letter
> the first word of each item in an outline and the letters that introduce major subsections of the outline
> the first, last, and all other important words in titles but not articles, conjunctions, or prepositions with fewer than five letters
> the pronoun *I*

Using Proper Capitalization

Underline the letters that should be capitals in each of the following items. If the sentence is correct, write **Correct**.

1. dear ms. taylor:

   please send me two tickets for your lecture on May 12.

   sincerely yours, _____

2. One of shakespeare's characters says, "all the world's a stage." _____

3. loveliest of trees, the cherry now

   is hung with bloom along the bough,

   and stands about the woodland ride

   wearing white for Eastertide.

   —A. E. Housman, from *A Shropshire Lad*

4. have you read the article "vernon jordan, past and present" in *ebony?* _____

5. two of my favorite short stories are "sixteen" and "strawberry ice cream soda." _____

6. ms. Cass exclaimed, "you should have seen the Viking exhibit at the

   Metropolitan!" _____

7. *The Outsiders* and other books by S. E. Hinton are popular with students. _____

8. *"The King and I,"* I told Julie, "is my favorite film." _____

9. ann Frank wrote, "i still believe that people are really good at heart." _____

10. "that was a great movie," said Tom. "now let's have something to eat." _____

First Words and the Pronoun I

A. Capitalizing First Words and the Pronoun I
Underline each letter that should be capitalized in the following numbered items.

1. I. energy
    a. present sources
        1. petroleum
        2. natural gas
        3. coal
    b. problems

      _____

2. dear mr. pappas:

    enclosed is a check for $10 to cover the cost of shipping the books.

    very truly yours,

      _____

3. *time* magazine gave a rave review of the play *phantom of the opera*.

      _____

4. "call me tonight," Rachel said, "and i'll give you the Spanish assignment."

      _____

5. Virginia Woolf wrote "a room of one's own" in lecture form for a college audience.

      _____

B. Capitalizing First Words and the Pronoun I
Underline each letter that should be capitalized in the following diary entry about a trip. Consider all the rules for capitalization in this chapter.

        last week i went to the southwest for the first time. my teacher, mrs. gomez, hired a coach from the blue line bus company, and our class toured arizona and new mexico.

        we saw the grand canyon, an indian pueblo, and several ranches. We crossed the rio grande and saw a film company making *southern highway*, a documentary. in a museum in santa fe, we saw turquoise jewelry, navajo blankets, and hopi sand paintings. at taos we visited adobe houses where indians have lived since a.d. 1000.

        the temperature was around 80° during the day. in the northern part of arizona, we saw snow at the rim of the canyon. the colorado river, which flows west of the great divide, was swollen by run-off.

End Marks

Use a **period** at the end of a declarative sentence, most imperative sentences, and an indirect question.

Declarative sentence	Michael Dukakis ran for President in 1988.
Imperative sentence	Put the dirty dishes in the sink.
Indirect question	The soldier asked if the supplies had come.

Also, use a period at the end of an abbreviation (*Col.* for *Colonel*), after an initial (*John F. Kennedy for John Fitzgerald Kennedy*), after each number or letter in an outline or a list, between dollars and cents (*$4.32*), and to indicate any other decimal.

Use a **question mark** after an interrogative sentence.

Interrogative sentence	Who fought in the War of the Roses?

Use an **exclamation point** after an exclamatory sentence and after a strong interjection.

Exclamatory sentence	Watch out for that oncoming car!
Strong interjection	Terrific! *or* Oh, boy!

Using End Marks
Add punctuation where necessary in the following sentences.

1. Who is that dancing with P J Collins

2. One mile is equal to 5,280 feet or 1,609 kilometers

3. Jennifer asked for the number of the J D Cohen Furniture Company

4. At Camp Willowtree, dinner is served promptly at 6:00 PM

5. Around 1000 BC the Phoenicians developed the system of writing on which our

   alphabet is based

6. Oh, no The quarterback fumbled the ball

7. The decimal 50 is the same as the fraction one-half.

8. Is the second floor of the White House open to the public

9. Did you see Grace at the skating rink

10. Use a food processor to knead bread dough

11. I British political parties

     A Conservative Party

     B Labour Party

     C Liberal Party

     D Social Democratic Party

12. This compact disc was advertised for only $950

13. Oh Is today their anniversary

14. Ask Jamal whether the bus leaves at 1:00 or at 2:00 PM

15. Dixie Express guarantees package delivery by 10:30 AM the next day

End Marks

A. Using End Marks
Add punctuation where necessary in the following sentences.

1. The defense attorney asked the witness for the prosecution if he had ever seen the defendant.

2. Hooray The Cardinals won the championship

3. Who fought in the Spanish-American War

4. Nick bought five almost new paperback books at the garage sale down the street for only $125 each

5. Dr Roger Harmon's specialty is sports medicine

6. In Great Britain high tea is served at around 5:00 PM

7. Can't you read the sign posted there It says: No Smoking Allowed

8. Did you know that the singer Englebert Humperdinck's real name is Arnold Dorsey

9. Actor Larry Hagman, who used to be in *I Dream of Jeannie,* now plays J R Ewing in the television series *Dallas.*

10. Ingrid's mother bought this sweater in 1970 for only $950 Can you believe it

11. Look There's a landslide over on that mountain

12. Tell me where I should plant the geraniums and azaleas

13. Have you heard a weather forecast for the weekend

14. How many centimeters are there in an inch

15. Are you the patient who said the noise from the visitors' lounge is too loud

B. Using End Marks in Writing
Add periods, question marks, and exclamation points where necessary in the following paragraph.

(1) Many changes have been made in the laws governing the United States monetary system during the last few decades **(2)** In 1965, President Lyndon B Johnson signed a bill eliminating silver from the dime and the quarter and reducing the silver content of the half dollar to 40 percent **(3)** In 1970, President Richard M Nixon signed a similar law that eliminated the use of silver in the silver dollar and removed the remaining silver from the half dollar **(4)** Do you have any silver dollars dated before 1970 **(5)** Save those US coins Because of their silver content, their value increases every year

The Comma (I)

Use a comma after every item in a series except the last one.

Ben Vereen is a dancer, a singer, and an actor.

Use a comma after words such as *first, second,* and *third* when they introduce parts of a series.

First, you must total debts; second, you must total assets; third, you must set up a budget for yourself.

Use a comma between two or more adjectives of equal rank that modify the same noun.

It was a dark, cold, rainy evening.

A. Using Commas Correctly
Add commas where necessary in the following sentences.

1. Dickens's character Ebenezer Scrooge was a mean stingy old man.

2. Your paper must include the following: first an outline; second three to five pages of text; third endnotes; and fourth a bibliography.

3. The driver stopped looked both ways and then proceeded.

4. Emily's favorite poets are Alice Walker Gwendolyn Brooks and Anne Sexton.

5. Sulfur has a strong unpleasant smell.

6. First check the card catalog; second look for the books you want; third take notes.

7. Picnickers brought sandwiches potato salad lemonade and fruit.

8. Our newspaper tour guide showed us reporters writing stories typesetters printing articles and the drivers of delivery trucks getting ready to deliver the papers.

9. Be sure to close the windows feed the cat and switch on a lamp.

10. Carolyn wore suede boots and thin handknitted wool knee socks.

B. Using the Comma
Add commas where they are missing in the following paragraph.

(1) Microorganisms include bacteria yeasts and molds. (2) They are tiny invisible creatures. (3) Whether you can see them or not, they are on your hands inside your body and in the air. Many microorganisms are harmful, but some can be useful. (4) First molds are used to make antibiotics other medicines and cheeses. (5) Second yeasts are used for making breads synthetic vitamins and some beverages. Microorganisms, which can be both harmful and useful, affect us in many ways.

The Comma (I)

A. Using the Comma

Add commas where they are missing in the numbered sentences.

In 1949 the golfer Ben Hogan was in a serious automobile accident. **(1)** He suffered a double fracture of the pelvis a broken collar bone broken ribs a fractured ankle and severe internal injuries. He survived, but the doctors were not optimistic when they responded to reporters' questions. **(2)** They said Hogan would live walk and resume some everyday activities. They doubted, however, whether he would ever play golf again.

Nevertheless, Hogan worked hard to make a comeback on the golf circuit. **(3)** First he tied his old rival Sam Snead in the Los Angeles Open. **(4)** Second Hogan entered the biggest most important tournament of all, the Masters at Augusta, Georgia. He began well, but his tired body could not maintain the pace. **(5)** Hogan's patient diligent effort finally paid off. Two months later he won the U.S. Open, and he went on to win other top tournaments as well.

B. Using the Comma in Writing.

Rewrite the sentences by following the directions in parentheses.

1. They packed for the journey. (Include a series of items.)

   _____

   _____

2. This was to be an adventure. (Include two adjectives of equal rank that modify the same noun.)

   _____

   _____

3. They wanted to experience the thrill; they wanted to test themselves. (Include *first* and *second* to introduce a series.)

   _____

   _____

4. The adventure was a memorable experience for many reasons. (Include a series of reasons.)

   _____

   _____

The Comma (II)

Use a comma after introductory words or mild interjections: *Yes, I heard you.*

Use a comma after two or more prepositional phrases at the beginning of a sentence: *At two o'clock on the dot, the first shift ends.*

Use a comma after verbal phrases and adverb clauses that begin a sentence: *Before we leave, let's call Pam.*

Use commas to set off one or more words that interrupt the flow of thought in a sentence: *Tea, for example, also contains caffeine.*

Use a comma to set off nouns of direct address: *Contestants, take your places.*

Use commas to set off most appositives. An **appositive** explains or identifies another word. The appositive directly follows the word it explains. Do not use commas with essential appositives.

> The house, a brick ranch, is for sale.
> The singer Willie Nelson is very popular.

Using Commas Correctly
Add commas where necessary in the following sentences.

1. Although Natalie likes old movies she has never heard of James Cagney.

2. Looking up at the night sky my father pointed out the planet Jupiter.

3. In the morning before breakfast Ron runs five miles.

4. A gecko I believe is a type of lizard.

5. Yes Paula you have three minutes for your rebuttal.

6. Exhausted from a hectic day at work Judy lay down for a while.

7. The hearing a joint investigation by Congress will be televised.

8. Well we will of course refund your money if you're not satisfied.

9. At the edge of the fairgrounds there is a vendor selling balloons.

10. Anthony will you take the minutes of the meeting?

11. Do you think Professor Jennings that the experiment will work?

12. Because she is ill Ms. Haywood will not return to work tomorrow.

13. Her attorneys moreover have asked for a delay.

14. Queen Victoria an English monarch ruled for sixty-four years.

15. If Rhonda makes this run we'll win the game!

16. This road I think leads to the stadium.

17. When she got the flu Felicia resolved to take better care of herself.

18. Let me take your coat Brenda and hang it up.

19. In the long line for tickets strangers began to talk to one another.

20. Mecca the birthplace of Mohammed is one of the two capitals of Saudi Arabia.

The Comma (II)

A. Using the Comma
Add commas where necessary in the following sentences.

1. With the increase in motor traffic after World War I there was great need for the construction of new roads.
2. Parkways the first highways were gently winding; freeways on the other hand were straight roads designed for high speeds.
3. Tunneling through mountains and spanning rivers the highways swept across the country.
4. At the exits of a highway cloverleafs made it easy to enter a city.
5. Consisting of three or four levels of interlocking highways some modern cloverleafs have been nicknamed "spaghetti bowls."
6. Encouraged by the availability of highways freight companies greatly increased the use of trucks.
7. Yes railway trains the traditional freight haulers did decline as a result.
8. In the small towns in the country many railway tracks lay abandoned.
9. In the older cities in the United States the four-lane superhighway often ends in narrow city streets.
10. Now because traffic jams have become common cities and states are restoring railways for commuter use.

B. Using the Comma in Writing
Rewrite the sentences by following the directions in parentheses.

1. At the end, they might offer her a full-time job. (Add another prepositional phrase to the beginning of the sentence.)

   _____

2. She will return to school. (Begin the sentence with the word *if*.)

   _____

3. This is valuable experience in the working world. (Include interrupters such as *of course* or *I think*.)

   _____

4. You should get involved in this program. (Begin with an introductory word and address a person directly.)

   _____

Orange Level, Copyright © McDougal, Littell & Company

The Comma (III)

Use commas to set off explanatory words that precede or follow a direct quotation.

> Michelle said, "Many people have called."
> "Many people have called," Michelle said.

Use a comma before a conjunction that joins the two main clauses of a compound sentence.

> Joan is already here, but Maria won't be flying in until tonight.

A. Using Commas Correctly
Add commas where necessary in the following sentences.

1. Senator Braun commented "The bill has a good chance of passing."

2. Maria overslept but she still made it to work on time.

3. "Where" the teacher asked "is Samoa located?"

4. Los Angeles has a larger area than New York City but New York has more people.

5. "*The New York Times*" said Mr. Schultz "was first published in 1851."

6. Did Debra resign or has she decided to stay?

7. The phone and the doorbell both rang and I answered the phone first.

8. A volcanic eruption was predicted and the town had to be evacuated.

9. "I know when the St. Lawrence Seaway opened" said Janice.

10. "The Pyramids were tombs for the pharaohs" explained Ms. Dixon.

11. The jurors have been selected and they are ready to hear the case.

12. "Well" the clerk replied "we don't have that item in stock right now."

13. I'd like to join you for lunch but I have to be at a meeting upstairs in ten minutes.

14. Steve's injury did not require surgery nor did he need physical therapy.

15. Was it Dolores who said "I'll take photos, sell ad space, or write articles"?

B. Using the Comma
Add commas where they are missing in the following dialogue.

(1) "My report" Doug told Eve "is on Jack Schaefer a Western novelist."

(2) I liked his short stories first and then I read the novel *Shane*."

(3) Eve said "Schaefer had never seen the West when he wrote *Shane*."

(4) "He must have had a great imagination" Doug declared. "The Western Writers of America organization gave *Shane* an important award so they must have found it to be very authentic."

(5) "Actually" Eve explained "Schaefer researched his subject thoroughly at Yale University."

The Comma (III)

A. Using Commas

Add commas where necessary in the numbered sentences in the following paragraph. Some sentences do not need commas.

(1) Mars is the closest planet to Earth and it has long captivated people's imaginations. (2) Giovanni Schiaparelli an Italian scientist discovered lines on the surface of Mars and called them *canali*. (3) The word is Italian for *channels* but it was translated into English as *canals*. (4) Study of these "canals" led to a whole Martian mythology and to speculation about life on Mars.

(5) "Long ago" wrote author Leigh Brackett ". . . there were oceans in equatorial and southern Mars." (6) Edgar Rice Burroughs and H. G. Wells wrote vividly about Martians and their activities. The space age, however, brought better knowledge of Mars. (7) The "Red Planet" turned out to be barren and rocky and this discovery greatly diminished the likelihood of life on Mars.

B. Using the Comma in Writing

Rewrite the sentences by following the directions in parentheses.

1. "I can't possibly enjoy this vacation." (Include explanatory words before the direct quotation.)

_____

2. "Traveling alone to stay with strangers feels *too* strange." (Include explanatory words following the direct quotation.)

_____

3. "I've met these cousins only once, and I may not like them at all." (Include explanatory words between parts of the direct quotation.)

_____

_____

4. "I haven't seen anyone my age waiting for this bus." (Include the conjunction *but* and another clause.)

_____

_____

5. "Hello, I've been looking for somebody my age." (Include the conjunction *and* and another clause.)

_____

_____

Orange Level Copyright © McDougal, Littell & Company

182   *Handbook 41   Punctuation*

The Comma (IV)

Use commas to set off nonessential clauses. A nonessential clause adds an extra idea to the sentence. The sentence would be complete without it.

Rita, who is very talented, won the scholarship.

Do not use commas to set off essential clauses. An essential clause is necessary for the meaning of the sentence.

The person who is considered the most important Italian composer of the nineteenth century is Giuseppi Verdi.

A. Using Commas Correctly
In the blank write **ESS** if the boldfaced clause is essential or **NON** if it is nonessential. Add commas where necessary.

1. All the students *whom you chose as class officers* seem outstanding. _____

2. The vise-grip *which is a wrenchlike tool* resembles pliers. _____

3. The watercolor *that Barbara painted* shows a lakeside scene in winter. _____

4. Anyone *who is familiar with our subway system* will tell you it was
   well planned. _____

5. An obelisk commemorates the Battle of Bunker Hill *which actually was*
   fought on Breed's Hill. _____

6. "Silent Cal" is the nickname *that was bestowed on President Coolidge.* _____

7. James Buchanan was the only President *who remained single.* _____

8. Two terms in office was a tradition *that Thomas Jefferson established*
   for U.S. Presidents. _____

9. Mrs. Farnaby *whom we named after the pet-shop owner* is our new cat. _____

10. Foods *that undergo little or no processing* are less expensive. _____

B. Using the Comma
Add commas where they are missing in the following paragraph. Some sentences do not need commas.

(1) The dancer whose farewell performance we attended was Rudolf Nureyev. **(2)** He was appearing with other ballet dancers in a special program that had six parts. **(3)** The part that I enjoyed most was an episode from the ballet *Sleeping Beauty*. **(4)** Teenager Jennifer Gelfand who rushed to the theater when another dancer was injured performed with a partner from the Bolshoi Ballet. **(5)** Boston's Wang Center for the Performing Arts which was redecorated recently was an impressive setting for the show.

The Comma (IV)

A. Using the Comma

The following sentences contain essential and nonessential clauses. Add commas where necessary. If a sentence is correct, write **Correct** in the blank.

1. Lila who is very talented won a scholarship to art school.

2. The Shaws need someone who can baby-sit after school.

3. Ms. Snyder whom you met yesterday is visiting from England.

4. The Mayor was the official who resolved the dispute.

5. Peter gave me his jacket which didn't fit him anymore.

6. The animal that we saw in the woods was a muskrat.

7. The United Nations delegates who met yesterday could not resolve the dispute.

8. This magazine needs someone who can write stirring adventures.

9. Amalia was the person who rescued the struggling swimmer.

10. Curling which is played on ice probably began in Scotland.

B. Using Commas in Writing

Combine the sentences by following the directions in parentheses. Use commas where necessary.

Example   The page follows this one. The page is missing.
          The page that follows this one is missing.

1. I got help from some neighbors. Some neighbors could recall outdated words. (Include an essential clause beginning with *who*.)

_____

2. They had used some of the words. They had seen others in old books. (Include two essential clauses beginning with *that*.)

_____

3. They knew a number of old words. They were willing to share old words. (Include a nonessential clause beginning with *which*.)

_____

_____

4. Cars have inspired many new words. People once called their cars *motors* or *machines*. (Include a nonessential clause beginning with *which*.)

_____

_____

The Comma (V)

Use a comma to separate the day of the month and the year. Do not use a comma when only the month and the year are given. When a date is part of a sentence, a comma also follows the year.

> February 29, 1992　　　　January 1991
>
> On June 6, 1990, we took a field trip.

Use a comma between the name of a city or town and the name of the state or country. When an address is part of a sentence, use a comma after each item. Do not use a comma between the state and the ZIP code.

> Los Angeles, California　　Geneva, Switzerland　　Boston, MA 02114
>
> Our trip to Los Angeles, California, was very exciting.

Use a comma after the salutation of a friendly letter. Use a comma after the complimentary close of a friendly letter or a business letter.

> Dear Sally Anne,　　　　　Sincerely yours,

Use a comma to avoid confusing a reader.

> Not far from the neighborhood, stores were opening up.

Using Commas Correctly

Add commas where necessary in the following sentences.

1. What event of national interest occurred on August 8 1974?

2. It was on October 29 1929 that America's first stock market crash occurred.

3. On either side of the handsome pewter dish pans hung gleaming.

4. Thomas E. Dewey lost the November 1948 presidential election.

5. A few feet beyond the closet doors opened onto a porch.

6. Write your senators at the U.S. Senate, Washington D.C. 20510-2102.

7. When the small fire started throughout the hospital the alarms sounded.

8. On January 26 1991 Monica Seles won tennis's Australian Open.

9. J. P. Whalen was born on July 23 1938 in Jamaica Plain Massachusetts.

10. Was the law passed in June 1990 or April 1991?

11.
> 4000 Dolphin Boulevard
>
> Orlando FL 32821
>
> July 16 1992

Dear Sharon

　　　　We finally arrived here last night. On our way down the highway we stopped in Norfolk Virginia and Savannah Georgia. Things seem different from the way they were the last time we visited here in June 1990. At our hotel rooms are small but comfortable. I'm having fun but missing everyone at home.

> Your friend
>
> Emily

The Comma (V)

Using the Comma in Writing

Rewrite each sentence using commas correctly. If a sentence is already correct, write **Correct.**

1. The last time I saw Derek Stephen and I heard him play the guitar.

_____

2. In fact, the two of us went to his guitar recital in January 1991.

_____

3. It was in Cleveland Ohio in the music school's auditorium.

_____

4. We flew to Cleveland on Saturday, January 16 the day of the recital.

_____

_____

5. For the morning of our flight reservations had been difficult to get.

_____

_____

6. The day before the airline had lowered its prices dramatically.

_____

7. In Cleveland, Derek told us he also planned to make guitars and repair them.

_____

8. He will be having a March 4 interview at a school where he can learn those skills.

_____

9. Remembering Derek said so many friends from high school days had made him eager to hear from them.

_____

_____

10. You can write to him at 3900 Carlin Court, Falls Church VA, 22046.

_____

_____

The Semicolon and Colon

Use a **semicolon** in the following ways: to join the parts of a compound sentence if no coordinating conjunction is used; to separate clauses when there are several commas in the parts of a compound sentence; to separate the parts of a series when there are commas within the parts; and before a conjunctive adverb that joins the clauses of a compound sentence.

Newts are brightly colored salamanders; efts are young newts.

Byzantine trade included furs such as sable, mink, and fox; precious stones, gold, and ivory; and fabrics such as silk, muslin, and damask.

California, New York, and Texas are the three most populous states; but the populations of Florida and Arizona are among the fastest growing.

Evan is a slow reader; however, he is an excellent student.

Use a **colon** in the following ways: to introduce a list of items; after the greeting of a business letter; between numerals indicating hours and minutes; between chapter and verse in a biblical reference; between two sentences when the second explains or summarizes the first; and to introduce a long or formal quotation.

You will need these items: work boots, warm clothing, and a backpack.
Dear Ms. Ellison:
The train will leave at 5:18 P.M.
It's clear your trip agreed with you: you look years younger.
In one of his essays, Emerson wrote: "Though we travel the world over to find the beautiful, we must carry it with us or we find it not."

Do not use a colon after a verb or a preposition unless the colon is being used to introduce a formal quotation.

| **Incorrect** | Peter likes to paint: horses, dogs, and cats. |
| **Correct** | Peter like to paint horses, dogs, and cats. |

Using Semicolons and Colons
Use semicolons and colons appropriately in the following sentences.

1. Jim enjoys history, literature, and psychology but Rebecca prefers math, science, and music.
2. Beethoven visited Vienna in 1787 Mozart heard him play there.
3. Dan is interested in Japan consequently, he enjoyed the novel *Shogun*.
4. The runner has trained for months unfortunately, yesterday he broke his ankle.
5. Before you paint, gather the following things paint, a palette, and brushes.
6. Let's ask Sylvia to play the piano she's the best pianist I know.
7. Rembrandt was a great painter nevertheless, he died penniless.
8. For skiing you need the following skis, poles, a warm jacket, a hat, and gloves.
9. E. B. White was an essayist however, he is best known for the book *Charlotte's Web*.
10. The following are jobs in advertising copywriting, editing, and design.

The Semicolon and the Colon

A. Using the Semicolon and the Colon
Add semicolons and colons where they are needed in the numbered sentences.

To jump start a car in cold weather, first find another car with a strong battery. **(1)** Then take the following safety precautions make sure that the cars do not touch turn off the ignitions of both cars turn off all accessories in both cars.

Now take a set of jumper cables coded with black and red markings. **(2)** Locate the positive terminals of the two batteries then connect the clamps of the red cable to the positive terminals. **(3)** Next, connect one clamp of the black cable to the negative terminal of the assisting battery connect the other clamp of the black cable to the engine block of the car to be started.

(4) When all the cables are connected, start the engine of the assisting car then start the engine of the other car. Once you have cut the engine of the assisting car, take one important final step, for safety's sake. **(5)** Remove the cable clamps in the reverse order from the way you connected them first, disconnect one of the black cable's clamps from the engine block then, disconnect the other from the assisting battery finally, disconnect the red cable's clamps from the positive terminals.

B. Using the Semicolon and Colon in Writing
Use semicolons and colons appropriately in the following sentences.

1. Ann was mesmerized by the city and its crowds, its broad streets, its skyscrapers.
2. Dear Mr. Perez

   Thank you for talking with me about a part-time job.
3. During our summer in Alaska, the sun was sometimes still shining at 10 30 P.M.
4. Linda hurried to the store however, it had already closed by the time she arrived.
5. You clearly won't be able to come to Andrew's party you have too much to do.
6. The biblical quotation "There is no new thing under the sun" is from

   Ecclesiastes 1 90.
7. Henry David Thoreau once said "To regret deeply is to live afresh."
8. The treasure included gold, silver, and copper a cannon, armor, and swords and

   many ancient maps.
9. In 1986 Ivan Lendl won the U.S. Open in tennis Stefan Edberg, the Australian

   Open and Boris Becker, Wimbledon.
10. Francis Bacon wrote "Prosperity is not without many fears and distastes adversity

    is not without comforts and hopes."

The Dash

Use **dashes** to set off an abrupt change of thought or an idea that breaks into the flow of a sentence. Also, use a dash after a series to indicate that a summary statement will follow.

A. Using the Dash
Add dashes where necessary in the following sentences.

1. Ants, bees, and people these organisms live in societies.
2. Ants and bees they both live in organized colonies communicate with one another by sound, gesture, or odor.
3. Bees communicate the location of food sources this has been proved through gesture.
4. One movement it is called a dance means that food has been found nearby.
5. Karl Von Frisch wrote he did research in the 1920's *Bees: Their Vision, Chemical Senses, and Language*.

B. Using the Dash
Rewrite each sentence, adding dashes where necessary.

1. A queen ant she is protected as the mother of the colony may live as long as twenty years.

   _____

   _____

2. Army ants they are sometimes called soldier ants have voracious appetites.

   _____

3. Young birds, lizards, snakes, even small mammals all these creatures may fall prey to hungry army ants.

   _____

   _____

4. Food-producing insects like aphids are herded sometimes even kept in shelters by some ants.

   _____

5. A sense of smell and color discrimination these are traits of bees.

   _____

The Dash

A. Identifying Correct Usage of the Dash

Decide if dashes are used correctly or should be inserted in the following sentences. In the blanks rewrite the sentences, using correct punctuation, or write **Correct.**

1. Nebulae, comets, asteroids these are all—studied by astronomers.

_____

2. The expensive menu listed I couldn't believe it—only two entrees.

_____

3. Time—would that I had more of it—always seems too short.

_____

4. Modern conveniences good plumbing, central heating, and even electricity—are often lacking in old houses.

_____

_____

5. If you had a wish—one pertaining to a foreign country you'd like to visit what would it be?

_____

_____

B. Using the Dash and Other Punctuation Marks

Add commas, semicolons, colons, and dashes where necessary in the paragraph.

(1) Ophthalmologists optometrists and opticians these are eye professionals. (2) Opticians specialize in eye care however they are not medical doctors. (3) They can repair broken glasses replace them if they are beyond repair and fit glasses and contact lenses. (4) Optometrists can also provide these services in addition they can examine eyes prescribe glasses and contact lenses and recommend eye exercises. (5) Ophthalmologists they are medical doctors can do everything opticians and optometrists do and more. (6) Unlike opticians and optometrists, ophthalmologists can do the following treat eye disorders and diseases prescribe medicines perform surgery.

(7) Before prescribing corrective lenses, the optometrist or ophthalmologist will do an examination none of it hurts. (8) One part is the Snellen test it's the test that requires you to read the chart with the big *E*. (9) Then the doctor checks the physical condition of your eyes he or she checks both inside and out. (10) A light is shone into each of your eyes this allows the doctor to examine the interior of your eyes.

The Hyphen

Use a **hyphen** at the end of a line to divide a word of two or more syllables. Use hyphens in compound numbers from twenty-one to ninety-nine, in fractions, in certain compound nouns, and between words that make up a compound adjective used before a noun.

The cut-rate store ran a twenty-four hour sale.
The drive-in is showing a double feature for one-half regular price.

Using the Hyphen

Add hyphens where necessary in the following sentences. If a sentence does not need a hyphen, write **Correct** in the blank.

1. Ms. Lopez sent her father in law a birthday card. _____

2. At forty three John F. Kennedy was the youngest person ever elected President. _____

3. The long lost son is a well worn theme of books and movies. _____

4. There were thirty three states in the Union at the outbreak of the Civil War. _____

5. An Irish setter is a large, red haired dog. _____

6. The senators defeated the bill by a two thirds majority. _____

7. Renee's grandmother gave her an antique jack in the box. _____

8. Mickey Mantle seemed to be an accident-prone athlete. _____

9. Only twenty three students signed up for the excursion. _____

10. In 1911, sixty three year old Bram Stoker wrote the novel *Dracula*. _____

11. During the arctic summer the sun shines twenty four hours a day. _____

12. Michael received on the job training as a carpenter's assistant. _____

13. My great grandfather was a Cherokee chief. _____

14. Agatha Christie wrote many best selling novels. _____

15. The governor of our state has become very well known. _____

16. These out of print books were donated to the library. _____

17. Visitors from out of town came in droves. _____

18. The Vice President spoke for forty five minutes. _____

19. A public speaker should be well prepared. _____

20. Hal's business venture was a short lived one indeed. _____

The Hyphen

A. Using the Hyphen

Add hyphens where necessary in the following sentences. Use a dictionary if necessary.

1. My brother in law has always wanted to go skiing in the Bugaboo Mountains in British Columbia.

2. One half of her income is used to pay the rent and buy food.

3. The wildlife movie we saw on television yesterday showed a man feeding a ten foot alligator.

4. The green covered booklet is designed to be a guide to the transport services available in the city.

5. In the 1950's Marc Chagall began making stained glass windows.

6. The coach scheduled a post game conference.

7. My ninety five year old great grandmother tells me stories about what life was like at the turn of the century.

8. I'd like to get a part time job next summer so I can start saving money to buy a car.

9. "Stopping by Woods on a Snowy Evening" is one of the best loved poems in American literature.

10. There are several well known actors in this movie, but still no one seems interested in going to see it.

B. Using the Hyphen

Add hyphens where necessary in the following paragraphs.

(1) Humans have two sets of teeth: primary teeth and permanent teeth. (2) The twenty primary teeth begin to erupt before a baby is one year old. (3) They may re main until the child is eleven or twelve. (4) There are thirty two permanent teeth. (5) The first of these erupt when the child is about six years old. (6) Thirteen year old children should have twenty eight permanent teeth. (7) The third molars, or wisdom teeth, generally erupt at around the age of eighteen, but they may come in later or not at all.

(8) Both sets of teeth can be protected against tooth decay by daily at home care and by regular professional care at the dentist's. (9) At home care should include thorough brushing and flossing. (10) Good tasting toothpaste may make brushing more pleasant. (11) Proper dental care can help prevent periodontics, which are diseases of the tooth supporting tissues. (12) Regular dental checkups and professional teeth cleanings are also all important.

The Apostrophe

To form the possessive of a singular noun, add an **apostrophe** and *s* even if the singular noun ends in *s*.

Bess's field trip was canceled.

To form the possessive of a plural noun ending in *s*, add only the apostrophe.

Both students' poems were read in class.

Plural nouns that do not end in *s* take an apostrophe and *s*.

The survey measured people's political opinions.

To form the possessive of an indefinite pronoun, use an apostrophe and *s*.

Someone's car is blocking traffic.

Do not use an apostrophe with a possessive personal pronoun.

hers   ours   yours   its   theirs

Use an apostrophe in a contraction and to show that numbers in a date have been omitted.

she's = she is   the class of '91

Use an apostrophe and *s* to form the plurals of letters, figures, and words that are used as words.

two *A's*   three *10's*   no *if's, and's,* or *but's*

Using the Apostrophe

Add apostrophes where necessary in the following sentences.

1. Is this someones idea of a joke? _____

2. Lucretia Mott was a supporter of womens rights in the mid-1800's. _____

3. Many school children remember George Washington as someone who

    couldnt tell a lie. _____

4. The baseball players strike interrupted the baseball season. _____

5. Cynthias poll resulted in ten *yess,* four *nos,* and two *undecideds.* _____

6. The employees union held a meeting at its new headquarters. _____

7. E. E. Cummings spelled his name with two small *es* and a small *c.* _____

8. Houdinis ability to escape almost any restraint was amazing. _____

9. The 56 Chevy and the 66 Mustang are Donalds favorite cars. _____

10. There were seven *90s,* ten *80s,* and five *70s* on the chemistry test. _____

The Apostrophe

A. Using the Apostrophe

Add apostrophes where necessary in the following paragraphs.

(1) There is great diversity of fish species in a coral reef. (2) Anyone whos interested in tropical fish should try scuba diving near a reef. (3) Reefs have many places in which fish can hide. (4) The waves tumbling action stirs up the water, bringing fresh nutrients and washing away residue. (5) Its important for a reefs residents to have both food and refuge.

(6) A fishs life is often threatened by a reefs numerous and diverse predators. (7) Two of the most common are moray eels and jacks. (8) Both are astonishingly fast, particularly for short bursts of about ten feet. (9) The morays body is streamlined. (10) The jacks fins and body shape are like those of a fighter jet. (11) Both morays and jacks rocket suddenly from behind a rocks cover to snap up fish prey. (12) The predators speed and stealth make them an ever-present danger to all the other fish on the reef. (13) The predators, however, help keep a natural balance of species in the worlds oceans.

B. Using the Apostrophe in Writing

Rewrite the following sentences to correct mistakes in the use of the apostrophe.

1. Marty received two *Bs'* and two *Cs'* on his report card.

_____

2. "I wandered lonely as a cloud" is the first line of Wordsworths' famous poem.

_____

3. Whose car shall we take, your's or mine?

_____

4. My two little sisters favorite story is "How the Crocodile Got It's Smile."

_____

5. His' truck sped out of control and crashed into the garage door.

_____

6. Vanessa couldnt keep up with Debras aerobic exercise class.

_____

Quotation Marks (I)

Use quotation marks at the beginning and at the end of a direct quotation. Use single quotation marks to enclose a quote within a quote.

Direct Quotation	"Ms. Parker will be with you shortly," she said.
Quote within a Quote	"Mikey said, 'Put the dirty pans in the oven,' so I did," explained my little sister.

When a quotation is divided by explanatory words, enclose each part of the quotation in quotation marks.

"If I am elected," the candidate declared, "I promise to cut the deficit."

Using Quotation Marks Correctly

Add quotation marks where necessary in each sentence.

1. "I'm sure you will enjoy J. D. Salinger's short stories, said Ms. Phillips.

2. "In the Middle Ages," said Dr. Lynch, "books were handwritten by monks.

3. Andrea said, In Shakespeare's *As You Like It* a character says, All the world's a stage.

4. We can never have enough of nature, wrote Henry David Thoreau.

5. Samuel Johnson wrote, Whatever you have, spend less.

6. Whoever said, Love is blind, was correct, said Mark.

7. I missed Mardi Gras, said Marni, but I went to the World's Fair.

8. A sonnet consists of fourteen lines, explained Mr. Jackson.

9. I plan to go to California, Matt said, if I can save enough money.

10. The Manx is a type of cat, explained Janet.

11. I know who wrote, The medium is the message, Clare said. It was Marshall McLuhan.

12. A rose, wrote Gertrude Stein, is a rose is a rose is a rose.

13. When Neil Armstrong stepped onto the moon, he said, That's one small step for a man, one giant leap for mankind.

14. Injustice anywhere is a threat to justice everywhere, wrote Martin Luther King, Jr.

15. Becky claimed that she agreed with the Shakespearean character who said, Neither a borrower nor a lender be.

16. When Thomas Paine wrote, These are the times that try men's souls, he was trying to win support for the American Revolution, Keith explained.

17. Marcia said, My parents remember the speech in which John F. Kennedy implored, Ask not what your country can do for you—ask what you can do for your country.

18. Anne Frank wrote in her diary, In spite of everything I still believe that people are really good at heart.

Quotation Marks (I)

A. Using Quotation Marks
Add quotation marks where necessary.

Shortly after 2:00 A.M. on April 15, 1912, the ship *Titanic* slid to its watery grave. The passenger liner, on its maiden voyage from England to New York, had struck an iceberg in the North Atlantic.

William Ryan, a geologist at Columbia University, believes the *Titanic* can be salvaged. The only question, he says, is how much money you're willing to spend. We're talking about hundreds of millions of dollars.

A French team has already brought up such items as trays and dishes from the wreck. In a magazine article the team leader says, None of the items we brought up will be sold for profit.

Ruth Blanchard, a survivor of the *Titanic,* opposes plans to disturb it. It's the graveyard of 1,500 people, she says. I believe they should be left in peace.

B. Correcting Misuse of Quotation Marks
Rewrite the following sentences, using quotation marks correctly. Delete any unnecessary quotation marks.

1. My great-grandmother, a survivor of the *Titanic* disaster, told me "about the ship's striking an iceberg and sinking."

   _____

   _____

2. "She said, Let me tell you about my experiences in one of the lifeboats."

   _____

3. I told her "that I would love to hear her story."

   _____

4. John Pierce plans to raise the ship. "The *Titanic,* he states, is coming up."

   _____

5. "I am dismayed, he said, by those who say, "Leave it alone."

   _____

6. 'I have mixed feelings about raising the *Titanic,'* Anna said.

   _____

Quotation Marks (II)

Place a comma after explanatory words that come before a direct quotation.

> Gina waved to me and called, "I'll phone you after dinner."

Commas and periods always appear inside closing quotation marks.

> "Wait a minute," Dena said, "until I find my keys."

Place question marks and exclamation points inside the quotation marks if they belong to the quotation itself.

> Rhoda asked, "How many computer languages exist today?"
> Ben exclaimed, "We're missing the last train home!"

Place question marks and exclamation points outside the quotation marks if they do not belong to the quotation.

> Didn't you hear the cashier call, "The register is down"?
> How amazed I was when our neighbor said, "I am nearly ninety years old"!

Using Quotation Marks with Other Punctuation

Punctuate the following sentences correctly, using commas, quotation marks, and end marks as necessary.

1. Mark Twain stated Courage is resistance to fear, mastery of fear—not absence of fear

2. Do you know who wrote No Truth or goodness realized by man ever dies

3. Look out below the hikers frantically yelled

4. A skid states the booklet *Winter Motoring* reflects poor driving technique

5. Which President made the statement If a man starts out to make himself President, he hardly ever arrives

6. Nowadays explained the nurse chemotherapy can be controlled by a small, computer-programmed, implanted device

7. How often inquired Ali does a longhaired cat need its fur brushed and combed

8. Who was the first person to remark A fool and his money are soon parted

9. Aquatic plants the saleswoman began are essential for keeping the fish in aquariums healthy

10. I can't believe exclaimed Anita that motion pictures were invented in 1891

11. What do you think of my choice of subject—the ground-nesting snowy owl Stephen was asking

12. Jennifer asked Why did John Donne say No man is an island

13. We heard Kareem exclaim My sister will be interviewed on Channel 4 tonight

14. Didn't Louisa May Alcott's father once say One must be a wise reader to quote wisely and well

15. Writing a piece of fiction begins with asking yourself What if . . .

Quotations Marks (II)

A. Writing Quotations Correctly

Rewrite the sentences to include direct quotations. Follow the directions in parentheses. Use quotation marks, commas, and end marks correctly.

1. Amy exclaimed that she found some great quotations for the bulletin board. (Put the explanatory words at the beginning.)

_____

_____

2. Voltaire stated that the secret of being a bore is to tell everything. (Put the explanatory words at the beginning.)

_____

_____

3. This famous French writer also said that common sense is not so common. (Put the explanatory words at the end.)

_____

_____

4. Wasn't it Benjamin Franklin who wrote that lost time is never found again? (Put the explanatory words at the beginning.)

_____

_____

5. Charles Kettering commented that we should all be concerned about the future because we will spend the rest of our lives there. (Put the explanatory words at the beginning.)

_____

_____

B. Using Quotation Marks with Other Punctuation

In the following sentences, correct any errors in the use of end marks and quotation marks. If a sentence contains no errors, write **Correct** on the line.

1. "What unusual characters I've encountered in fiction"! said Clara. _____

2. A famous poem by Christina Rossetti begins, "Who has seen the wind?" _____

3. Didn't O. Henry say, "About the only chance for the truth to be told is in fiction?" _____

4. The novelist Willa Cather wrote, "There are only two or three human stories." _____

Orange Level, Copyright © McDougal, Littell & Company

198   *Handbook 41 Punctuation*

Quotation Marks (III)

Use quotation marks to enclose the titles of magazine articles, chapters, short stories, TV episodes, essays, poems, and songs.

"The Best Advice I Ever Had"   "The Most Dangerous Game"

Underline the titles of books, newspapers, magazines, plays, movies, TV series, works of art, epic poems, and long musical compositions.

<u>Annie John</u>   <u>Our Town</u>   <u>Boston Globe</u>

Identifying Titles Correctly

Find the titles in the following sentences and add quotation marks or underlining correctly.

1. The movie Cyrano de Bergerac is based on Edmond Rostand's play.
2. Edgar Degas, a French Impressionist, created bronze sculptures and produced numerous paintings, among them The Bellelli Family, a group portrait.
3. Markings was a book of diary entries by Dag Hammarskjöld, a United Nations Secretary General; it was published after his death.
4. The title song The Rose, in the film of that name, has a theme of hope.
5. Millions of Americans read either Time or Newsweek every week.
6. Songs like Paul Simon and Art Garfunkel's Sounds of Silence synchronize the talents of the composer and the lyricist.
7. A recording of the musical score from the film Chariots of Fire has sold widely.
8. Lullaby for Peregrine is Robert P. Tristram Coffin's poem for the first Pilgrim child born in the New World.
9. The Life and Death of a Western Gladiator is an article about a rattlesnake; it was written by Charles Finney for Harper's magazine.
10. Columnist Sydney J. Harris wrote the essay We're Not Fit to Colonize Space.
11. My favorite episode of the Nova television series is called Case of the Flying Dinosaur.
12. The title Seventeen was used long ago by Booth Tarkington for a novel about a teenaged boy; it is now the title of a magazine for girls.
13. In Jessamyn West's short story Sixteen, a girl struggles with the conflicts of growing up.
14. The Song of Roland is the national epic of France.
15. Robert Louis Stevenson, known for his adventure novels, also wrote volumes of essays; one of his most popular essays is Walking Tours.

Quotation Marks (III)

Correcting Misuse of Quotation Marks

Rewrite any sentence in which underlining or quotation marks are not correctly used. Delete any unnecessary quotation marks. If a sentence has no error, write **Correct.**

1. The painting "Pilgrims Landing at Cape Cod" depicts a historic event.

   _____

2. The book Founding Mothers tells how women fought for American independence.

   _____

3. Emerson's famous essay Nature demonstrated Transcendental thought.

   _____

4. We heard all of Bach's <u>Brandenburg Concerto No. 5 in D Major</u>.

   _____

5. "Animals" magazine features such articles as The Magic of Cedar Swamps.

   _____

6. Many readers enjoy Gwendolyn Brooks's poem The Ballad of Late Annie.

   _____

7. One of Stephen Crane's best-known stories is <u>The Blue Hotel</u>.

   _____

8. Old Possum's Book of Practical Cats, which includes such poems as Growltiger's Last Stand, provided the lyrics for Cats, a musical comedy.

   _____

   _____

9. An episode of "The Golden Girls" TV series is titled <u>Rose Fights Back</u>.

   _____

10. "The Spirit of '76," a chapter in Stephen Schlesinger's book <u>The New Reformers</u>, describes events of 1976.

   _____

   _____

Directions One or more of the underlined sections in the following sentences may contain errors of grammar, usage, capitalization, punctuation, or spelling. Write the letter of each incorrect section; then rewrite the item correctly. If there is no error in an item, write *E.* Write your answers on your own paper or on an answer sheet, as your teacher directs.

Example   Tomorrows' emergency meeting of the Foreign Relations
                 A   B

              committee will be held promptly at 9:30 A.M.   No error
                C   D   E

Answer   A—Tomorrow's   B—Foreign Relations Committee

1. "A rose is a rose is a rose" stated Gertrude Stein in what is perhaps the
    A   B C

   best known line from her poetry.   No error
     D   E

2. Aaron Burr who was Vice-President of the United States under Thomas Jefferson,
    A   B   C

   shot, and killed Alexander Hamilton in a duel.   No error
     D   E

3. The doctor said that "no one was to visit the patient for at least twenty-four
              A   B   C

   hours after the surgery."   No error
           D   E

4. Among the numerous novels that portray the horrors of war is Eric Maria
                 A   B

   Remarque's *All Quiet on the Western Front,* set in World War I.   No error
            C   D   E

5. The actor Martin Sheen who's sons are also movie actors, was originally named
       A   B   C   D

   Ramon Estevez.   No error
          E

6. Unfortunately Kirsten and Chris's skit has been cut from the show.   No error
    A   B   C   D   E

7. Flying out of <u>Long Island, New York,</u> in <u>May 1927,</u> Charles Lindbergh
                      A   **B**

    took 33 hours to cross the <u>Atlantic Ocean;</u> on <u>September 1, 1974,</u> a pair
                                C   **D**

    of pilots flew across the same ocean in less than two hours. <u>No error</u>
                                                            E

8. <u>Your</u> absolutely right that the most common <u>English surname</u> is <u>Smith, however,</u>
    A   **B**   **C**

    the most common surname in the world is the <u>Chinese name Chang.</u> <u>No error</u>
                                                    D   **E**

9. The tallest skyscrapers <u>include:</u> the <u>Sears tower in Chicago, Illinois;</u> the <u>World</u>
                            A   **B**

    <u>Trade Center in New York City, New York;</u> and the <u>Texas Building in Houston,</u>
                            C   **D**

    <u>Texas.</u> <u>No error</u>
             E

10. "The <u>post-game parade,"</u> said the coach <u>enthusiasticly,</u> <u>"will</u> be led
            A   **B**   **C**

    by <u>whomever</u> scores the most runs." <u>No error</u>
       D   **E**

11. Charles said <u>"that</u> his <u>aunt</u> would be <u>visiting</u> him this <u>Summer."</u> <u>No error</u>
                      A   **B**   **C**   **D**   **E**

12. The speaker from the planetarium told us that among <u>Jupiter's</u> largest <u>Moons</u> are
                                                  A   **B**

    <u>Io, Europa,</u> and Ganymede. <u>No error</u>
    C   **D**   **E**

13. <u>"Yes, Mother,</u> I do know <u>who</u> wrote the Declaration of <u>Independence."</u> Howard said
     A   **B**   **C**   **D**

    impatiently. <u>No error</u>
                 E

14. Imported products from the <u>far east</u> include <u>Japanese</u> items such as
                              A   **B**

    <u>Sony Televisions</u> and <u>Nikon cameras.</u> <u>No error</u>
           C   **D**   **E**

15. After the first <u>inning,</u> of the <u>game,</u> Jason <u>said, "What's</u> wrong with our team
                  A   **B**   **C**

    <u>today</u>"? <u>No error</u>
     D   **E**

Directions Read the passage and choose the word or group of words that belongs in each numbered space. Write the letter of the correct answer on your own paper or on an answer sheet, as your teacher directs.

Example In the years before ___(1)___ the fire ant came to the United States from South America. Though at first limited to the South, it is now threatening to spread to ___(2)___.

1. A. World war II
   B. World War II
   C. world war II,
   D. World War II,

2. A. the states of new Mexico, and Arizona
   B. the states of New Mexico and Arizona
   C. the States of New Mexico and Arizona
   D. the states of New Mexico, Arizona

Answers 1—D   2—B

At Washington's ___(16)___ the air traffic controller was the person ___(17)___ talking into three microphones and listening to ten loudspeakers. "The ___(18)___ almost unbearable." The tower had to handle from 600 to 700 takeoffs and ___(19)___ only maps and radios to track flights. However, after 128 people died in a collision over the ___(20)___ improvements were made. In particular, the ___(21)___ ordered the installation of radar.

16. A. National Airport in 1946
    B. National airport, in 1946
    C. national Airport in 1946,
    D. National Airport in 1946,

17. A. who looked out the window while
    B. who looked out the window; while
    C. which looked out the window, while
    D. whom looked out the window while

18. A. clamor, said an observer, was
    B. clamor," said an observer, "was
    C. clamor," said an observer, "Was
    D. clamor" said an observer "was

19. A. landings: using
    B. landings, using
    C. landings; using
    D. landing's using

20. A. Grand Canyon in June 1956,
    B. Grand Canyon in June, 1956,
    C. grand canyon in June 1956,
    D. Grand Canyon in June 1956

21. A. Civil Aeronautics Administration,
    B. civil aeronautics administration
    C. Civil Aeronautics Administration
    D. Civil Aeronautics administration

Even with the aid of radar, the controller's job is demanding. Why is it so ___(22)___ traffic is heavy, and the controller is the only ___(23)___ track of all planes. Furthermore, there are often more planes than air space.

Air traffic controllers train at the Federal Aviation Administration Academy in Oklahoma City. They begin with the ___(24)___ aviation regulations, radio navigations, ___(25)___ They must spend three years in courses and on-the-job training before passing into the system.

22. A. difficult. Air
    B. difficult? Air
    C. difficult! Air
    D. difficult; air

23. A. one who keeps
    B. one, who keeps
    C. one whom keeps
    D. one whom keep

24. A. basics; weather,
    B. basics, weather,
    C. basics. Weather
    D. basics: weather,

25. A. air lanes and communications.
    B. air lanes, communications,
    C. air lanes, and communications.
    D. air lanes; and communications.

Proofreading Practice: The Sentence and Its Parts

Writing Sentences Correctly Read the passage below. Then use proofreading marks to correct all errors in capitalization, punctuation, spelling, and grammar. Look especially for sentence fragments and run-on sentences.

Does inteligent life exist elsewhere in our galaxy. Researchers from the National Aeronautics and Space administration (NASA), the SETI Institute (Search for Extraterrestrial Intelligence), and the Jet Propulsion Laboratory are working on a major program that may provide an answer to this question. On Columbus Day 1992 the researchers began the more intensive search ever conducted. For evidence of Extraterrestrial life within our galaxy. They turned on new high-powered equipment that is searching the galaxy for radio signals possibly being transmited by alien civilizations.

The SETI program consists of two search strategys—a targeted search and a sky survey. The targeted search uses the most largest radio telescopes in the world to focus on 800 nearby stars and listen for radio signals. The sky survey uses 34-meter antennas to scan the entire sky for signals coming from places not on the targeted search list the researchers expect the two search strategies to continue until about the year 2002.

According to Deputy Chief Bernard M. Oliver at the SETI program office, "Theirs nothing unique about our sun and its planets that one would not expect to find duplicated in millions of other places in the galaxy. Oliver explains that since there are over 10 billion sunlike stars in the Milky way alone, a large number of these stars may have planetary systems therefore it is highly likely that within those systems are planets with an earthlike environment that can support intelligent life forms. On the basis of this likelihood, the researchers on the SETI team believes that it is just a matter of time before contact with a distant civilzation will be made.

Proofreading Practice: Complete Sentences

Writing Sentences Correctly Read the business letter below. Then use proofreading marks to correct the errors in capitalization, punctuation, spelling, and grammar. Look especially for sentence fragments and run-on sentences.

7523 Powers Street

Shelby Iowa 51570

October 17, 19—

Dear Chef Clarisse

I like to watch your show, *Cooking with Clarisse,* on saturday afternoons. I especially like when you prepare foods that are popular with kids and teens. I have invented a snack that I make when some of my friends comes over to my house. We all think it's great, and it's real easy to make. Heres the recipe:

Marks mini-Taco Pizza snacks

10 refrigerator biscuits	1/4 c. of grated cheddar cheese
1 6-oz. can of enchilada sauce	1 choped onion
1/2 envelope of taco seasoning	1/2 c. of water
1/2 lb. of ground beef	

Preheat your oven to 425°. Brown the ground beaf and onion, and drain the fat. Add the taco seasoning and water, and stir the mixture. After you have brung it to a boil. Reduce the heat and simmer it for 15-20 minutes.

On a greased baking sheet. Flaten each biscuit to a four-inch circle and make a rim. Fill the biscuits with enchilada sauce. Add the ground beef and onion sprinkel the cheese on top. Bake them in the bottom half of your oven for 10 minutes. Enjoy!

I hope you make this recipe on your show. Happy cooking!

Sincerely

Mark Ulrich

Proofreading Practice: Using Nouns

Using Nouns Correctly Read the article below. Then use proofreading marks to correct all errors in capitalization, punctuation, spelling, and grammar. Pay special attention to the use of nouns.

Most Chicagoans agree that the Chicago Air and Water show is one of their cities most exciting events. Held every summer on Lake Michigan's spectaculer shoreline, the event attracts hundreds of thousands of spectators. men, womens, and children all take delight in the shows daring and dramatic performances. Among the most popular attractions are the military groups who demonstrate their special skills, such as parachuting, assault procedures, and rescue operations.

The highlight of each show is the final act. A loud roar seems to come out of nowhere as spectaters are greeted by the sudden appearence of a military jet team— the U.S. Air Force Thunderbirds, the U.S. Navy blue angels, or the Canadian Snow Birds. Members of the team risks their lifes as they carry out a series of aerial maneuvers that do not never cease to amaze and excite the crowd. In one thrilling feat, two or more planes fly straight toward each other. At several hundred miles per hour. Loud oohs and aahs can be heard in the crowd as the planes veer away from each other at the last second.

What daring flight heros and performances will dazzle the crowd at the next Chicago Air and Water Show. Time will tell, but if passed shows are any indication, the star lineup will undoubtedly meet most Chicagoans expectations. As the show draws near, familys, couples, and individuals who just wouldnt miss this annual event will be making there plans for another exciting after noon on the lake front.

Orange Level, Copyright © McDougal, Littell & Company

Proofreading Practice: Using Pronouns

Using Pronouns Correctly Read the news story below. Then use proofreading marks to correct all errors in capitalization, punctuation, spelling, and grammar. Pay special attention to the use of pronouns.

Driving on a lonely desert road on a trip to california, Margaret Starr had car trouble. An hour earlier, she had turned off the main highway to take a shortcut. Now her and her two children, eight-year-old Madge and eleven-year-old Andy, were stranded. "How long can the kids and me last without water?" she wondered. It wasn't long before the heat in the car became unbearible. Margaret opened the trunk and pulled out a blanket. She set about making a half tent by using rocks to secure one end of the blanket to the top of the car and the other end to the ground in the shade of the shelter, it seemed a little less hotter

The next day, Margaret knew she had to find water. She drained her car radiator and tasted it. "Its undrinkable," she muttered disappointedly, but she didn't throw it out. She dampened a rag and used it to cool her childrens faces. Then she tried digging for water. She didn't find any but she noticed that the ground was cooler a foot or so down. She asked Andy to help her dig shallow pits for Madge and he to lay in. Then she covered their bodys with sand and smeared they're faces with cold cream. Later, Margaret slashed pieces of cactus. She and the children squeezed them cactus pieces to get every bit of moisture.

By the third day, Margaret knew that she and her children could not survive much longer. She set out in the direction of the main high way. On the fourth day, two rockhounds whom were out prospecting found Margaret laying in the road. They revived her and then rescued her children.

Margaret hadn't never thought of herself as a particularly clever person. However, experts said that her creative thinking had saved both her and her children. She and them survived against incredable odds.

Proofreading Practice: Using Verbs

Using Verbs Correctly Read the passage below. Then use proofreading marks to correct all errors in capitalization, punctuation, spelling, and grammar. Pay special attention to the use of verbs.

Inspector Swift was hot on the trail of another bold and cunning criminal. The night before, there had been a robbery at the home of Mr. and Mrs. Howard Smythe, one of the towns wealthyest couples. A valueable painting had been stole from the Smythes' den and the police report suggested that the robber had broken a window and then had entered the room. In addition, a tiny peice of blue fabric laying next to the glass on the floor suggested that the robber had tore his shirt as he crawled through the window. However on the basis of his own investigation, Inspector Swift was convinced that the robber had went into the room through the door, not the window. The Inspector already knowed that the outcome of this case would rise some eyebrows.

"By the end of the day, thought Inspector Swift I will have spoke to every one of the Smythes household employees. I'll crack this case in no time!"

None of the employees were spared the inspector's careful questioning, not even Mrs. Sedwick the smythes' cook and most trusted worker. Mrs. Sedwick walked into the living room, where the inspector had been waiting, and set down. She sqirmed uneasily and then shouted, "Leave me go! I didn't steal no painting!

"On the contrary, Mrs Sedwick, you did steal the painting, and I can prove it, replied the inspector. He held up a plastic bag that contained fabric like the piece that had been finded on the den floor. "We found this fabric in your sewing basket *you* broke the window yourself and planted this clue so that the police would beleive that someone had broke into the house."

Proofreading Practice: Using Modifiers

Using Modifiers Correctly Read the announcement below. Then use proofreading marks to correct all errors in capitalization, punctuation, spelling, and grammar. Pay special attention to the use of modifiers.

West Fest

Step into the past and relive the exciting days of the Old West. Don't miss none of these thrilling attractions and activities at the incredibly 50-acre site of Colorado's West fest extravaganza. Look what's in store for you:

Western Stage Show

Enjoy good knee-slapping and foot-stomping performances by some of the more talented stars of todays country music.

Musical Entertainment

Join in the fun of line dancing and two-stepping to the livly music of several excelent country bands.

Horseback Riding

Take a trail ride in the beautifulest country setting imagineable.

Square Dancing

Expert caller Joe "Smoothie" Jones always calls out the dance movements very clear. Even beginners dance quite good to Joes directions.

Hearty Cowpoke Supper

Tasty chow will be served between 5:00 and 8:00 pm daily. Hungry cowpokes can wander over to the most nearest chuck wagon for some real hearty edibles.

Old-Time Photo Shop

Individuals, couples, and groups can have there pictures taken in period costumes customers can also have them photos framed.

General Store

Shop in the supermarket of yesterday. This here store has great gifts and souvenirs.

Call 555-WEST for more details, partner.

Proofreading Practice: Using Prepositions, Conjunctions, and Interjections

A. Using Prepositions, Conjunctions, and Interjections Correctly Read the description below. Then use proofreading marks to correct all errors in capitalization, punctuation, spelling, and grammar. Pay special attention to the use of prepositions, conjunctions, and interjections.

Unbeleivable! Incredible. Wow! Words of surprise like these are frequently uttered by visitors standing above on the rim of the majestic Grand canyon for the first time. Gazing upon the canyon's multicolored cliffs and wondrous vistas is an experience of a lifetime! However no visit to the Grand Canyon is complete without going down in the canyon. Visitors who travel down the mountainous trails in the canyon walls discovers unique and diverse rock formations. They can also observe an abundance of plants, flowers, and animals that have adapted good to the canyons dessert environment. The more adventurus travelers complete the one-mile descent to the bottom of the canyon, where they are greeted by the raging waters of the mighty Colorado river.

B. Using More Prepositions, Conjunctions, and Interjections Correctly
Read the postcard below. Then use proofreading marks to correct all errors.

Dear Naomi

Guess where I went to today! I took a mule trip into the Grand Canyon. What an adventure! My mules' name was Ida, and, oh yes she was stubborn! Of all the mules in the group, she was the more stubborn one, and beside that, she insisted on stopping to nibble at the bushes all along the trail. When I finaly got her back in line, she proceeded to walk on the outside of the trail, where the drops were very steep. The guide said not to worry though, because mules are sure-footed I guess he was right, because Ida didn't loose her footing even once. All in all, the mule trip was thrilling but I'm stiff and soar from being into the saddle so long. Ouch.

Jan

Proofreading Practice: Reviewing Parts of Speech

Using Parts of Speech Correctly Read the survey below. Then use proofreading marks to correct all errors in capitalization, punctuation, spelling, and grammar. Look for words that have been used incorrectly.

The management team of Teen Scene want to make improvments in its store, and you can help. Please take the time to fill out this survey your comments will be took very serious as the team tries to create a better store for their valued customers.

1. Describe the stile of casual clothes you like best. _____

   _____

2. What fabrics are most appealing to you in casual clothes?

   _____

   What types of fabrics does you avoid? _____

3. Check *True* or *False?*

   The clothes at Teen Scene are made real good. True _____ False _____

4. Check the statement below that tells how you feel about the prices at Teen scene:

   The prices are very good. _____

   Only some of the clothes is within my budget. _____

   I can only look. The prices are much too high. _____

5. Check the statement below that tells how you feel about the service you recieve

   at Teen Scene:

   I always get friendly courteous, and helpful service. _____

   Some of the salespeople give good service but others act uncaring. _____

   The service is always poor. _____

6. Check *True* or *False.*

   There are always enough salesclerks during a sale in the fitting rooms and at the

   checkout counters. True _____ False _____

Optional: Write your name and a phone number where you can be reached at.

_____

Proofreading Practice: Using Verbals and Appositives

Using Verbals and Appositives Correctly Read the passage below. Then use proofreading marks to correct all errors in capitalization, punctuation, spelling, and grammar. Look especially for misplaced modifiers, dangling modifiers, and split infinitives.

Wiggling back and forth, many people are disgusted at the sight of a long, slimy worm. Indeed, a worm is not a visualy attractive creature to human beings. In fact the word *worm* has become a generic name for any lowly life form. However, such a negative image is undeserved. In reality, worms are truely amazing little creatures and serve many useful purposes that far outvalue their usefulness as fish bait. Knowing them there purposes, worms might be shown the respect and appreciation they deserve.

Boring their way through the upper soil, worms are sometimes called natures plow. There burrows allow air and water to pass through the soil easy, promoting plant growth. In addition, consuming about 30 percent of their own weight daily in plant matter and minute animals and dirt, useful excrement is left on the surface of the soil. The excrement of worms transform barren soil into rich, fertile loam.

Population figures for worms are staggering! Researchers estimate that there are more than four thousand earthworm species varying greatly in habit and diet and the list grows by a dozen or so new species each year. While some species lives in rain-forest treetops and dine on decomposing material found in Bromeliads, a type of pineapple plant, other species live as much as eight feet underground and consume protozoa, bacteria, and other microorganisms from the soil. Some species even dine on other earth worms!

Worms are also a good source of protein. There is no need to, however, worry that earthworms will become a secret ingredient in fast food hamburgers. Obtaining the tremendus number of worms that would be reqired for human consumption on a regular basis would be much too costly.

Proofreading Practice: Subject-Verb Agreement

Using Subjects and Verbs Correctly Read the description below. Then use proofreading marks to correct all errors in capitalization, punctuation, spelling, and grammar. Look especially for sentences in which the subject and verb do not agree in number.

Upon entering an Amish settlement, visitors notice the homes painted white, the horses and buggies, and the plain clothing of the residents. The Amish are hard working and gentle people who practices a simple way of life. Some of the men are farmers, while others work in various trades, such as furniture making. The women are homemakers who spend their spare time making quilts and other crafts. Both the men and women are very skilled craftspersons their products are sold in Amish stores nationwide and are of high quality.

Since the 1600s, the Amish has held firm to their beliefs and traditions in a world that has made giant technological advances. They do not oppose progress but they have rejected much of modern technology, including radioes and television. Beleiving that they must be "in the world, but not of it," the Amish have a culture and a value system that emphasizes family and community. Regarding radio and television as a threat to family life, amish families spend their leisure time reading. At mealtime, neither radio nor television interrupt the quiet time needed for family conversation

There are an abundance of good food and social activitys in the comunity. The Amish cherishes their families, relatives, and friends and regularly travel to each other's homes for both informal visits and formal occasions such as baptisms, worship services, weddings, and funerals many of the Amish enjoys group games, such as volleyball and baseball.

The Amish also truly model the meaning of community spirit. When a disaster strikes an Amish household, the neighbors does that familys chores for them, takes care of their children, and harvests their crops. When a barn burns down, everyone work together to rebuild it.

Proofreading Practice: Using Clauses

A. Using Clauses and Sentence Structure Correctly Read the news story below. Then use proofreading marks to correct all errors in capitalization, punctuation, spelling, and grammar. Pay special attention to the use of clauses.

Some people might call truck driver Chester A. Sutter an ordinery man but the citizens of middleton call him a hero. As Mr. Sutter was driving down Waverly Avenue on the afternoon of May 3. He spotted smoke poring out of the third-floor windows of the Sunset view apartment building. He later told reporters that when he saw two women and a baby on the ledge of one of those windows he knew he had to do something quick. He parked his truck under the window which was a huge eighteen-wheeler. He climbed on top of the trailer and braced himself with his arms stretched out in front of him.

After only a moment's hesitation, Dina Gardner dropped six month old Kyle down toward Mr. Sutter. He caught baby Kyle, whom was uninjured in the fall. Mrs. Gardner and her sister Rosa, both of who jumped onto the truck, also was uninjured. In recognition of that heroic act, mayor Thorndike has named Chester A. Sutter Middletons Citizen of the week.

B. Getting More Practice with Clauses and Sentence Structure Read the sports report below. Then use proofreading marks to correct all errors.

There was not a seat at the park that was empty during Saturday's exciting game between the Valesburg Vipers and the Bayberry Bulldogs. Even though the Vipers played very competitive. They were held scoreless against the undefeated Bulldogs, whom scored a whoping nine runs. The crowd gave rousing cheers for Ricardo Lopez, the Bulldogs star first baseman, who caught four line drives and hit three home runs. After the game, Lopez talked appreciativly about the crowd, who had cheered him in an interview with a local news reporter.

Proofreading Practice: Capitalization

Capitalizing Words Correctly Read the letter below. Then use proofreading marks to correct all errors in capitalization, punctuation, spelling, and grammar. Pay special attention to the use of capital letters.

May 15, 19—

Dear Aunt Aiko and uncle hoshi,

My class trip to Washington, d.c., was great! It took us all day and all night to get there I hadn't never slept on a train before. I found out that those berths really are as small as they look in the movies!

We checked into our hotel on Tuesday afternoon. Then we went straight to the white house. I could hardly beleive I was walking into the home of the president! I was hoping to see the oval office, the official office of the President, but the public doesn't get to see that. Too bad! We saw five beautiful rooms on the first floor. They are used for formal dinners, big parties, and meetings with goverment dignitarys. Some of the fancy furniture there don't look very comfortable to sit in, but it is real pretty. I especially liked the portraits of passed Presidents

On the second day, we visited the museums at the Smithsonian Institution. In the National Museum of natural history, we saw exibits of animals from all over the world. Believe it or not, there was a enormous skeleton of a Blue Whale on the ceiling! Did you know that blue whales can grow up to 100 feet long?

After the Smithsonian, we went to capitol hill and toured the United States Capital. We saw the chambers where the senate and house of representatives meet and many beautiful works of art that show people and events from american History. We also saw the rotunda, the grand circular room beneath the Capitol's dome.

Well I have to go now because mom needs my help in the kitchen.

Your Loving Niece,

Lee

Proofreading Practice: Punctuation

Using Correct Punctuation Read the movie review below. Then use proofreading marks to correct all errors in capitalization, punctuation, spelling, and grammar. Pay special attention to the use of punctuation marks.

Looking for adventure. Well you don't have to look far. *Adventure on Vintar,* an exciting futuristic thriller, opens Friday in theaters everywhere.

In the opening scene Earth's world leaders and top scientists are meeting with highly advanced creatures from vintar, a distant planet in our galaxy. For several months, a scientific research team on Earth have been transmiting radio mes sages to the Vintarians through space in order to arrange this historic meeting. Discussion centers on a plan for transportting a group of earths top scientists to Vintar, where they will study the Vintarians method of eliminateing starvation pollution, and illness. In addition, an Earth family that have been chose to live in a Vintarian household and experience family life on Vintar will accompany the scientists.

Brian Tuscany and Marlena Muldair give very convincing performances as Willie and Wanda, the two clever teenagers who uncover the real purpose of the Vintarians contact with Earth.

"This is my best role yet, says Muldair, and I hope the public will begin to see me now as more than just a supporting actress."

Tuscany who had never played a leading role before admits that he was challenged by the role of Willie: That scene in which I made one last attempt to convince the doubting Dr Horn that the Vintarians were not the compassionate beings that they presented themselves to be was especially difficult for me Im really not an outspoken kind of guy like Willie.

When all seems lost, it is up to Willie and Wanda to save the Earth however they are up against tremendous odds. If you like fast-paced action, don't miss *Adventure on Vintar.* Its terrific.

Answer Key

Handbook 29

Page 1, Form A
Exercise A

1. S	5. F	9. F
2. F	6. F	10. F
3. S	7. S	
4. S	8. S	

Exercise B *Answers will vary. Possible answers shown below.*
1. Mark was signing up for football.
2. Beef cattle are raised on a ranch in Wyoming.
3. Janice slipped on the skateboard at the end of the sidewalk.
4. I saw a huge worm while I was working in the garden.
5. The questions on the test were easy.

Page 2, Form B
Exercise A

1. S	5. S	9. F
2. F	6. S	10. S
3. F	7. F	
4. S	8. S	

Exercise B *Answers will vary. Possible answers shown below.*

All the people in our kingdom have been praying to the gods for a good harvest this year. We need the floods from the Nile River because most of the country is desert. By the end of the flooding, we will plant crops. Once the crops have been gathered, we will plan our festival. We will celebrate the harvest by offering gifts to the gods.

Page 3, Form A
Exercise A

1. INT; ?	4. INT; ?	7. INT; ?
2. DEC; .	5. EXC; !	8. DEC; .
3. EXC; !	6. IMP; .	9. IMP; .
		10. DEC; .

Exercise B *Answers for new sentences will vary.*

1. DEC; .	3. EXC; !
2. INT; ?	4. IMP; .

Page 4, Form B
Exercise A

"Is this John?"
"Yes."
"Would you like to baby-sit for Justin?"
"OK."
"I would be willing to pay you extra, since it's short notice."
"That would be great."
"Do you have any baby-sitting experience?"
"Well, I do have a little brother."
"I will be gone for four hours. Are you sure that you would like to baby-sit?"
"Yes, Mrs. Murray."
"Terrific! Can you be here at 6:30?"
"That will be fine. I'll see you then."

Exercise B *Answers will vary.*

Page 5, Form A
Exercise A
1. Many people | mispronounce the words *library* and *February.*
2. The crowd | swayed with the rhythm of the cheerleaders' chant.
3. A major earthquake | devastated San Francisco in 1906.
4. Michiko | has an exotic collection of seashells.
5. The majestic Rocky Mountains | rose in the distance.
6. A dromedary, a camel with one hump, | is used for racing.
7. Elaine | is traveling to Denver on the *California Zephyr.*
8. The countries of Central America | have a complex history.
9. Tall people | have an advantage in basketball.
10. Abraham Lincoln's vision of democracy | endures.

Exercise B *Answers for sentence completion will vary.*

1. S	5. P	9. P
2. P	6. S	10. S
3. S	7. P	
4. S	8. S	

Page 6, Form B
Exercise A *Answers for sentence completion will vary.*

1. CS	3. CS	5. CS
2. CP	4. CP	

Exercise B *Answers will vary. Possible answer shown below.*

Tortoises and turtles have changed very little through time. The term *tortoise* commonly refers to the land species, whereas *turtle* commonly refers to the aquatic species. Some tortoises are enormous, weighing over 500 pounds. Tortoises often have long life spans. The Galapagos tortoise, for example, may live up to 150 years.

Page 7, Form A

Simple Subject	Verb
1. chatter	bothers
2. Williamsburg	is
3. band	practices
4. Visitors	enjoy
5. committee	designed
6. dictionary	is
7. Hostels	are
8. Anita	played
9. Ms. Voorhees	arranged
10. auditorium	was
11. swimmers	demonstrated
12. restaurant	opens
13. we	installed
14. captain	requested
15. bands	play
16. Meredith	was
17. screen	flashed
18. I	remember
19. hotel	offers
20. Marianne	travels
21. David	presented
22. bus	stalled

23. boss   announced
24. poster   is
25. Gian Lorenzo Bernini   was

Page 8, Form B
Exercise A

Simple Subject	Verb
1. Boston Marathon	is
2. runners	come
3. race	begins
4. finish line	is
5. runners	eat
6. carbohydrates	give
7. runners	hit
8. racers	stop
9. people	enter
10. many	return

Exercise B *Answers will vary. Possible answers shown below.*
1. The host put five hot dogs on the grill to begin the all-day barbecue.
2. Is the repair service sending someone to fix the broken laundry machine?
3. Alejandro walked through the dense forest in the hope that he could find the cabin.
4. Didn't you hear the fire alarm ten minutes ago?
5. The doctor was thoroughly absorbed in her scientific experiments.

Page 9, Form A

Simple Subject	Verb
1. kookaburra	is
2. friend	is recruiting
3. *Orthodontics*	comes
4. Jane Marple	had solved
5. Thoreau	lived
6. counselor	could have given
7. I	will need
8. stamp	has
9. polka	has remained
10. Tony	may have been selling
11. Karen	was waltzing
12. Eddie	may have met
13. storm	must have been
14. students	bike
15. dad	had been waiting
16. librarian	went
17. Mr. Vincent	does want
18. Janet	claimed
19. She	can do
20. Nobody	could see

Page 10, Form B
Exercise A *Answers will vary. Possible answers shown below.*
1. Telephones with special features are becoming more common.
2. Long-forgotten memories can surprise us by popping into our minds.
3. Our natural environment should be everyone's concern.
4. Photography is enjoying a revival of popularity.
5. Recent inventions have included the miniature television set and the fax machine.

Exercise B *Answers will vary. Possible answers shown below.*
    I have just completed an unusual type of class. The instructor's enthusiasm might have been a result of the quality of the students. A typical student had saved money to attend because of great interest in the workshop or might have been sponsored by school officials. Criticism of one's work was offered by professional writers. I really enjoyed being surrounded by people of such great talent and humor.

Page 11, Form A
Exercise A

Simple Subject	Verb
1. (You)	Write
2. exhibit	is
3. Francine	Does, play
4. (You)	check
5. tickets	are
6. group	did, raise
7. wreath	hung
8. meeting	will be
9. families	are
10. key	is
11. photographers	went
12. (You)	Save
13. noise	was
14. Lauren	Has, heard
15. Anna	did tell
16. mansion	is
17. (You)	Start
18. Phyllis	is, coming
19. bridesmaids	were
20. you	have been

Page 12, Form B
Exercise A
1. A new *movie* (simple subject) *is opening* (verb) at the cinema next Friday.
2. Large colorful *billboards* (simple subject) *stood* (verb) all along the road.
3. The latest *statistics* (simple subject) on the health risks of smoking *are* (verb) here.
4. A *woman* (simple subject) from Czechoslovakia *lives* (verb) in the apartment down the hall.
5. Several *cars* (simple subject) are *parked* (verb) across the street.

Exercise B
1. There *is* (verb) a *message* (simple subject) for you on your desk.
2. Here *are* (verb) the *snapshots* (simple subject) from our vacation.
3. *Did* (verb) Ken's *mother* (simple subject) *buy* (verb) a personal computer?
4. *Send* (verb) your entry to the radio station. (You)
5. There *is* (verb) a popular swimming *area* (simple subject) under the bridge.

Page 13, Form A

	Direct Object	Indirect Object
1.	noise	
2.	table	parents
3.	equipment	
4.	people	
5.	Latin	students
6.	boxes	
7.	letter	aunt
8.	party	students
9.	medals	
10.	flag	
11.	costume	sister

12. trout
13. mud
14. cameras
15. picture   cousin
16. knot
17. brakes
18. seat   me
19. tickets   us
20. umbrella   me

Page 14, Form B
Exercise A

1. N	5. DO	9. N
2. DO	6. DO	10. IO
3. DO	7. DO	
4. IO	8. IO	

Exercise B *Answers will vary for indirect objects. Possible answers shown below.*
1. DO = self-confidence; My trip with Outward Bound last year taught me self-confidence.
2. DO = plans; Elena told her advisor her plans for the long summer.
3. DO = souvenir; Dave brought his girlfriend a souvenir from his trip to Nova Scotia.
4. DO = way; Jenny showed me the way to the new restaurant.
5. DO = information; The guide gave the tourists interesting information about the caverns.

Page 15, Form A

	Linking Verb	**Subject Complement**
1.	is	movement
2.	taste	good
3.	appeared	calm
4.	is	quarterback
5.	is	part
6.	seem	blurry
7.	felt	tired
8.	are	friends
9.	is	she
10.	looked	beautiful
11.	tastes	salty
12.	is	cashier
13.	will be	captain
14.	appears	cloudy
15.	are	creatures
16.	are being	stubborn
17.	smelled	delicious
18.	will become	architect
19.	grew	tense
20.	seemed	excited

Page 16, Form B
Exercise A

	Linking Verb	**Subject Complement**
1.	has become	mathematician; PN
2.	was	scout; PN
3.	smells	delicious; PA
4.	was	leader; PN
5.	is	I; PN
6.	looks	bigger; PA
7.	Has, remained	holiday; PN
8.	has become	dilapidated; PA
9.	is	afraid; PA
10.	is	state; PN

Exercise B *Answers will vary. Possible answers shown below.*
1. Our camping trip last summer was a <u>disaster</u>. (PN)
2. Once we reached the campsite, we felt <u>exhausted</u>. (PA)
3. The site, next to the river in a small clearing, looked <u>tiny</u>. (PA)
4. The wind in the trees sounded <u>spooky</u>. (PA)
5. The water in the river was a dark <u>torrent</u>. (PN)
6. The wild blueberries we found tasted <u>sour</u>. (PA)

Page 17, Form A
1. Hayrides, quilting bees; S
2. stories, poems; DO
3. damp, moldy; PA
4. United States, Canada; DO
5. Kangaroos, koalas; S
6. Lewis, Clark; IO
7. Come, join; V
8. manager, captain; PN
9. sanded, varnished; V
10. neatness, punctuality; DO
11. original, practical, affordable; PA
12. architect, inventor, writer; PN
13. Luis, Jill; IO
14. smallpox, polio; DO
15. Berlin, Dresden; S

Page 18, Form B
Answers will vary. Possible answers shown below.
1. We returned the books and tapes to the library.
2. The fireworks sparkled and glittered in the dark summer sky.
3. Maria sent Nick and me a post card.
4. In this part of the country, the winters are long and snowy.
5. The only typewriter for sale at the flea market was old and broken.
6. The news shop on the corner has various magazines and journals.
7. After the meeting, the secretary will write and file a report.
8. John found an old photograph and an antique frame in the attic.
9. Ellen and Linda studied all day at the library.
10. The students in the last four rows are sophomores and juniors.

Handbook 30
Page 19, Form A
Exercise A

1. F	5. S	9. F
2. F	6. F	10. S
3. S	7. S	
4. F	8. F	

Exercise B *Answers will vary. Possible answers shown below.*
1. Paul fell asleep at the movies.
2. Finally, the superintendent of the apartment building repaired the elevators.
3. The defeated pitcher slumped on the dugout bench.
4. An enormous crowd of anxious spectators watched the firefighter.
5. Because the lake had dried up, the wild animals left the area.

Page 20, Form B

Exercise A *Answers will vary for revision of fragments. Possible answers shown below.*

1. He was chosen in the first-round draft.
2. Correct
3. I fell while riding a dirt bike.
4. There was a power failure during the thunderstorm.
5. Salt is often used on highways during the winter.
6. I saw Lucy at the library.
7. Correct
8. When his father died, he became king of the tiny country.
9. Correct
10. Sign your name at the bottom of the application.

Exercise B *Answers will vary. Possible answer shown below.*

The Aboriginal people were the first people to inhabit Australia. They have lived in northern Australia for over 20,000 years. This area is now a national park and contains rock paintings that record the Aboriginal people's traditions. Some Aboriginal people still live in this area, but their youth are losing interest in old ways. The traditions that were once passed down are gradually being lost.

Page 21, Form A

Exercise A

1. Run-on	5. Run-on	9. Run-on
2. Run-on	6. Run-on	10. Correct
3. Correct	7. Run-on	
4. Run-on	8. Correct	

Exercise B *Answers will vary. Possible answers shown below.*

1. Last summer we camped, and we had the best vacation ever.
2. We saw an old Hitchcock film. It was a classic thriller.
3. Diane tried to skate backwards; she ended up with a badly sprained arm.
4. Burnett noticed the leaves of the bush, and he realized that it was a poisonous plant.

Page 22, Form B

Exercise A *Answers will vary. Possible answers shown below.*

1. Russia sold Alaska to the United States; the price was two cents an acre.
2. Paul's brother works for United Airlines. He's a flight attendant.
3. Court stenographers must listen well, and they must also type rapidly.
4. Eyes are delicate organs. Have them examined every two years.
5. *Dendrophobia* is a medical term; it means "fear of trees."

Exercise B *Answers will vary. Possible answer shown below.*

The senior-class production of Shakespeare's *Macbeth* was fantastic. The stars were all members of the senior class, but some juniors played supporting roles. It is clear that the students put in a lot of time; they must have rehearsed for many weeks. The stage crew deserves credit, too; the sets, lighting, costumes, and makeup were all exceptional. The hard work of the entire cast and crew paid off.

Handbook 31

Page 23, Form A

Exercise A

1. success; show; actors
2. Anthony; saxophone; band
3. book; freedom; wartime
4. Connors; ball; net
5. Janet; lifeguard; North Beach
6. Victoria Woodhull; President; 1872
7. witnesses; disaster; skill; determination; paramedics
8. contest; trip; Hawaii
9. Cuba; island; miles; Key West; Florida
10. helicopter; Logan Airport
11. Leroy; prize; exhibit; planets
12. Neil; card; books; Southwest
13. Spring; season; people
14. results; election; Wednesday
15. Sachems; championship; year; row

Exercise B *Answers will vary. Possible answers shown below.*

1. cat; car
2. December; month; winter
3. architect; California
4. computer; patience; practice
5. boat; stream

Page 24, Form B

Exercise A

PE TH TH TH
Oliver Wendell Holmes wrote a poem and entitled it "Old Ironsides." His title
TH TH TH
refers to the American frigate Constitution. The ship was nicknamed "Old Ironsides"
TH PE
because it was damaged so little during the War of 1812. Holmes learned that the
TH PL PL PE
ship was about to be demolished in a shipyard at Boston. The poet published the
TH TH TH TH
poem in a local newspaper in an effort to save the ship. "Old Ironsides" was reprinted
PL TH TH
throughout the country. The ringing first line of the poem quickly became famous:
TH TH
"Ay, tear her tattered ensign down!" It was so effective that the Constitution was
PE PL TH TH
saved. Many tourists who visit Boston board this frigate. It is the oldest warship
TH PL PL TH
afloat in any navy of the world. It sails in the harbor at Boston on Independence Day
TH ID ID/TH ID TH
each year. Its survival is evidence of the power of the poetic word.

Exercise B *Answers will vary. Possible answers shown below.*

1. Many people enjoy playing *baseball* (noun), a game that builds *strength* (noun) and *dexterity* (noun).
2. *Baseball* (noun) is especially popular in the *United States* (noun) and *Canada* (noun).
3. To play *baseball* (noun) well requires *concentration* (noun).
4. Even the best players must guard against injuries to their *wrists* (noun) and *shoulders* (noun).
5. Players can improve their performance by studying the techniques of someone like *Wade Boggs* (noun).

Page 25, Form A

Exercise A

1. groups = common, collective; changes = common, abstract
2. practices = common, abstract; demand = common, abstract
3. trend = common, abstract; food chain = common, compound, abstract

4. Amazon = proper, concrete; tributaries = common, concrete

Exercise B *Answers will vary. Possible answers shown below.*
1. The committee decided to sponsor the amendment.
2. My grandfather's wish is to live to the year 2020.
3. San Diego is the name of a city in California.
4. Confidence may influence the result of an examination.

Page 26, Form B
Exercise A

1. Lincoln = PRO, CON; life = COM, ABS; boy = COM, CON; education = COM, ABS
2. family = COM, COLL, CON; Illinois = PRO, CON; law = COM; ABS
3. campaign = COM, ABS; Lincoln, Douglas = PRO, CON; fame, subject, and slavery = COM, ABS
4. commander-in-chief = COM, CON; efficiency, strength = COM, ABS
5. conflict = COM, ABS; end = COM, ABS

Exercise B *Answers will vary. Possible answers shown below.*
1. The snorkler saw an angelfish near Paula.
2. The girl admired the coral beneath the water's surface.
3. A good snorkler has skill and training.
4. Only one-third of our group went snorkeling in Bluestone Bay.
5. Another class agreed to take a challenge.

Page 27, Form A
Exercise A

1. PN	3. IO	5. DO
2. S	4. DO	

Exercise B *Answers will vary. Possible answers shown below.*
1. *Lee Corporation* (S) is hiring new computer *operators* (DO).
2. The *doctor* (S) gave the *patient* (IO) *medicine* (DO).
3. *Bud Hopkins* (S) fixes *cars* (DO).
4. *Rosa Ruiz* (S) sells *customers* (IO) *appliances* (DO).
5. *Ms. Schwartz* (S) is a forest *ranger* (PN).

Page 28, Form B
Exercise A *Answers will vary. Possible answers shown below.*
1. One of the most common medicines is *aspirin* (PN).
2. Most families keep *aspirin* (DO) in the medicine cabinet.
3. People take *aspirin* (DO) for colds, fever, or headaches.
4. Doctors whose patients have digestive problems must give *aspirin* (IO) and its side effects special consideration, however.
5. People should not take *aspirin* (DO) frequently, except under a doctor's supervision.

Exercise B *Answers will vary.*

Page 29, Form A

1. elephants	16. boxes
2. ladies	17. ferries
3. snowmen	18. banjos
4. monkeys	19. brushes
5. footsteps	20. staffs
6. cameos	21. dresses
7. moose	22. knives
8. fish, fishes	23. heroes
9. glasses	24. flies
10. roofs	25. tomatoes
11. sofas	26. dwarfs, dwarves
12. raspberries	27. sons-in-law
13. toys	28. teeth
14. lives	29. pushups
15. bunches	30. enemies

Page 30, Form B
Exercise A

1. taxes	6. cargoes
2. armies	7. leaves
3. cliffs	8. sisters-in-law
4. grandchildren	9. cupfuls
5. parties	10. zoos

Exercise B
1. oboes, basses, pianos
2. scores, bookshelves
3. technicians, microphones, echoes
4. pianists, brothers-in-law, maestros
5. rhythms, melodies, keys, sessions

Page 31, Form A
Exercise A

1. bicyclist's	11. lawyers'
2. students'	12. Los Angeles's
3. year's	13. the Jacksons'
4. tree's	14. lady's
5. Dennis's	15. group's
6. bus's	16. knives'
7. oxen's	17. sailors'
8. writers'	18. teacher's
9. sheep's	19. library's
10. minibike's	20. children's

Exercise B

1. boy's	6. monkeys'
2. winners'	7. wineglass's
3. gentlemen's	8. year's
4. Galileo's	9. knights'
5. Miss Thomas's	10. travelers'

Page 32, Form B

1. girls'	14. Hobbes's
2. Kim Soo's	15. Secretaries'
3. Andersons'	16. Curtises'
4. Carlos's	17. geese's
5. Armadillos'	18. lioness's
6. nation's	19. Keats's
7. families'	20. Women's
8. men's	21. neighbors'
9. James's	22. Dickens's
10. board's	23. ferry's
11. Clemens's	24. Yankees'
12. tenants'	25. Marx's
13. deer's	

Handbook 32

Page 33, Form A

Pronoun	Antecedent
1. it, it	budget
She	mayor
2. it	discussion
3. My	Gina
I	Gina
we	sister, I
4. his	Champollion
5. she, her	Billie Holiday
6. her	Susan
7. it	music
8. its, it	Timbuktu
9. her	Willa Cather's
it	novel
10. his	Malcolm
their	Malcolm and his friends
11. their	Europeans
12. it	turban
13. they, they, their	Picts
14. their	soldiers
15. its	water boatman

Page 34, Form B

Exercise A

1. Over two hundred cheering fans turned out to welcome their team back home.
2. The players and the coach were pleased when they saw how many fans had come out in the cold rain to welcome them back.
3. Coach Breen praised the team and said it was one of the finest teams he had ever worked with.
4. When quarterback Doug Brown started to speak, the cheerleaders led a cheer for him.
5. The pep rally was better than anyone had thought it would be.

Exercise B *Answers will vary.*

Page 35, Form A

Exercise A

1. I
2. she
3. We, you, your
4. yours, theirs
5. you, me, I, she

Exercise B

1. their—third person, P
2. you—second person, S; I—first person, S
3. it—third person, S
4. we—first person, P; them—third person, P; your—second person, S
5. His—third person, S; mine—first person, S

Page 36, Form B

1. The freshly unpacked leaves of spring made a comforting roof over his head as he walked along.
2. Nothing he has described here has importance, except to him, and to those few thousands who thanks to chance also live or have lived in Shillington.
3. He had expected to be told who he was, and why, and he had not been entirely disappointed.
4. He was "where the people are."
5. A passing car slowed suspiciously, diluting his intense happiness.

Page 37, Form A

Exercise A

1. P	3. O	5. O
2. N	4. N	6. P

Exercise B

Pronouns	Case
1. their	P
2. its	P
3. you, your	N, P
4. him	O

Page 38, Form B

Exercise A

Pronoun	Case
1. me	O
2. I	N
Your	P
3. We	N
4. They	N
me	O
5. their	P
6. them	O
7. us	O
8. ours	P
our	P
9. Your	P
mine	P
10. she	N

Exercise B *Answers will vary.*

Page 39, Form A

Exercise A

Pronoun	Type
1. himself	reflexive
2. itself	intensive
3. themselves	intensive
4. myself	reflexive
5. themselves	reflexive
6. yourself	intensive
7. ourselves	reflexive
8. herself	reflexive
9. herself	intensive
10. herself	reflexive

Exercise B

1. myself	6. itself
2. himself/herself	7. herself
3. ourselves	8. myself
4. myself	9. himself
5. himself/herself	10. themselves

Page 40, Form B

Exercise A

Pronoun	Type
1. himself	intensive
2. themselves	reflexive
3. yourself	reflexive
4. ourselves	intensive
5. himself	intensive
6. himself	reflexive
7. itself	intensive
8. themselves	reflexive
9. myself	reflexive
10. themselves	reflexive

Exercise B
1. Only she herself had ever been to this camp.
2. The teachers themselves had to perform all activities.
3. The climb itself was not too hard.
4. We had to rappel down ourselves.
5. Before rappelling down, I asked myself why I was so scared.

Page 41, Form A
Exercise A
1. that
2. those
3. Those
4. these
5. these, those
6. Those
7. That
8. that
9. This
10. these

Exercise B
1. Those
2. This
3. This
4. Those
5. That
6. These
7. That
8. those
9. That
10. Those
11. That
12. these
13. Those
14. those
15. this

Page 42, Form B
Exercise A *Answers will vary. Possible answers shown below.*
1. This is one of the most interesting cities for sightseeing.
2. That, in the distance, is the tallest building.
3. Those circling the monument are all American flags.
4. That is a statue that is especially dramatic at night.

Exercise B
1. This has been such an exciting trip so far!
2. I have visited other Scandinavian countries before, but this is my first visit to Norway.
3. Those are just some of nature's wonders on the west coast.
4. That is Norway's second-largest city.
5. Do those sound awful?

Page 43, Form A
Exercise A
1. One
2. none
3. Each
4. Few
5. some
6. Neither
7. Both
8. No one
9. None
10. everyone

Exercise B

Indefinite Pronoun	Number
1. Everyone	singular
2. Most	plural
3. Anybody	singular
4. few	plural
5. all	plural
6. Somebody	singular
7. Everybody	singular
8. any	plural
9. someone	singular
10. Both	plural

Page 44, Form B
Exercise A *Answers will vary. Possible answers shown below.*
1. Anybody
2. Many
3. Several
4. both
5. all
6. Some
7. Others
8. No one

Exercise B *Answers will vary. Possible answers shown below.*
1. Do all of the contestants need identification badges?
2. Nobody thinks Willie has a chance to win.
3. Many of the students in school think Tino will win.
4. One of the girls in my physical education class is running for the first time.
5. Some of the eight competitors in the track meet are already in place.

Page 45, Form A
Exercise A
1. Who
2. Which
3. What
4. Whose
5. What

Exercise B *Answers will vary. Possible answers shown below.*
1. Who met Will at the pizzeria yesterday?
2. What broke into pieces?
3. Who owns an antique locket?
4. Which computers sold well in November?
5. Whose camera was lost as the girls ran for the bus?

Page 46, Form B
Exercise A
1. Who was appointed to the Supreme Court in 1988?
2. What is the role of the Senate?
3. Who was appointed Chief Justice in 1986?
4. Of the nine justices, who is the only woman?
5. Whose is the responsibility for leading the Court?

Exercise B
1. Who is trying to regenerate flocks of ducks and other migratory birds?
2. What is the main reason for the decreasing number of birds?
3. Whose are the remaining breeding grounds that the governments want to protect?
4. Which decreased more in the 1980's—the number of ducks or the number of geese?
5. Who will try to make the birds' habitats more productive?

Page 47, Form A
Exercise A

Relative Pronoun	Word Modified
1. whose	Japan
2. that	island
3. which	Tokyo
4. who	samurai
5. that	recovery

Exercise B

Pronoun	Type
1. who	REL
2. What	INT
3. Which	INT
4. whose	REL

5. that		REL
6. Whom		INT
7. whom		REL
8. who		REL
9. Who		INT
10. that		REL

Page 48, Form B

Answers will vary. Possible answers shown below.

1. The 1920's, which was an era of prosperity, preceded the Great Depression.
2. F. Scott Fitzgerald was a gifted American novelist who immortalized the Jazz Age.
3. Women's suffrage, which was won in 1920, reflected a changing society.
4. King Harold of England, whom William the Conqueror defeated in 1066, is one of the people depicted in the Bayeux Tapestry.
5. The accident that took place at the Chernobyl nuclear plant in the U.S.S.R. on April 25, 1986, caused families for miles around to evacuate.
6. Charles Lindbergh, who flew alone across the Atlantic, earned instant fame.
7. Francois Duvalier, whom many people feared, was dictator of Haiti.
8. Charles Babbage designed a machine that was the forerunner of the computer.
9. Dick Francis wrote the novel *Reflex,* which he based on his career as a jockey.
10. Crocuses are popular flowers that bloom early in spring.

Page 49, Form A

Exercise A

Pronoun	Antecedent
1. their	prospectors
2. her	Michelle
3. she	Vera
4. himself	Javier
5. its	chameleon
6. yours	José
7. he	Mr. Birdseye
8. its	earth
9. themselves	twins
10. his	Carlos

Exercise B

Possessive Pronoun	Antecedent
1. their	cardinals
2. their	Juan, Louis
3. its	rose
4. his	George Bernard Shaw
5. her	Shirley Temple
6. their	directors
7. their	Katie, Abbie
8. her	seal
9. their	Brazilians
10. its	panther

Page 50, Form B

1. their	7. their
2. its	8. we, our
3. his	9. your
4. her	10. its
5. their	11. it, his
6. my	12. they

Page 51, Form A

Exercise A

Indefinite Pronoun	Possessive Pronoun
1. Several	their
2. Everyone	his or her
3. Many	their
4. None	its
5. All	their
6. Neither	her
7. anyone	him or her
8. Nobody	his or her
9. Both	their
10. Neither	his or her
11. Everything	its
12. Some	their
13. Each	its
14. Everyone	his or her
15. Most	its

Exercise B *Answers will vary. Possible answers shown below.*

1. Some, P
2. Everything, S
3. anyone, S
4. Each, S
5. someone, S

Page 52, Form B

Exercise A

1. Several, A
2. Everyone, S
3. Any, A
4. Some, S
5. All, A

Exercise B *Answers will vary. Possible answers shown below.*

1. Few of the fans remained in their seats until the last inning.
2. One of my favorite places is Yosemite National Park.
3. Both of his brothers are majoring in accounting.
4. Neither of the bookcases was made of solid teak.
5. Several of my cousins are planning a long trip in their camper.
6. All of the actors know their lines.
7. All of the cake is gone.
8. Everybody has taken his or her break.
9. Most of the story is well written.
10. Most of the books are here.

Page 53, Form A

Exercise A

Pronoun	Antecedent
1. he	vague
2. their	Paul and Martin
3. his	vague
4. it	vague
5. they	missing

Exercise B *Answers will vary. Possible answers shown below.*

1. her; Mrs. Castillo was asked about her voting preferences by Mrs. Jackson.
2. it; The newspapers predict snow.
3. they; Before playing a concert, the musicians set up their speakers.
4. he; The coach was very calm when he spoke to the referee.

5. they; When you write a letter to the editor, the editor never answers.

Page 54, Form B
Exercise A *Answers will vary. Possible answers shown below.*
1. Amy took the novel *Jane Eyre* from the bag and laid the book on the table.
2. This novel shows the writing talents of Charlotte Brontë, one of the famous Brontë sisters.
3. In reading Emily Brontë's *Wuthering Heights,* Amy discovered the author's tragic view of love and the forces of nature.
4. *Wuthering Heights* was made into a movie starring Laurence Olivier.

Exercise B *Answers will vary. Possible answers shown below.*
1. My cousin Theresa recently worked as an extra for the filming of *Nightmare in Flight.*
2. Theresa expected to see glamorous stars but spent many dull hours waiting in an airport.
3. When Theresa did see the leading lady, the actress looked tired and cranky.
4. When the cast was finally ready, the director had the crew shoot the scene twelve times.

Page 55, Form A
1. I; N	8. him; O
2. me; O	9. me; O
3. he; N	10. me; O
4. she; N	11. she; N
5. him; O	12. us; O
6. me; O	13. We; N
7. I; N	14. me; O
	15. me; O

Page 56, Form B
1. him; Carl and he are diving to locate the mooring for their boat.
2. Correct
3. her; Can you and she represent us at the next Junior Achievement meeting?
4. Correct
5. Correct
6. us; Those pedestrians and we witnessed the accident, called the police, and offered evidence.
7. me; You and I can get aerobic exercise just by doing some fast walking every day.
8. she; Nobody had told Yvette and her that they could have bought artistic posters in the federal building's bookstore.
9. Correct
10. I; Candidates for public office always need the support of citizens like you and me.

Page 57, Form A
Exercise A
1. their	6. their
2. I	7. she
3. her	8. their
4. his	9. I
5. I	10. her

Exercise B
1. she	6. I
2. we	7. he
3. she	8. we

4. she	9. I
5. I	10. I

Page 58, Form B
Exercise A
1. its
2. I
3. their
4. I (Other possible answers: *he, she, we, they*)
5. his
6. their
7. I (Other possible answers: *he, she, we, they*)
8. their
9. her
10. she

Exercise B
(1) Either a student or a teacher tells of his or her impression that our school is going to be closed. (2) Correct (3) The principal then learns that a high-tech firm wants the building for office space, and no one is more surprised than he. (4) The students realize they could all be sent to different schools, and no one tries harder than they to save the school.

Page 59, Form A
1. Who's	9. Whose
2. your	10. its
3. We	11. us
4. they're	12. Who
5. It's	13. whom
6. those	14. those
7. Their	15. Whom
8. us	

Page 60, Form B
Exercise A
1. us	9. It's
2. you're	10. whom
3. its	11. We
4. Who	12. they're
5. Whose	13. Those
6. Your	14. their
7. those	15. those
8. Whom	

Exercise B *Answers will vary. Possible answers shown below.*
1. Who has a great plan to raise money for Central High?
2. We members of the student council would like to hear your ideas for fund-raising activities.
3. Anyone who thinks he or she has an original and creative idea should submit his or her proposal by Friday to the student council.
4. We will consider all of your proposals.

Skills Assessment 1
Pages 61–63
1. B—1800's. By (or: 1800's; by)
2. A—Among   B—Andrew, Carlos, and me,
3. E
4. A—mythology, the   D—skies
5. E
6. A—those streamers   C—Sara's brother-in-law
7. B—musicians
8. C—country's

9. A—These	D—yours			
10. C—Hugo and me	D—dangerous			
11. A—Whose	D—February			
12. A—himself	C—Address;			
13. B—ourselves	D—her and me.			
14. E				
15. C—her	D—gymnastics			

16. B	18. D	20. D	22. C	24. C
17. B	19. C	21. A	23. B	25. D

6. might	apply
7. Can	operate
8. have	completed
9. has	made
10. could	walk
11. will be	staying
12. may	live
13. Can	set
14. has	written
15. will	circulate

Handbook 33

Page 65, Form A

Exercise A

Verb	Type
1. streaked	action
2. strutted	action
3. was	linking
4. whisked	action
5. seems	linking

Exercise B *Answers will vary. Possible answers shown below.*

Verb	Type
1. is	linking
2. occupied	action
3. live	action
4. sell	action
5. become	linking
6. seem	linking
7. attracts	action
8. buy	action
9. holds	action
10. look	linking

Page 66, Form B, Exercise A

> A   L
> Many authorities believe that the domestic cat is a descendant of an African
> A
> wildcat. Ancient Egyptians tamed the wildcat, possibly as early as 3500 B.C. These
> A
> cats controlled the population of mice, rats, and snakes on farms and in grain
> L   A
> storehouses. Eventually these cats became pets. Artisans frequently honored such
> cats in paintings and sculptures.
> A   A
> After about 1500 B.C., the Egyptians considered cats sacred. If a person killed a
> L   A   A
> cat, the punishment was usually death. When a pet cat died, owners shaved off their
> A   A
> own eyebrows as a sign of mourning. Egyptians also mummified and buried dead
> L
> cats. Scientists discovered an ancient cat cemetery in Egypt with more than 300,000
> cat mummies.

Exercise B *Answers will vary. Possible answers shown below.*
1. Marilyn sounded the alarm.
2. Mr. Olaf grew tomatoes in his garden.
3. Janet proved her arguments.
4. I smelled the exquisite roses.
5. That particular star appears near the horizon.

Page 67, Form A

Helping Verb(s)	Main Verb
1. will	request
2. was	describing
3. Has, been	sending
4. should	leave
5. Did	prove

Page 68, Form B

Exercise A

Helping Verb(s)	Main Verb
1. will	visit
2. Could	help
3. has	found
4. could	open
5. Have	located
6. should	change
7. Does	expect
8. may, have	memorized
9. must	reach
10. are	risking

Exercise B *Answers will vary. Possible answers shown below.*

Helping Verb(s)	Verb Phrase
1. Are	are going
2. should have	should have reported
3. Has	has pitched
4. should	should read
5. has been	has been singing
6. Has	has played
7. must be	must be running
8. Have, been	have been going
9. must have	must have been kidding
10. Did	did try
11. Will, be	will be running
12. will, be	will be riding

Page 69, Form A

Verb	Type	Direct Object
1. canceled	transitive	show
2. originated	intransitive	
3. have	transitive	senses
4. used	transitive	system
5. forms	intransitive	
6. make	transitive	trips
7. attracts	transitive	seekers
8. spawn	intransitive	
9. was coming	intransitive	
10. Put	transitive	mustard
11. felt	intransitive	
12. Do have	transitive	ticket
13. has played	transitive	percussion
14. Can understand	transitive	logic
15. have heard	transitive	performance
16. look	intransitive	
17. broke	transitive	loaf
18. broke	intransitive	
19. tighten	transitive	strap
20. seemed	intransitive	

Page 70, Form B

Answers will vary. Possible answers shown below.
1. intransitive; The morning sun melted the ice sculptures.

2. intransitive; The band entertained the fans at the game.
3. transitive; The ship's crew sailed around the world.
4. transitive; Mattie and Louise ate slowly.
5. intransitive; Yesterday I drove my mother's car for the first time.
6. transitive; The temperature increased steadily throughout the day.
7. intransitive; Have you ever danced the tango?
8. transitive; The population in this area expanded rapidly during the last decade.
9. transitive; I studied for an hour before dinner.
10. intransitive; The central character changes her mind frequently.

Page 71, Form A
1. raced; A
2. was built; P
3. is owned; P
4. were composed; P
5. attract; A
6. wrote; A
7. is derived; P
8. won; A
9. thanked; A
10. includes; A
11. are written; P
12. accompanied; A
13. has been enlarged; P
14. were overwhelmed; P
15. has contributed; A
16. were completed; P
17. was expressed; P
18. observes; A
19. reaches; A
20. were being groomed; P

Page 72, Form B
Exercise A *Answers will vary. Possible answers shown below.*
1. refinished
2. were bought
3. offers
4. packed
5. were listed

Exercise B
1. An ambulance rushed Joanne to the nearest community hospital.
2. The outing committee elected Clare chairperson by a vote of 10 to 8.
3. Poet Robert Lowell wrote the prize-winning volume *Lord Weary's Castle.*
4. Dr. Thomas Whitecloud wrote "Blue Winds Dancing," an essay about his Native American heritage.
5. After dark, search-van drivers offer homeless persons a ride to a shelter.

Page 73, Form A
Exercise A
1. continuing; continued; continued
2. hoping; hoped; hoped
3. walking; walked; walked
4. purchasing; purchased; purchased
5. wandering; wandered; wandered

Exercise B
1. enjoy
2. loved
3. playing
4. received
5. cook
6. finished
7. developed
8. frying
9. earned
10. carried

Page 74, Form B
Exercise A
1. taste
2. denied
3. slithered
4. reply
5. removed
6. drafted
7. Prove
8. telephone
9. rescued
10. exercise

Exercise B
1. Cartoonists are always looking for fresh ideas.
2. At this point, she or he is using a pencil.
3. The cartoonist is approaching a crucial step.
4. On the comics page, your favorite comic strip is waiting for you.

Page 75, Form A
1. put
2. taught
3. brought
4. broke
5. cost
6. set
7. burst
8. wore
9. frozen
10. spoke

Page 76, Form B
Exercise A
1. led
2. burst
3. lost
4. sitting
5. wore
6. choosing
7. set
8. taught
9. broken
10. brought

Exercise B
1. brought = past participle
2. spoken = past participle
3. worn = past participle
4. hit = past participle
5. taught = past
6. lost = past participle
7. cost = past participle
8. sitting = past participle
9. set = past participle
10. teaching = present participle

Page 77, Form A
1. drank
2. swum
3. sang
4. rung
5. began
6. sung
7. shrank
8. begun
9. rang
10. begun
11. sank
12. drunk
13. sunk
14. swam
15. shrunk
16. Sang
17. rung
18. drunk
19 sung
20. sunk
21. drinking
22. sinking
23. shrank
24. swum
25. ringing

Page 78, Form B
Exercise A
1. sung = past participle
2. drinking = present participle
3. rang = past
4. begun = past participle
5. sang = past
6. drunk = past participle
7. sinking = present participle

8. swum = past participle
9. shrank = past
10. sank = past

Exercise B
1. sung = sang
2. begun = began
3. Correct
4. shrunk = shrank
5. rung = rang
6. Correct
7. drunk = drank
8. sunk = sank
9. began = begun
10. sank = sunk

Page 79, Form A
1. saw, giving
2. fell, did
3. thrown
4. gone
5. seen
6. wrote, grown
7. knew, eaten
8. rode
9. taken
10. did
11. run
12. come
13. known
14. written
15. rose, drove

Page 80, Form B
Exercise A
1. saw; seen
2. gave; given
3. knew; known
4. seen; saw
5. threw; thrown
6. rode; ridden
7. Correct
8. knowed; knew
9. come; came
10. wrote; written

Exercise B
1. Sherlock Holmes has brought fame to his author, Sir Arthur Conan Doyle.
2. Holmes's cases began as newspaper stories in the 1880's.
3. Conan Doyle wrote about Sherlock Holmes in fifty-six short stories and four novels.
4. In fact, Holmes could have taught science.

Page 81, Form A
Exercise A

Verb	Tense
1. saw	past
2. will begin	future
3. had designed	past perfect
4. hibernate	present
5. have extinguished	present perfect
6. will have been	future perfect
7. has taken	present perfect
8. will answer	future
9. had saved	past perfect
10. were	past

Exercise B
1. seemed
2. had moved
3. scores
4. will have sold
5. will go
6. cooks
7. had been
8. took
9. will help
10. has had

Page 82, Form B
Exercise A

Verb	Tense
1. will have owned	future perfect
2. set	past

3. like — present
4. will need — future
5. have won — present perfect
6. had wanted — past perfect
7. have written — present perfect
8. will finish — future
9. had had — past perfect
10. extended — past

Exercise B *Answers will vary. Possible answers shown below.*
1. After the game, the team will travel to the next city.
2. Has anyone learned how to run this program on the computer?
3. The wind changed suddenly, and the sky turned dark.
4. By this time next year, we will have found a nicer apartment.
5. The balloonists had hoped for a light wind.
6. Emily writes long entries in her diary every day.

Page 83, Form A
1. will be visiting = future progressive
2. is telling = present progressive
3. had been sitting = past perfect progressive
4. had been rumbling = past perfect progressive
5. was erupting = past progressive
6. were filling = past progressive
7. were dying = past progressive
8. had been fleeing = past perfect progressive
9. were looking = past progressive
10. have been uncovering and restoring = present perfect progressive
11. had been removing = past perfect progressive
12. were losing = past progressive
13. are keeping = present progressive
14. will have been lying = future perfect progressive
15. have been learning = present perfect progressive

Page 84, Form B
Exercise A
1. is lifting
2. have been attending
3. will have been working
4. were skiing
5. will be renting
6. had been collecting
7. are being
8. will have been jogging
9. was opening
10. will be giving

Exercise B *Answers will vary. Possible answers shown below.*

People of tomorrow will be living in a controlled climate. Fans will enjoy their favorite sports out-of-doors all year long. Robots will be cooking the food and cleaning the homes. Most people will shop by television, and physical illnesses will decline. People will be living in safer but very controlled environments.

Page 85, Form A
Exercise A
1. was studying, was reading; A
2. is enjoying, had complained; S
3. coaxes, will exchange; S
4. is playing, is acting; A
5. came, likes, raves; S

Exercise B
1. Charlie likes tennis and practices his backhand stroke for many hours.
2. Marita will draw the still life, and I will paint a self-portrait.
3. We will play charades now, and we will have a snack later.
4. Matt was late as usual, but Eva was prompt.
5. We won the first-place trophy, and Joy won an honorary medal.

Page 86, Form B
Exercise A
1. Today, artists admire cave paintings and marvel at their beauty.
2. When these paintings were first found, they were called fakes.
3. Today, scientists have instruments that test the age of objects such as paintings.
4. Experts believe that the ancient artists probably perched on ledges as they painted.

Exercise B *Answers will vary.*

Page 87, Form A
1. taught	10. leaves	19. take
2. let	11. brought	20. letting
3. take	12. learn	21. teach
4. learned	13. take	22. took
5. brought	14. letting	23. bring
6. teach	15. let	24. taught
7. take	16. took	25. let
8. let	17. teaching	
9. Teach	18. brought	

Page 88, Form B
Exercise A
1. Correct	6. Correct
2. Correct	7. Correct
3. taught	8. Let
4. Correct	9. took
5. let	10. Correct

Exercise B
1. Take the *Wild Nature* magazines that are sitting on the sofa back to the library.
2. Take the masks that I made for the Chinese play to Jenny and Alex Po.
3. Teach Jeffrey how to use the school's public address system.
4. Let Consuelo Paz have my collection of baseball cards.

Page 89, Form A
Exercise A
1. set	10. rose	19. lies
2. lay	11. rise	20. sat
3. sit	12. sat	21. laid
4. raised	13. lying	22. raised
5. risen	14. raised	23. sits
6. set	15. rise	24. lies
7. laying	16. risen	25. sat
8. lain	17. Raise	
9. laid	18. set	

Page 90, Form B
Exercise A
1. lay	6. Raising
2. sets	7. Sit
3. Correct	8. Lie

4. sat	9. rose
5. Correct	10. Correct

Exercise B
The incorrect sentences are 1, 2, 5, 7, and 10. The corrected sentences follow.
1. Sally first tried to lie in a hammock at camp during free time one day.
2. She had taken a magazine outdoors and sat on the grass to relax.
5. Setting her magazine on the hammock, Sally scrambled in and lay down.
7. The startled girl cautiously raised her head and pushed outward and down with her palms.
10. "I seem to be back where I started," Sally muttered, raising herself from the ground.

Handbook 34
Page 91, Form A
Exercise A
1. Good
2. large, powerful
3. western
4. beautiful, expensive
5. metric, English
6. exotic, hard, many
7. Supersonic, fast
8. French, German
9. proper, regular, important
10. Lush, tropical, long, wet

Exercise B
	Adjective	**Word(s) Modified**
1.	several	classes
	photographic	journalism
2.	quiet	audience
	thoughtful	audience
3.	new	models
	less	fuel
	better	mileage
4.	yellow	shirt
	white	jeans
5.	senior	class
	modern European	history
6.	large	volcano
	Hawaiian	islands
7.	McIntosh	apples
	crisp	apples
	juicy	apples
8.	insightful	questions
9.	secret	documents
	old	suitcase
10.	long	career
	brilliant	career
11.	terrifying	ordeal
12.	cool	water
	refreshing	water
13.	travel	magazine
	Japanese	gardens
14.	young	playwright
	delightful	comedy
15.	important	Punctuality

Page 92, Form B
Exercise A
1. pear; predicate
2. ambassador; proper

3. furniture; predicate
4. music; proper
5. engines; predicate
6. torch; proper
7. religion; proper
8. food; proper
9. Jogging; predicate
10. He; predicate

Exercise B *Answers will vary. Possible answer shown below.*

The adorable young girl had curly black hair and brown eyes. "She must be about twelve years old," I thought. She looked impish and mischievous. She asked me the time. Was she nervous? I couldn't tell.

Page 93, Form A
Exercise A

Adjective	Word(s) Modified
1. stone	walls
their	vaults
2. Whose	paintings
oil	paintings
3. Some	newspapers
4. office	building
5. sculpture	exhibit
art	museum
6. car	door
7. These	books
Which	one
8. kitchen	table
her	bags
9. Which	program
television	program
their	ancestors
10. metal	frames

Exercise B *Answers will vary. Possible answers shown below.*

1. her
2. Many
3. wool
4. Ann's
5. paper
6. Those
7. several
8. Tom's
9. What
10. gift

Page 94, Form B
Exercise A *Answers will vary. Possible answers shown below.*

(1) In 1921, a jury in Massachusetts handed down *its* historic verdict of guilty in the Sacco-Vanzetti murder case. (2) People throughout the country, however, believed that *these* two men were innocent. (3) What was the real issue in *this* case? (4) Sacco and Vanzetti were Italian immigrants who were charged with killing two men during a robbery, but *many* people believed they were really being tried for political beliefs. (5) Sacco and Vanzetti were professed anarchists (anarchists are against any form of government), and the jury made *its* decision of guilty even though the trial evidence was very weak.

Exercise B *Answers will vary.*

Page 95, Form A
Exercise A
1. never too
2. more deeply
6. clearly, swiftly
7. Patiently

3. quite
4. higher, tightly
5. immediately
8. still, long
9. smoothly
10. together

Exercise B

Adverb	Word(s) Modified
1. recently	signed
2. thoroughly	cleaned
3. yesterday	rearranged
4. very	careful
5. still	are being counted
6. exceptionally	fine
7. quite	expensive
8. utterly	adored
9. often	holds
10. beautifully	played
11. too	dangerous
12. honestly	answer
13. bitterly	cold
14. immediately	rushed
15. frankly, effectively	spoke

Page 96, Form B
Exercise A
1. spoke; V
2. new; ADJ
3. well; ADV
4. depleted; ADJ
5. tired; ADJ
6. hard; ADV
7. slammed; V
8. satisfied; ADJ
9. coldly; ADV
10. set up; V
11. like; V
12. easy; ADJ
13. sounded; V
14. gently; ADV
15. excited; ADJ

Exercise B *Answers will vary. Possible answers shown below.*
1. never; have traveled
2. everywhere; have looked
3. Nervously; dialed
4. always; expresses
5. consistently; late

Page 97, Form A
Exercise A
1. tenaciously
2. really
3. vigorously
4. awfully
5. suspicious
6. obvious
7. hilarious
8. steadily
9. bad
10. wistfully

Exercise B

Adverb	Word(s) Modified
1. beautifully	sang
2. thoughtful	person
3. steadily	dripped
4. suddenly	stopped
5. quickly	produces
6. easily	opened
7. accurate	description
8. bitter	tastes
9. soothing	feels
10. nervously	paced
11. lazily	reclined
12. carefully	checked
13. wonderful	smells
14. loudly	laughed
15. terribly	upset

Page 98, Form B
Exercise A

	Modifier	Word Modified
1.	well (ADV)	warm (V)
2.	shadowy (ADJ)	forest (N)
3.	extremely (ADV)	happy (ADJ)
4.	so (ADV)	loudly (ADV)
5.	naturally (ADV)	curious (ADJ)
6.	favorably (ADV)	was reviewed (V)
7.	long (ADJ)	journey (N)
8.	wonderfully (ADV)	grow (V)
9.	hungry (ADJ)	it (PRON)
10.	ever (ADV)	Have run (V)

Exercise B *Answers will vary.*

Page 99, Form A
Exercise A

1.	S	5.	C	9.	C
2.	S	6.	C	10.	C
3.	C	7.	S		
4.	S	8.	S		

Exercise B
1. most likely
2. Correct
3. harder
4. most
5. Correct
6. older
7. bigger
8. the less helpful
9. best
10. the most beautiful

Page 100, Form B
Exercise A
1. the most gracefully; Correct
2. tallest; taller
3. worse; worst
4. more deeply; Correct
5. more tall; taller
6. more happy; happier
7. smallest; Correct
8. more; most or the most
9. the farther; the farthest
10. best than; better than

Exercise B *Answers will vary. Possible answers shown below.*
1. This movie is the funniest of the three comedies.
2. This piano player is better than that piano player.
3. Of the three books, this one is the most interesting.
4. She drives more slowly than he does.
5. My sister Susan is older than my sister Meg.

Page 101, Form A
Exercise A

1.	DC	3.	IC	5.	DC
2.	IC	4.	IC		

Exercise B
1. In this day and age, we have many more labor-saving machines than earlier generations did.
2. Today, people can sew faster with a sewing machine than by hand.
3. Correct
4. Computers can perform many tasks faster than people can.
5. A microwave oven now cooks faster than any other oven used at home.

Page 102, Form B
Exercise A
1. The day we took the training wheels off my sister Kristen's bike was one of the happiest days of her life.
2. The old bike with the missing fender was more rickety than the new one, but she loved that battered heap.
3. When I saw her trying to balance, I thought she looked cuter than any other child I'd seen.
4. The first turn Kristen tried was more difficult than any other turn she'd tried.
5. That photo of her is funnier than the photo of you in your clown costume.

Exercise B *Answers will vary.*

Page 103, Form A
Exercise A

1.	any	9.	had
2.	any	10.	any
3.	ever	11.	ever
4.	any	12.	could
5.	can	13.	anybody
6.	are	14.	anything
7.	could	15.	any
8.	has		

Exercise B
1. couldn't hardly; could hardly
2. can't never; can't ever *or* can never
3. nothing; anything
4. couldn't scarcely; could scarcely
5. shouldn't never; should never *or* shouldn't ever
6. Didn't nobody; Did nobody *or* Didn't anybody
7. doesn't want none; doesn't want any
8. hasn't told me nothing; hasn't told me anything *or* has told me nothing
9. don't give the baby no; don't give the baby any
10. didn't want nobody; didn't want anybody

Page 104, Form B
Exercise A *Answers will vary. Possible answers shown below.*
1. I don't know what to do about this broken television set. (*or* I hardly know)
2. Correct
3. That teacher never gives any homework for weekends or vacations.
4. Correct
5. Since she's always lived in the Midwest, Melinda hasn't ever seen the ocean. (*or* has never seen the ocean)

Exercise B *Answers will vary. Possible answer shown below.*
Last summer my family went on a camping trip in the mountains. We had camping equipment, but we didn't have any room to carry extra food or supplies. I had never been fishing before, but there was no choice—we had to fish to eat. I could hardly believe it when I caught a huge trout!

Page 105, Form A
Exercise A

1.	good	9.	these
2.	these	10.	those
3.	That	11.	well
4.	those	12.	That

5. this   13. this
6. good   14. well
7. that   15. well
8. well

Exercise B
1. This here
2. That sorts
3. These kind
4. feeling good
5. tastes really well
6. These kind
7. that there
8. This sort
9. hear too good
10. look well

Page 106, Form B
Exercise A
1. I can't sleep because that baby is crying so much.
2. Correct
3. That kind of movie is too childish; or Those kinds of movies are too childish.
4. Do you like those miniature televisions?
5. Correct

Exercise B *Answers will vary. Possible answer shown below.*

Last month I attended that benefit concert for the homeless. I couldn't see the stage very well, but I did hear some bands that played really well. I think these kinds of fundraisers are very important. Supporting them makes me feel good.

Skills Assessment 2
Pages 107–109
1. D—Most famous
2. D—more loudly
3. A—raised   D—had fallen
4. A—Those   C—farther
5. E
6. B—was written   D—rhyme
7. A—really familiar C—has never seen
8. B—long, thick, and warm
9. B—noisier   D—these kinds
10. A—doesn't   B—well,
11. A—lost
12. D—provided
13. A—ever
14. B—any other   D—won
15. A—carefully   C—lower

16. D   18. C   20. D   22. A   24. B
17. B   19. A   21. C   23. C   25. D

Handbook 35
Page 111, Form A
Exercise A
1. for; of
2. with; from
3. of; beside
4. in; from; to
5. around; in
6. behind; under
7. According to
8. Because of
9. Over; above
10. ahead of

Exercise B
1. to quadruplets
2. Between the two houses
3. from China
4. near Lake Cumberland
5. since breakfast
6. in a pouch

7. inside the submarine
8. except Jan
9. during the winter
10. below the nose
11. into the sea
12. for two months

Page 112, Form B
Exercise A
1. for freedom, for = P, freedom = OP; of the press, of = P, press = OP
2. into high drifts, into = P, drifts = OP; beside the road, beside = P, road = OP
3. to the movie, to = P, movie = OP; along with Robert and me, along with = P, Robert, me = OP
4. behind their house, behind = P, house = OP
5. to the cabin, to = P, cabin = OP
6. among the weeds, among = P, weeds = OP; in the field, in = P, field = OP
7. by Chad, by = P, Chad = OP; about incidents, about = P, incidents = OP;
8. in addition to food and water, in addition to = P, food, water = OP
9. against the wind, against = P, wind = OP
10. by birth, by = P, birth = OP; by conviction, by = P, conviction = OP

Exercise B *Answers will vary for the prepositions. Possible answers shown below.*

During the evening of July 20–21, 1969 (OP), millions of people around the world (OP) sat in front of their TV sets (OP) to watch the Apollo 11 space mission bring the first human beings to the moon (OP). The Lunar Module landed on the moon (OP) on July 20 (OP) at 8:17 P.M. (OP) GMT (Greenwich Mean Time). Neil Armstrong, the first astronaut to emerge from the Lunar Module (OP), stepped onto the moon (OP) at 2:56 A.M., GMT, "taking one giant leap for mankind." (OP) It was now July 21 in England (OP), but because of the time difference (OP) between England (OP) and the United States (OP), it was still July 20 in America (OP).

Page 113, Form A
1. of the country; name; ADJ
2. of my favorite songs; one; ADJ
3. In the cave; had painted; ADV
4. Along the path; planted; ADV
5. in the dark; Can see; ADV
6. over the fence; flew; ADV
7. in the distance; mountain; ADJ
8. from 1954; song; ADJ
9. of the hockey players; One; ADJ
10. with enthusiasm; shouted; ADV
11. at 8:30; will leave; ADV
12. in scientific research; career; ADJ
13. through the net; dropped; ADV
14. During the storm; stopped; ADV
15. in the red dress; girl; ADJ

Page 114, Form B
Exercise A
1. around the theater; stretched; ADV
2. of the silver rings; Two; ADJ
3. of hit tunes; medley; ADJ
4. on the plane; worked; ADV
5. down the hill; raced; ADV
6. of the joke; end; ADJ
7. into the pool; jumped; ADV

8. on the tape; voice; ADJ
9. at the next corner; Turn; ADV
10. of the plant; roots; ADJ

Exercise B *Answers will vary. Possible answers shown below.*
1. The woman at the bus stop gave me the information.
2. I looked in the attic, but I couldn't find the photo album.
3. I am now reading a book about baseball.
4. Mother and Dad went to the soccer game with us.
5. Dolores was happy about the news.

Page 115, Form A
Exercise A
1. and
2. or
3. Neither, nor
4. whether, or
5. both, and
6. either, or
7. but
8. for
9. yet
10. not only, but also

Exercise B *Answers will vary. Possible answers shown below.*
1. not only, but also = CR
2. but = CD
3. both, and = CR
4. but = CD
5. or = CD
6. both, and = CR
7. whether, or = CR
8. Neither, nor = CR
9. Whether, or = CR
10. and = CD

Page 116, Form B
Exercise A *Answers will vary. Possible answers shown below.*
1. and = CD
2. but = CD
3. Either, or = CR
4. or = CD
5. Both, and = CR

Exercise B *Answers will vary. Possible answers shown below.*
1. At the age of nineteen months, Helen Keller was stricken with an illness that left her both deaf and blind.
2. Neither her mother nor her father knew what to do with such a child.
3. Within two years Helen had learned not only the manual alphabet but also braille.
4. Helen learned to speak, but she was hard to understand, and she required an interpreter.
5. Both Helen Keller and Anne Sullivan deserve much credit for what they accomplished.

Page 117, Form A
1. when = SC; furthermore = CA
2. so that = SC
3. thus = CA
4. consequently = CA
5. if = SC
6. After = SC
7. in order that = SC
8. so that = SC
9. therefore = CA
10. Because = SC

Page 118, Form B
Exercise A
1. I didn't realize that the lake was so close to the city; otherwise, I would have gone there sooner.
2. Since it is raining, the game will probably be canceled.
3. Because Prague, the capital of Czechoslovakia, has many churches, it has been called the "City of a Hundred Spires."
4. The car overheated; therefore, Jan did not arrive in time for the first act.

Exercise A *Answers will vary. Possible answers shown below.*
1. Many adults in the United States do not know how to read; *consequently* (CA), these people live under a terrible handicap.
2. *Because* (SC) they are unable to fill out application forms, they have difficulty finding jobs.
3. Illiterate adults cannot read directions; *therefore* (CA), they have to ask people for help.
4. They should go to adult education centers *where* (SC) adults can learn to read.

Page 119, Form A
Exercise A
1. Oh, no!
2. Good grief!
3. Oh,
4. Incredible!
5. wow,
6. Horrors!
7. Oh, dear,
8. Ugh!
9. Congratulations!
10. Never again!

Exercise B *Answers will vary. Possible answers shown below.*
1. Boom; Crash
2. Welcome
3. No
4. Help
5. Terrific
6. Hooray
7. Ouch
8. Yes
9. Never
10. Well

Page 120, Form B
Answers will vary. Possible answers shown below.
1. Never again! It isn't worth running to catch a bus.
2. Well! Was it necessary to shout at us?
3. All right! You're precisely on target.
4. Congratulations! Your friends are truly proud of you.
5. Hurry! The bus is coming!
6. Indeed! You can carry your own luggage.
7. The waiter dropped the platter on the floor. Crash!
8. Help! My leg is broken!
9. "Welcome! My name is Count Dracula."
10. Never! I will not watch that horror film.

Handbook 36
Page 121, Form A
Exercise A
1. nouns
2. adverb
3. adjectives
4. conjunctions
5. pronoun
6. interjection
7. preposition
8. verb
9. pronoun
10. adjective

Exercise B *Answers will vary. Possible answers shown below.*
1. school; project
2. explore; short story
3. and; provide; magazines

4. several; with
5. attentively; careful; later

Page 122, Form B
Exercise A *Answers will vary. Possible answers shown below.*
1. V; You shouldn't be mean to your little sister.
2. N; Name your favorite singer.
3. ADJ; Elliot accidentally broke a saucer while washing the dishes.
4. ADV; Meg parked near the blue jeep.

Exercise B *Answers will vary. Possible answers shown below.*
1. David left school early.
   Take a left turn at the corner.
2. The tractor plow is being repaired.
   Rita plowed forty acres today.
3. French is my favorite subject.
   Don't subject me to that loud music.
4. Great! That's wonderful news.
   That's a great idea.

Handbook 37
Page 123, Form A
Exercise A
1. joining two separate hulls together; joining
2. Leaving a little space between the two hulls; Leaving
3. tying two logs together; tying
4. Using paddles and sometimes sails; Using
5. skimming over the water; skimming
   attracting the attention of curious onlookers, attracting

Exercise B
1. hearing; DO
2. Washing cars; S
3. Speaking another language; S
4. listening to my explanation; OP
5. dieting; PN
6. Flying a glider; S
7. solving math problems; OP
8. roller skating; PN
9. planning parties; DO
10. walking on water; OP

Page 124, Form B
Exercise A
1. Eating tomatoes; S
2. growing the first tomato in the United States; DO
3. believing the tomato poisonous; OP
4. appreciating the tomato's value; DO
5. classifying it as a fruit or a vegetable; OP
6. Labeling it as a fruit; S
7. using a fruit in soups and sauces; S
8. deciding the issue; OP
9. satisfying both the scientific and nonscientific worlds; PN
10. classifying the tomato as a vegetable for purposes of trade only; OP

Exercise B *Answers will vary. Possible answers shown below.*
1. A popular modern sport is parachuting from the sky; parachuting from the sky = gerund phrase
2. Jumping from an airplane and falling freely at a speed in excess of one hundred miles per hour are

the skydiver's challenges; jumping from an airplane, falling freely at a speed in excess of one hundred miles per hour = gerund phrases
3. The pilot's task is flying the plane at a height of up to fifteen thousand feet; flying the plane at a height of up to fifteen thousand feet = gerund phrase
4. Performing stunts with other divers during the free-fall is part of the sport; performing stunts with other divers during the free-fall = gerund phrase

Page 125, Form A
1. baked *modifies* potato
2. Soothed by the music *modifies* Linda
3. Packing hurriedly *modifies* Tara
4. endangered *modifies* species
5. examining me *modifies* doctor
6. flooded *modifies* basement
7. laughing *modifies* audience
8. Tired after the long practice *modifies* athlete
9. ripped *modifies* jacket
10. driving recklessly through the town *modifies* motorist
11. leaping several feet into the air *modifies* Andrea
12. buried *modifies* treasure
13. Founding *modifies* Fathers
14. Using combinations of leaves and stems *modifies* Japanese
15. Increased *modifies* demand
16. bound *modifies* book
17. stuffed into a corner of his dresser drawer *modifies* socks
18. having weighed 3,024 carats in its rough state *modifies* diamond
19. observing Florida law *modifies* Fred
20. scraping *modifies* sound

Page 126, Form B
Exercise A *Answers will vary. Possible answers shown below.*
1. Hearing the music, Olenka knew that her neighbors were having a party; *modifies* Olenka
2. Written in Gothic script, the medieval manuscript was difficult to read; *modifies* manuscript
3. Running down the street, Sam hoped he would reach the bus stop in time; *modifies* Sam
4. Finding no one at home, Steve left a note saying he'd stop by again later; *modifies* Steve
5. Exhausted from a full day of biking yesterday, Justine decided to stay in last night; *modifies* Justine

Exercise B *Positioning of gerund phrases in sentences may vary.*
1. Known as *origami,* Japanese paper folding is of two kinds: traditional and creative.
2. Calling for folding colored paper into simple figures such as a butterfly or frog, traditional origami has the greatest appeal for children.
3. Requiring cutting, combining, and pasting, creative origami is used to make original, complex figures.

Page 127, Form A
Exercise A
1. to become
2. to throw
3. to go
4. to revive
5. to earn
6. to learn
7. to clean
8. To save
9. To listen
10. to miss

Exercise B

1. To understand the difference between a democracy and a republic; N
2. to offer tutoring services to younger children; ADJ
3. to take a trip to Australia next year; N
4. to regain control of the foundering ship; ADV
5. to denounce his principles; N
6. to circumnavigate the globe; ADJ
7. To win an Olympic medal; N
8. to watch the fireworks; ADJ
9. to stay physically fit; ADV
10. to attend regular practice sessions; N

Page 128, Form B
Exercise A
1. to strike it rich; ADV
2. to make furniture; ADV
3. To take karate lessons; N
4. to visit; ADV
5. to find a new route to India; N

Exercise B *Answers will vary. Possible answers shown below.*
1. They struggled to revive the victim speedily.
2. To arrange flowers attractively takes an artistic eye.
3. A catcher must practice to provide a good target for the baseball pitcher.
4. To swim in the Olympics, one must have both talent and dedication.
5. To explore the depths of the ocean, one must be physically fit.
6. It takes practice and concentration to become fluent in French.
7. It is difficult for me to recall the year of the blizzard.
8. To write a best seller is Peggy's ardent wish.

Page 129, Form A
Exercise A
1. Having traveled over three thousand miles from coast to coast
2. While mowing the lawn
3. To win friends and influence people
4. Having learned to say the alphabet and count to twenty
5. laughing a good deal
6. built with the aid of an anonymous donor
7. To study effectively
8. Opening the front door
9. Eating half a grapefruit, toast, and cereal for breakfast
10. Jogging along the woodland path

Exercise B
1. Used as paddles or flippers
2. Living in the oceans
3. Tapered and streamlined
4. Diving as experts
5. Returning to land or a cake of ice

Page 130, Form B
Answers will vary. Possible answers shown below.
1. Sitting on the front porch, we heard the sound of thunder.
2. To carry bulky packages on the bus, you should tie them together.
3. Liking the color red, Arthur chose a new car of brilliant flamingo.
4. Pointing out good methods of study, the program was beneficial to all students.

5. Riding in the country in early spring, I found the air so refreshing.
6. Stan saw the runaway dog chasing the car down the street.
7. Jonathan swept up the pieces of the lamp that lay shattered beyond repair.
8. Holding ice to her forehead, Ellie was driven to the clinic by a teammate.
9. In prehistoric times, gigantic creatures living on land and in the sea were larger than any animal alive today.
10. The head of the whale constitutes about one-third of the total mass of the whale, which weighs over 125 tons and is over 100 feet long.

Page 131, Form A
1. the Lion-Hearted
2. the motion picture actress
3. a member of the camel family
4. the famed architect
5. an orchid
6. John Constable and Joseph M. W. Turner
7. the highest peak in North America
8. Aaron Copland
9. an automobile race
10. the capital of Denmark
11. an English clergyman
12. a drama in verse by T. S. Eliot
13. the Eighth
14. honesty and kindness
15. the crane operator
16. *In Cold Blood*
17. Jennie
18. a dog that came from China or Japan
19. a land that offers a marvelous variety of wild animals
20. to find projectile points

Page 132, Form B
Exercise A
1. *Mustelids,* the name of the group of animals to which otters belong, means "weasels."
2. Otters love water, an environment well suited to them because of their webbed feet, thick tails, and dense fur.
3. Two kinds of otters, the freshwater otter and the sea otter, are found in North America.
4. The sea otter, a large animal, has white whiskers, a feature that gives the otter its nickname of "old man of the sea."

Exercise B *Answers will vary.*

Handbook 38
Page 133, Form A
Exercise A

1. identifies	4. was
2. are	5. use
3. were	

Exercise B

1. belong	5. are	9. Correct
2. is	6. is	10. are
3. oversees	7. offers	
4. are	8. Correct	

Page 134, Form B
Exercise A
1. Jade, has
2. impurities, make
3. type, comes
4. Correct
5. pieces, have

Exercise B *Answers will vary.*

Page 135, Form A
Exercise A
1. has
2. are
3. have
4. are
5. is
6. promise
7. have
8. experience
9. meet, form
10. is

Exercise B
1. provide
2. is
3. go
4. Correct
5. Correct
6. help
7. are
8. is
9. are
10. Correct

Page 136, Form B
Exercise A
1. seek
2. are
3. are
4. Correct
5. dislike
6. favor
7. Correct
8. are
9. are
10. conceal

Exercise B
1. rocks, slabs, are quarried
2. stone, stone, are quarried
3. gravel, sand, provide
4. rock, stone, is used
5. quarry, quarry, is established

Page 137, Form A
1. write
2. are
3. posts
4. speak
5. votes
6. are
7. loses
8. tallies, gives
9. follows
10. is
11. is
12. are
13. appear
14. signals
15. eyes
16. seem
17. behave
18. understand
19. is
20. requests

Page 138, Form B
Exercise A
1. Correct
2. is
3. look
4. is
5. Correct
6. knows
7. looks
8. approve
9. Correct
10. try

Exercise B
1. prances
2. stand
3. leaps, balances
4. jumps
5. head, begin

Page 139, Form A
1. consists
2. are
3. Correct
6. travels
7. doesn't, doesn't
8. Don't

4. Correct
5. Correct
9. is
10. are

Page 140, Form B
Exercise A
1. is
2. is
3. doesn't
4. has
5. are
6. is
7. was
8. Does
9. is
10. prefer

Exercise B
1. Where do bush pilots usually fly?
2. Two hundred miles is a short distance to fly to deliver supplies, food, and medicine.
3. A bush pilot doesn't have access to many weather stations.
4. Therefore, news with accurate weather details is not available.
5. Since isolated areas are decreasing today, this group of heroes is fast disappearing.

Skills Assessment 3
Pages 141–143
1. B—is
2. A—have used
3. B—is
4. E
5. A—Hasn't
6. A—"Wow!
7. A—who
8. D—is taking
9. C—flag,
10. B—1863,
11. B—are
12. E
13. C—definitely
14. B—wants
15. A—frontier

B—the term *Yankee*
C—guaranteed

B—except
D—amazing." (or amazing!")
D—strength

D—represent
D—oldest

D—too much
C—program; nevertheless,
C—was

16. B   17. C   18. A   19. D   20. D

Handbook 39
Page 145, Form A
Exercise A
1. SUB
2. IND
3. SUB
4. IND
5. SUB
6. SUB
7. SUB
8. IND
9. SUB
10. SUB

Exercise B
1. IND+IND
2. SUB+IND
3. IND+IND
4. IND+SUB
5. SUB+IND

Page 146, Form B, Exercise A
1. SUB+IND
2. IND+SUB
3. SUB+IND
4. SUB+IND
5. IND+SUB

Exercise B *Answers will vary. Possible answers shown below.*
1. If you are considering the purchase of a home computer, you should do some careful research about what computer is right for you. Subordinate

clause = If you are considering the purchase of a home computer
2. Cost is a major factor, but you must also consider your needs. (no subordinate clause)
3. Since certain types of computers and software are appropriate only for specific needs, you should decide exactly what your needs are. Subordinate clause = Since certain types of computers and software are appropriate only for specific needs
4. Your parents may want to use the computer for their financial planning, and you may want to use it for school reports, graphics, and games. (no subordinate clause)
5. Remember, even the best computer can be worth nothing to you if you do not know how to use it. Sub-ordinate clause = if you do not know how to use it

Page 147, Form A
Exercise A
1. adjective clause = which consists of more than two hundred species of hoofed animals
modified noun = *Ungulate* order
2. adjective clause = where the horse was first domesticated about five thousand years ago;
modified noun = Central Asia
3. adjective clause = which is used for riding, driving, and racing;
modified noun = light horse
adjective clause = which is a strong work animal;
modified noun = draft horse
4. adjective clause = that knights rode into battle;
modified noun = work horses

Exercise B *Answers will vary. Possible answers shown below.*
1. Jacques Cousteau, who is an ocean scientist, makes underwater nature films.; who is an ocean scientist
2. Cousteau was an ocean diver who had been diving with the French Navy.; who had been diving with the French Navy
3. Gagnan, who was an engineer, knew a great deal about all kinds of valves.; who was an engineer
4. Gagnan was able to make the valve, which was just what Cousteau had in mind.; which was just what Cousteau had in mind.

Page 148, Form B
1. adjective clause = who wrote a number of successful novels set in Maine
modified noun = Mary Ellen Chase;
introductory word = who
2. adjective clause = whose habits are clearly similar to those of lions in the wild
modified noun = cats;
introductory word = whose
3. adjective clause = I most admire
modified noun = people; none
4. adjective clause = that were once used for delicate operations such as eye surgery
modified noun = knives;
introductory word = that
5. where President Jimmy Carter spent a night with an average American family
modified noun = town;
introductory word = where
6. adjective clause = which are given annually
modified noun = Nobel Prizes;
introductory word = which

7. adjective clause = young female readers enjoyed years ago
modified noun = books; none
8. adjective clause = he first saw a concert grand piano and a big double-bass violin
modified noun = day; none
9. adjective clause = why she exercises, watches her weight, and eats healthful foods
modified noun = reason;
introductory word = why
10. adjective clause = whose sharp eyes spot typographical errors in materials about to be published
modified noun = proofreader;
introductory word = whose
11. adjective clause = you find on the first floor of the state office building
modified noun = clerk; none
12. adjective clause = which appear at the foot of the Statue of Liberty
modified noun = lines;
introductory word = which
13. adjective clause = where he had been pronounced incapable of learning
modified noun = class;
introductory word = where
14. adjective clause = when the arts flourished in Western Europe
modified noun = time;
introductory word = when
15. adjective clause = whose achievements were outstanding this year
modified noun = students;
introductory word = whose

Page 149, Form A
1. who developed the modern quick-freezing process; ESS
2. , which is considered one of the Lipari Islands,; NON
3. , which is a Yorkshire word,; NON
4. , which is a very popular house plant,; NON
5. that is most nutritious; ESS
6. , which is the state bird of Kentucky,; NON
7. , which is a popular name among European royalty,; NON
8. who inspired *Alice's Adventures in Wonderland.*; ESS
9. that is most commonly used; ESS
10. who is indifferent or hostile to the arts; ESS
11. , whose real name was Samuel Clemens,; NON
12. , who loves chocolate,; NON
13. who wrote this book; ESS
14. , which was published in 1854, NON
15. where the first modern Olympic Games were held; ESS

Page 150, Form B
Answers will vary. Possible answers shown below.
1. There go the workers who are resurfacing our street.
2. I found the page that was missing from my notebook.
3. Let me show you my best piece of writing, which I plan to enter in a short-story contest.
4. Yolanda, who hates to use a map, finally found our house.
5. Our director, who thinks we deserve the best, distributed the new band uniforms.

6. The curb that I tripped over yesterday has not been repaired.
7. A Boston artist who draws in chalk on pavements attracts many onlookers.
8. My favorite piece of needlework, which took me months to complete, has been damaged.
9. Not everything that you may hear is necessarily true.
10. The fire alarm that awakened us last night went off accidentally.

Page 151, Form A
Exercise A
1. Although early zippers were not very reliable
2. Because this early slide fastener might pop open by itself
3. so that it could not be opened or closed
4. when Gideon Sundback of Sweden invented a new, more reliable slide fastener
5. Since the slide fastener had been unreliable
6. when the B. F. Goodrich Company used the name to describe galoshes with slide fasteners
7. As leading fashion designers of the 1930's began to use zippers extensively
8. where there is a need to fasten and unfasten two adjoining edges of material
9. since some disabled people cannot grasp a zipper's metal tab
10. After Velcro® was invented

Exercise B
1. If the weather is inclement *modifies* may be canceled
2. before he attended the stage performance *modifies* read
3. than he had expected *modifies* better
4. If Christina has a good crop of vegetables this year *modifies* will sell
5. as George does *modifies* fast
6. Because Marina could not sleep *modifies* got up, read
7. to win the decathlon *modifies* felt
8. where everyone could easily see it *modifies* placed
9. when water moves suddenly from side to side *modifies* occur
10. although the hours are long *modifies* likes

Page 152, Form B
Exercise A *Answers will vary. Possible answers shown below.*
1. Stanley plans to visit his grandparents in Florida when school is out.
2. Grandfather Perkins likes to go fishing every morning while the rest of the family is asleep.
3. Because he is interested in the future, Stan hopes to spend time at Epcot Center's exhibits.
4. Grandmother Perkins will tour the World Showcase even though her feet ache.

Exercise B *Answers will vary. Possible answers shown below.*
1. After Mary found an apartment, she went to a downtown department store to buy furniture.
2. Although she didn't have much money, she still wanted to create a comfortable home.
3. A Bentwood rocker looked very comfortable, so she headed straight for it.
4. She couldn't buy the chair because she didn't have enough money.

Page 153, Form A
1. Where the treasure is buried; S
2. how he will cross the Australian Desert in a car with no air conditioning; OP
3. what we hear on the news; OP
4. Whomever the principal hires for the teaching position; S
5. why Jesse did not win the history award; DO
6. whoever crossed her path; IO
7. whatever grows in the ground; DO
8. Whoever attempts to climb a mountain; S
9. why the coach chose him as the lead-off batter; DO
10. Whoever sells the most tickets to the class carnival; S
11. when Gretchen spilled her soup; PN
12. that he would pick up the package at the post office later today; DO
13. whoever answers the phone; IO
14. How Amanda ever managed to stay upright on those skis; S
15. which one was to blame; OP

Page 154, Form B
Exercise A
1. that we should apologize; PN
2. why Penny became so angry; DO
3. what life was like in the Middle Ages; OP
4. whoever had been with the company for over one year; OP
5. when the next full moon would be; DO
6. how she could break the bad news to the yearbook staff; DO
7. What pleased Alex most; S; that he would be at a beach for his vacation; PN
8. whether I'll be able to make it to the meeting next week; DO
9. How global warming affects out planet; S
10. whoever answers our ad; IO

Exercise B *Answers will vary. Possible answers shown below.*
1. The owls hooted at *whoever and whatever dared disturb the peace and quiet of their wooded home.*
2. *I don't know why I continued my journey.*
3. *That I could hear my heart pounding* was distressing.
4. My determination was *what helped me make it home.*

Page 155, Form A
1. S	8. CP	15. S
2. CP	9. S	16. CP
3. S	10. S	17. CP
4. CP	11. CP	18. S
5. S	12. S	19. CP
6. CP	13. CP	20. S
7. S	14. S	

Page 156, Form B
Exercise A
1. S	6. CP
2. CP	7. CP
3. S	8. S
4. CP	9. S
5. S	10. CP

Exercise B *Answers will vary. Possible answers shown below.*
1. A balloon is a spherical bag made of paper, rubber, silk, or a rubberized fabric. (S)

2. The balloon is filled with a light gas, and it may have a basket attached to the bag. (CP)
3. A balloon may lose some of its gas and begin to sink. (S)
4. The gas in the balloon may be hot air or helium. (S)

Page 157, Form A
Exercise A
1. CX
2. S
3. CX
4. CP
5. CX
6. S
7. CX
8. CP
9. CX
10. S

Exercise B *Answers will vary. Possible answers shown below.*
1. President Franklin Roosevelt used leg braces because his legs were paralyzed.
2. The disease that had left him paralyzed was polio.
3. Though his mother felt he should live like an invalid, Eleanor, his wife, insisted on his using his talents.
4. The point is that Roosevelt was a very courageous man.

Page 158, Form B
Exercise A *Answers will vary. Possible answers shown below.*
1. As freezing rain was falling yesterday, roads quickly became icy.
2. The problem was that the storm occurred at rush hour.
3. Driving became even more hazardous because motorists found visibility very poor.
4. Workers who wanted to get home safely became anxious.

Exercise B *Answers will vary. Possible answers shown below.*
1. After we saw an ad in the paper, we helped Mom buy a freezer at the warehouse sale.
2. Because we had such a small freezer, we were shopping for food several times a week.
3. Our family can now stock up on frozen foods that are on sale.
4. My parents, who hate making frequent trips to the grocery store, are very pleased with the purchase.

Page 159, Form A
Exercise A
1. Monopoly is a game of strategy, but it has an element of chance. (CP)
2. Hangman is a word game that both children and adults enjoy. (CX)
3. Chinese checkers is played with marbles; it is an easy game to learn. (CP)
4. Chess, which probably originated in India in the 600's, is still played throughout the world. (CX)
5. A game that is played on a checkered board of sixty-four squares is called checkers in the United States, but it is called draughts in Great Britain. (CP-CX)
6. Checker-type games were played by the ancient Egyptians, Greeks, and Romans, but checkers as it is played in the United States dates back only to the 1500's. (CP-CX)
7. In chess, international rules govern the playing of the game, but in checkers, each nation has its own rules. (CP)
8. Horseshoe pitching is a game that may be traced to Roman soldiers of about A.D. 100. (CX)

9. Ninepins must be at least several hundred years old, since the story "Rip Van Winkle" depicts colonial settlers playing it in colonial days. (CX)
10. Children are still playing ring-around-a-rosy, and this is a game that dates back to medieval times. (CP-CX)

Page 160, Form B
Exercise A
1. CX
2. CX
3. CX
4. CP
5. CX
6. CP
7. CX
8. CP-CX
9. CX
10. CP-CX

Exercise B *Answers will vary. Possible answers shown below.*
1. In the 1940's, a phone was always black, and it had a straight cord. (CP)
2. The phone had no dial, since operators placed all calls. (CX)
3. A caller lifted the receiver and waited until the operator said, "Number, please."
4. Because there was little automation in those days, there were no call-forwarding or call-waiting features, and there were no answering machines. (CP-CX)

Page 161, Form A
Exercise A
1. S
2. F
3. F
4. S
5. F
6. F
7. S
8. F
9. S
10. F

Exercise B *Answers will vary. Possible answers shown below.*
1. Since the entire cast had spent so much time making the scenery, the production seemed very professional.
2. The actors, to whom the audience responded enthusiastically, took at least four curtain calls.
3. Correct
4. Because the play was a musical, we asked band members to be the orchestra.

Page 162, Form B
Answers will vary. Possible answers shown below.
1. People are shopping at home from catalogs much more than they used to.
2. Shoppers, who enjoy the catalog's colorful pages, read the booklets eagerly, looking for things to buy.
3. Stores have found success with mailing catalogs, since so many people would rather shop at home.
4. Today, when most customers have fewer hours free, people find catalog shopping a good way to save time.
5. Many catalogs are sent regularly throughout the year from department stores, while others come from specialty stores.
6. You can order just about anything from catalogs, whether you want books, quilts, tools, gadgets, cassettes, or clothes.
7. Although some catalog items are expensive, you can find catalogs that advertise close-outs or other special values.
8. There even are catalog guides, which are directories of other catalogs.

9. The order forms of catalogs offer clear instruction for customers so that merchandise can be exchanged.
10. Because people's lives keep getting busier, the future of catalog shopping looks bright.

Page 163, Form A
1. misplaced clause: when he visited us last Sunday
   modified word: asked
2. misplaced clause: that was manufactured by Philco
   modified word: radio
3. Correct
4. misplaced clause: as it roared into the night sky
   modified word: airplane
5. Correct
6. misplaced clause: as he listened to each dramatic adventure
   modified word: Granddad
7. misplaced clause: who brought outlaws to justice
   modified word: rider
8. Correct
9. misplaced clause: when he began barking
   modified word: showed
10. misplaced clause: when he was at home alone in the daytime, sick and bored
    modified word: felt
11. Correct
12. misplaced clause: when they came on the air
    modified word: pleased
13. misplaced clause: that Granddad most wanted to hear
    modified word: serial
14. Correct
15. Correct

Page 164, Form B
Exercise A *Answers will vary. Possible answers shown below.*
1. The child whose parents had gone out for the evening pleaded for the toy.
2. She went to the store to buy some paper that she could use for typing.
3. At the library, I browsed through a book that was about American folk art.
4. The car that we had owned for many years stalled on the expressway.
5. In Florence, I went to see the statue of David, which was sculpted by Michelangelo.

Exercise B *Answers will vary. Possible answers shown below.*
(1) In Boston's North End, Katarina Witt and Brian Boitano starred in an ice show that demonstrated their athletic skills. (2) The show, "Skating II," which was on tour, proudly featured these Olympic gold medalists. (3) Their daring jumps and spins, which are figure skaters' unique trademarks, won bursts of applause. (4) Other routines that the audience liked included those of Russians and Germans who were appearing in the show.

Page 165, Form A
Exercise A
1. S	6. S
2. OP	7. S
3. S	8. OP
4. PN	9. PN
5. DO	10. DO

Exercise B
1. who
2. whom
3. whoever
4. who
5. who

Page 166, Form B
Exercise A
1. whom
2. who
3. whom
4. who
5. who

Exercise B *Answers will vary.*

Handbook 40
Page 167, Form A
1. Correct
2. A book in the Old Testament tells of Jonah's experiences with a sea creature.
3. Did General Dwight D. Eisenhower lead the United States forces in Korea?
4. Both Dad and Aunt Polly will be attending the variety show.
5. The Bible contains the words of God and of His prophets.
6. The Secretary of the Treasury decides when currency should be printed.
7. According to Dr. Purzansky, Phyllis may need to get braces on her teeth.
8. Did Mr. Simon appear on the talk show?
9. Correct
10. Rudolf Diesel invented the famous engine that was named after him.
11. Some characters in one Walt Disney film are Sneezy, Grumpy, and Bashful.
12. My lawyer's formal title is William J. Smithers, Esq.
13. Correct
14. Our teacher, Professor Silverstein, often quotes Shakespeare.
15. Correct

Page 168, Form B
Exercise A
1. What position did Miss Harriet Lane hold when Buchanan was President?
2. Did you know that Pope John Paul I served for only thirty-four days?
3. We enjoyed talking with Grandmother about the 1940's.
4. Prince William of England will probably be King William someday.
5. Mr. and Mrs. Mullin are traveling with my mother and aunt.
6. The Chief Justice of the Supreme Court reviewed the case.
7. Have you read any poems by Langston Hughes?
8. Correct
9. Staff Sgt. Daniel G. Hernandez spoke to the platoon.
10. Mr. Agube read a hymn from the Koran, the sacred book of the Moslems.
11. Correct
12. The artist Michelangelo painted frescoes that depict God creating the world.
13. Gerald Casazza was once the mayor of our town.

14. Last month Aunt Josie celebrated her ninety-fifth birthday.
15. A young American woman, Lisa Halaby, became Queen Noor of Jordan.

Exercise B

Many people do not know that America's favorite uncle, Uncle Sam, was a real person. Until a quarter of a century ago, most people believed that Uncle Sam was a mythical figure. Then evidence was found in an 1830 newspaper showing that Uncle Sam was a man named Samuel Wilson, who was born in 1766. Interestingly enough, Sam Wilson was a childhood playmate of another figure from both history and legend—John Chapman, better known as Johnny Appleseed. Johnny Appleseed traveled across America preaching Scripture and planting apple orchards.

Page 169, Form A
1. The Southwest has hotter summers than New England does.
2. Red beans and rice is a traditional Louisiana dish.
3. Some dangerous mudslides have occurred along the Pacific Coast Highway in California.
4. Jeanette, who is from Atlanta, Georgia, has a lovely Southern accent.
5. If you drive west on Interstate 30, you will reach Dallas, Texas.
6. The Rocky Mountain goat is really an antelope.
7. Correct
8. The most photographed mountain in the Far East is Mt. Fujiyama, near Tokyo, Japan.
9. The Danube is the second-longest river in Europe.
10. The Southern Cross is a constellation visible from the Southern Hemisphere.
11. Carlsbad Caverns in New Mexico is one of the Southwest's most impressive tourist attractions.
12. Mercury and Venus are the only planets without at least one moon.
13. The name of Sixth Avenue was changed to Avenue of the Americas.
14. Two of Hawaii's beautiful islands are Maui and Kauai.
15. As you might guess, the Finger Lakes in New York are long and narrow.

Page 170, Form B
Exercise A
1. Parts of the Ohio River sometimes freeze over.
2. The Black Hills of South Dakota contain countless fossils.
3. Correct
4. The Atlantic washes East Coast beaches; the Pacific washes West Coast ones.
5. Do you know that Chicago is the largest city in the Midwest?
6. Jupiter, Saturn, and Uranus are gaseous planets circling the sun.
7. The Himalayas are a mountain system in southern Asia.
8. The Union of Soviet Socialist Republics is the official name of the Soviet Union.
9. Reservations are required for camping at Yellowstone National Park.
10. Correct
11. All of Australia is located in the Southern Hemisphere.
12. The Big Dipper is part of the constellation Ursa Major.

13. Lake Michigan is the only one of the Great Lakes entirely within the United States.
14. Correct
15. In cold weather deer from the Rocky Mountains seek food in cities.

Exercise B

The capital of the United States is Washington, D.C. It is also known as the District and D.C. The Potomac River separates the District of Columbia from its neighbors, Virginia and Maryland. Historic Georgetown lies on the banks of the Potomac. Since D.C. has a height limit for buildings, Crystal City has sprung up in Arlington, Virginia. From this high-rise complex there is a view of landmarks such as the Capitol, the Jefferson Memorial, and the towering Washington Monument. This obelisk is set in the National Mall, a parklike area that stretches from Capitol Hill. Tourists know this area well, and many visit the Smithsonian Institution buildings there.

Page 171, Form A
1. Most of the French people are Roman Catholic.
2. Lyndon Johnson guided the Civil Rights Act through Congress in 1964.
3. Pedro loves art from the Renaissance and the Middle Ages.
4. Ernest Hemingway served as an ambulance driver during World War I.
5. The first Olympics were held in 776 B.C.
6. The Society for the Prevention of Cruelty to Animals was formed in 1866.
7. One of the most important Jewish holidays is Rosh Hashana.
8. Are you taking Algebra 2, chemistry, and French?
9. The *Mayflower* carried the first Pilgrims to America.
10. The holiday known as Thanksgiving is celebrated on a designated Thursday in November.
11. Correct
12. A member of the International Red Cross spoke at Mayfield High School.
13. The luncheon menu included German potato salad and Swedish meatballs.
14. Many people regard Memorial Day as the beginning of summer.
15. Pulitzer Prizes are awarded annually by Columbia University.

Page 172, Form B
Exercise A
1. The Hospital Volunteers of America has an active chapter at Rock County Hospital; the chapter holds a blood drive every spring.
2. Several Cambodian and Vietnamese refugees live in our apartment building.
3. The Battle of Concord was fought during the Revolutionary War.
4. Two holidays in May are Mother's Day and Memorial Day.
5. Will the twenty-first century begin at 12:01 A.M. in A.D. 2000 or 2001?
6. The *Amtrak Limited* will take us to the stadium for the first World Series game.
7. In history class we studied the construction of the Golden Gate Bridge.
8. The TV ad for Berry-Good granola bars features animated talking strawberries.
9. The Canadians celebrate Thanksgiving in October.

10. The ancient Greek civilization existed from about 900 to 200 B.C.

Page 173, Form A
1. Dear Ms. Taylor:
   Please send me two tickets for your lecture on May 12.
   Sincerely yours,
2. One of Shakespeare's characters says, "All the world's a stage."
3. Loveliest of trees, the cherry now
   Is hung with bloom along the bough,
   And stands about the woodland ride
   Wearing white for Eastertide.
       A. E. Housman, "Loveliest of Trees"
4. Have you read the article "Vernon Jordan, Past and Present" in *Ebony*?
5. Two of my favorite short stories are "Sixteen" and "Strawberry Ice Cream Soda."
6. Ms. Cass exclaimed, "You should have seen the Viking exhibit at the Metropolitan!"
7. Correct
8. Correct
9. Anne Frank wrote, "I still believe that people are really good at heart."
10. "That was a great movie," said Tom. "Now let's have something to eat."

Page 174, Form B
Exercise A
1. I. Energy
   A. Present sources
      1. Petroleum
      2. Natural gas
      3. Coal
   B. Problems
2. Dear Mr. Pappas:
   Enclosed is a check for $10 to cover the cost of shipping the books.
   Very truly yours,
3. *Time* magazine gave a rave review of the play *Phantom of the Opera.*
4. "Call me tonight," Rachel said, "and I'll give you the Spanish assignment."
5. Virginia Woolf wrote "A Room of One's Own" in lecture form for a college audience.

Exercise B
Last week I went to the Southwest for the first time. My teacher, Mrs. Gomez, hired a coach from the Blue Line Bus Company, and our class toured Arizona and New Mexico.

We saw the Grand Canyon, an Indian pueblo, and several ranches. We crossed the Rio Grande and saw a film company making *Southern Highway,* a documentary. In a museum in Santa Fe, we saw turquoise jewelry, Navajo blankets, and Hopi sand paintings. At Taos we visited adobe houses where Indians have lived since A.D. 1000.

The temperature was around 80° during the day. In the northern part of Arizona, we saw snow at the rim of the canyon. The Colorado River, which flows west of the Great Divide, was swollen by run-off.

Handbook 41
Page 175, Form A
1. P. J. Collins?
2. kilometers.

3. J. D. Cohen Furniture Company.
4. P.M.
5. B.C. . . . is based.
6. Oh, no! The quarterback fumbled the ball!
7. decimal .50 . . . one-half.
8. open to the public?
9. skating rink?
10. bread dough.
11. I.   British political parties
        A. Conservative Party
        B. Labour Party
        C. Liberal Party
        C. Social Democratic Party
12. $.9.50
13. Oh! Is today their anniversary?
14. P.M.
15. 10:30 A.M. the next day.

Page 176, Form B
Exercise A
1. The defense attorney asked the witness for the prosecution if he had ever seen the defendant.
2. Hooray! The Cardinals won the championship!
3. Who fought in the Spanish-American War?
4. Nick bought five almost new paperback books at the garage sale down the street for only $1.25 each.
5. Dr. Roger Harmon's specialty is sports medicine.
6. In Great Britain high tea is served at around 5:00 P.M.
7. Can't you read the sign posted there? It says: No Smoking Allowed.
8. Did you know that the singer Engelbert Humperdinck's real name is Arnold Dorsey?
9. Actor Larry Hagman, who used to be in *I Dream of Jeannie,* now plays J. R. Ewing in the television series *Dallas.*
10. Ingrid's mother bought this sweater in 1970 for only $9.50. Can you believe it?
11. Look! There's a landslide over on that mountain!
12. Tell me where I should plant the geraniums and azaleas.
13. Have you heard a weather forecast for the weekend?
14. How many centimeters are there in an inch?
15. Are you the patient who said the noise from the visitors' lounge is too loud?

Page 177, Form A
Exercise A
1. Dickens's character Ebenezer Scrooge was a mean, stingy old man.
2. Your paper must include the following: first, an outline; second, three to five pages of text; third, endnotes; and fourth, a bibliography.
3. The driver stopped, looked both ways, and then proceeded.
4. Emily's favorite poets are Alice Walker, Gwendolyn Brooks, and Anne Sexton.
5. Sulfur has a strong, unpleasant smell.
6. First, check the card catalog; second, look for the books you want; third, take notes.
7. Picnickers brought sandwiches, potato salad, lemonade, and fruit.
8. Our newspaper tour guide showed us reporters writing stories, typesetters printing articles, and the drivers of delivery trucks getting ready to deliver the papers.
9. Be sure to close the windows, feed the cat, and switch on a lamp.

10. Carolyn wore suede boots and thin, handknitted, wool knee socks.

Exercise B
1. Microorganisms include bacteria, yeasts, and molds.
2. They are tiny, invisible creatures.
3. Whether you can see them or not, they are on your hands, inside your body, and in the air.
4. First, molds are used to make antibiotics, other medicines, and cheeses.
5. Second, yeasts are used for making breads, synthetic vitamins, and some beverages.

Page 178, Form B
Exercise A
1. He suffered a double fracture of the pelvis, a broken collar bone, broken ribs, a fractured ankle, and severe internal injuries.
2. They said Hogan would live, walk, and resume some everyday activities.
3. First, he tied his old rival Sam Snead in the Los Angeles Open.
4. Second, Hogan entered the biggest, most important tournament of all, the Masters at Augusta, Georgia.
5. Hogan's patient, diligent effort finally paid off.

Exercise B *Answers will vary. Possible answers shown below.*
1. They packed a tent, backpacks, and a canteen for the journey.
2. This was to be a risky, exciting adventure.
3. First, they wanted to experience the thrill; second, they wanted to test themselves.
4. The adventure reinforced an appreciation of the beauty of nature, of the importance of self-reliance, and of the value of cooperation.

Page 179, Form A
1. old movies, she has never
2. night sky, my father pointed
3. before breakfast, Ron runs five
4. A gecko, I believe, is a type
5. Yes, Paula, you have three
6. at work, Judy lay down
7. The hearing, a joint investigation by Congress, will
8. Well, we will, of course, refund your money
9. the fairgrounds, there is a
10. Anthony, will you take
11. you think, Professor Jennings, that the experiment
12. is ill, Ms. Haywood will
13. Her attorneys, moreover, have asked for
14. Queen Victoria, an English monarch, ruled
15. this run, we'll win the
16. This road, I think, leads to the
17. the flu, Felicia resolved to
18. your coat, Brenda, and hang it
19. for tickets, strangers began to
20. Mecca, the birth place of Mohammed, is one

Page 180, Form B
Exercise A
1. after World War I, there was great
2. Parkways, the first highways, were gently winding; freeways, on the other hand, were
3. Tunneling through mountains and spanning rivers, the highways
4. At the exits of a highway, cloverleafs made it easy
5. Consisting of three or four levels of interlocking highways, some modern

6. Encouraged by the availability of highways, freight companies
7. Yes, railway trains, the traditional freight haulers,
8. In the small towns in the country, many railway tracks
9. In the older cities in the United States, the four-lane superhighway
10. Now, because traffic jams have become common, cities and states

Exercise B *Answers will vary. Possible answers shown below.*
1. At the end of the internship, they might offer her a full-time job.
2. If it doesn't work out, she will return to school.
3. This is, of course, valuable experience in the working world.
4. Yes, Lisa, you should get involved in this program.

Page 181, Form A
1. commented, "The bill has
2. overslept, but she still
3. "Where," the teacher asked, "is Samoa located?"
4. City, but New York
5. *"The New York Times,"* said Mr. Schultz, "was first published
6. resign, or has she
7. both rang, and I answered
8. predicted, and the town
9. opened," said Janice.
10. the pharaohs," explained Ms.
11. been selected, and they are
12. "Well," the clerk replied, "we don't have that
13. for lunch, but I have
14. surgery, nor
15. said, "I'll

Exercise B
(1) "My report," Doug told Eve, "is on Jack Schaefer, a Western novelist. (2) I liked his short stories first, and then I read the novel *Shane.*"
(3) Eve said, "Schaefer had never seen the West when he wrote *Shane.*"
(4) "He must have had a great imagination," Doug declared. "The Western Writers of America organization gave *Shane* an important award, so they must have found it to be very authentic."
(5) "Actually," Eve explained, "Schaefer researched his subject thoroughly at Yale University."

Page 182, Form B
Exercise A
(1) Mars is the closest planet to Earth, and it has long captivated people's imaginations. (2) Giovanni Schiaparelli, an Italian scientist, discovered lines on the surface of Mars and called them *canali.* (3) The word is Italian for *channels,* but it was translated into English as *canals.* (4) Study of these "canals" led to a whole Martian mythology and to speculation about life on Mars.
(5) "Long ago," wrote author Leigh Brackett, " . . . there were oceans in equatorial and southern Mars." (6) Edgar Rice Burroughs and H. G. Wells wrote vividly about Martians and their activities. The space age, however, brought better knowledge of Mars. (7) The "Red Planet" turned out to be barren and rocky, and this discovery greatly diminished the likelihood of intelligent life on Mars.

Exercise B
Answers will vary. Possible answers shown below.
1. Lee said to herself, "I can't possibly enjoy this vacation."
2. "Traveling alone to stay with strangers feels *too* strange," she mumbled unhappily.
3. "I've met these cousins only once," she sighed, "and I may not like them at all."
4. "I haven't seen anyone my age waiting for this bus, but I think someone is coming over now."
5. "Hello, I've been looking for somebody my age, and you look about fifteen."

Page 183, Form A
Exercise A
1. ESS; no commas
2. NON; The vise-grip, which is a wrenchlike tool, resembles pliers.
3. ESS; no commas
4. ESS; no commas
5. NON; An obelisk commemorates the Battle of Bunker Hill, which actually was fought on Breed's Hill.
6. ESS; no commas
7. ESS; no commas
8. ESS; no commas
9. NON; Mrs. Farnaby, whom we named after the pet-shop owner, is our new cat.
10. ESS; no commas

Exercise B
(1) The dancer whose farewell performance we attended was Rudolf Nureyev. (2) He was appearing with other ballet dancers in a special program that had six parts. (3) The part that I enjoyed most was an episode from the ballet *Sleeping Beauty.* (4) Teenager Jennifer Gelfand, who rushed to the theater when another dancer was injured, performed with a partner from the Bolshoi Ballet. (5) Boston's Wang Center for the Performing Arts, which was redecorated recently, was an impressive setting for the show.

Page 184, Form B
Exercise A
1. Lila, who is very talented, won a scholarship to art school.
2. Correct
3. Ms. Snyder, whom you met yesterday, is visiting from England.
4. Correct
5. Peter gave me his jacket, which didn't fit him anymore.
6. Correct
7. Correct
8. Correct
9. Correct
10. Curling, which is played on ice, probably began in Scotland.

Exercise B
Answers will vary. Possible answers are shown below.
1. I got help from some neighbors who could recall outdated words.
2. Some were words that they had used, but others were ones that they had noticed in old books.
3. They knew a number of old words, which they were willing to share.
4. Cars, which people once called *motors* or *machines,* have inspired many new words.

Page 185, Form A
Exercise A
1. August 8, 1974?
2. October 29, 1929,
3. pewter dish, pans hung
4. no comma necessary
5. closet, doors opened
6. Washington, D.C. 20510-2102
7. started, throughout the hospital
8. On January 26, 1991, Monica
9. July 23, 1938,
   Jamaica Plain, Massachusetts.
10. no comma necessary
11.
   4000 Dolphin Boulevard
   Orlando, FL 32821
   July 16, 1992

Dear Sharon,
   We finally arrived here last night. On our way down the highway, we stopped in Norfolk, Virginia, and Savannah, Georgia. Things seem different from the way they were the last time we visited here, in June 1990. At our hotel, rooms are small but comfortable. I'm having fun but missing everyone at home.

   Your friend,
   Emily

Page 186, Form B
1. The last time I saw Derek, Stephen and I heard him play the guitar.
2. Correct
3. It was in Cleveland, Ohio, in the music schools's auditorium.
4. We flew to Cleveland on Saturday, January 16, the day of the recital.
5. For the morning of our flight, reservations had been difficult to get.
6. The day before, the airline had lowered its prices dramatically.
7. Correct
8. Correct
9. Remembering, Derek said, so many friends from high school days had made him eager to hear from them.
10. You can write to him at 3900 Carlin Court, Falls Church, VA 22046.

Page 187, Form A
1. psychology; but
2. 1787; Mozart
3. Japan; consequently
4. months; unfortunately
5. following things: paint
6. piano; she's *or* piano: she's
7. painter; nevertheless
8. following: skis, poles
9. essayist; however
10. advertising: copywriting

Page 188, Form B
Exercise A
1. Then take the following safety precautions: make sure that the cars do not touch; turn off the ignitions of both cars; turn off all accessories in both cars.
2. Locate the positive terminals of the two batteries; then connect the clamps of the red cable to the positive terminals.

3. Next, connect one clamp of the black cable to the negative terminal of the assisting battery; connect the other clamp of the black cable to the engine block of the car to be started.
4. When all the cables are connected, start the engine of the assisting car; then start the engine of the other car.
5. Remove the cable clamps in the reverse order from the way you connected them; first, disconnect one of the black cable's clamps from the engine block; then, disconnect the other from the assisting battery; finally, disconnect the red cable's clamps from the positive terminals.

Exercise B
1. the city: its crowds
2. Dear Mr. Perez:
3. at 10:30 P.M.
4. to the store; however
5. to Andrew's party: you have
6. from Ecclesiastes 1:9.
7. once said: "To regret deeply
8. copper; a cannon . . . swords; and
9. tennis; Stefan . . . Open;
10. wrote: "Prosperity is not without many fears and distastes;

Page 189, Form A
Exercise A
1. and people—these organisms live in societies.
2. Ants and bees—they both live in organized colonies—communicate
3. sources—this has been proven—through
4. movement—it is called a dance—means
5. Karl Von Frisch wrote—he did research in the 1920's—*Bees:*

Exercise B
1. A queen ant—she is protected as the mother of the colony—may live
2. Army ants—they are sometimes called soldier ants—have
3. Young birds, lizards, snakes, even small mammals—all these creatures
4. aphids are herded—sometimes even kept in shelters—by some
5. A sense of smell and color discrimination—these are traits

Page 190, Form B
Exercise A
1. Nebulae, comets, asteroids—these are all studied by astronomers.
2. The expensive menu listed—I couldn't believe it—only two entrees.
3. Correct
4. Modern conveniences—good plumbing, central heating, and even electricity—are often lacking in old houses.
5. If you had a wish—one pertaining to a foreign country you'd like to visit—what would it be?

Exercise B
1. Ophthalmologists, optometrists, and opticians—these are eye professionals.
2. Opticians specialize in eye care; however, they are not medical doctors.

3. They can repair broken glasses, replace them if they are beyond repair, and fit glasses and contact lenses.
4. Optometrists can also provide these services; in addition, they can examine eyes, prescribe glasses and contact lenses, and recommend eye exercises.
5. Ophthalmologists—they are medical doctors—can do everything opticians and optometrists do and more.
6. Unlike opticians and optometrists, ophthalmologists can do the following: treat eye disorders and diseases, prescribe medicines, perform surgery.
7. Before prescribing corrective lenses, the optometrist or ophthalmologist will do an examination—none of it hurts.
8. One part is the Snellen test—it's the test that requires you to read the chart with the big *E*.
9. Then the doctor checks the physical condition of your eyes; he or she checks both inside and out.
10. A light is shone into each of your eyes; this allows the doctor to examine the interior of your eyes.

Page 191, Form A
1. father-in-law
2. forty-three
3. long-lost; well-worn
4. thirty-three
5. red-haired
6. two-thirds
7. jack-in-the-box
8. Correct
9. twenty-three
10. sixty-three-year-old
11. twenty-four hours
12. on-the-job
13. great-grandfather
14. best-selling
15. Correct
16. out-of-print
17. Correct
18. Vice-President; forty-five
19. Correct
20. short-lived

Page 192, Form B
Exercise A
1. My brother-in-law
2. One-half
3. a ten-foot alligator
4. The green-covered booklet
5. stained-glass
6. a post-game conference
7. My ninety-five-year-old great-grandmother
8. a part-time job
9. enthusiasm was short-lived
10. best-loved

Exercise B
1. Correct
2. Correct
3. They may re-
4. thirty-two permanent teeth
5. Correct
6. Thirteen-year-old children; twenty-eight permanent teeth
7. Correct
8. daily at-home care
9. At-home care
10. Good-tasting

11. tooth-supporting
12. all-important

Page 193, Form A
1. someone's idea of a joke?
2. women's rights
3. couldn't tell a lie.
4. players' strike interrupted
5. Cynthia's poll resulted in ten *yes's,* four *no's,* and two *undecided's.*
6. The employees' union held
7. two small *e's* and a small *c.*
8. Houdini's ability to escape
9. The '56 Chevy and the '66 Mustang are Donald's favorite cars.
10. seven *90's,* ten *80's,* and five *70's* on the chemistry

Page 194, Form B
Exercise A
1. Correct
2. Anyone who's interested
3. Correct
4. The waves' tumbling action
5. It's important for a reef's residents
6. A fish's life . . . a reef's numerous
7. Correct
8. Correct
9. The moray's body is streamlined.
10. The jack's fins and
11. behind a rock's cover
12. predators' speed
13. in the world's oceans.

Exercise B
1. Marty received two *B's* and two *C's* on his report.
2. "I wandered lonely as a cloud" is the first line of Wordsworth's famous poem.
3. Whose car shall we take, yours or mine?
4. My little sister's favorite story is "How the Crocodile Got Its Smile."
5. His truck sped out of control and crashed into the garage door.
6. Vanessa couldn't keep up with Debra's aerobic exercise class.

Page 195, Form A
1. "I'm sure you will enjoy J. D. Salinger's short stories," said Ms. Phillips.
2. "In the Middle Ages," said Dr. Lynch, "books were handwritten by monks."
3. Andrea said, "In Shakespeare's *As You Like It,* a character says, 'All the world's a stage.'"
4. "We can never have enough of nature," said Henry David Thoreau.
5. Samuel Johnson wrote, "Whatever you have, spend less."
6. "Whoever said, 'Love is blind,' was correct," said Mark.
7. "I missed Mardi Gras," said Marni, "but I went to the World's Fair."
8. "A sonnet consists of fourteen lines," explained Mr. Jackson.
9. "I plan to go to California," Matt said, "if I can save enough money."
10. "The Manx is a type of cat," explained Janet.
11. "I know who wrote 'The medium is the message,'" Clare said. "It was Marshall McLuhan."
12. "A rose," wrote Gertrude Stein, "is a rose is a rose, is a rose."

13. When Neil Armstrong stepped onto the moon, he said, "That's one small step for a man, one giant leap for mankind."
14. "Injustice anywhere is a threat to justice everywhere," wrote Martin Luther King, Jr.
15. Becky claimed that she agreed with the Shakespearean character who said, "Neither a borrower nor a lender be."
16. "When Thomas Paine wrote, 'These are the times that try men's souls,' he was trying to win support for the American Revolution," Keith explained.
17. Marcia said, "My parents remember the speech in which John F. Kennedy implored, 'Ask not what your country can do for you—ask what you can do for your country.'"
18. Anne Frank wrote in her diary, "In spite of everything I still believe that people are really good at heart."

Page 196, Form B
Exercise A
Shortly after 2:00 A.M. on April 15, 1912, the ship *Titanic* slid to its watery grave. The passenger liner, on its maiden voyage from England to New York, had struck an iceberg in the North Atlantic.
William Ryan, a geologist at Columbia University, believes the *Titanic* can be salvaged. "The only question," he says, "is how much money you're willing to spend. We're talking about hundreds of millions of dollars."
A French team has already brought up such items as trays and dishes from the wreck. In a magazine article the team leader says, "None of the items we brought up will be sold for profit."
Ruth Blanchard, a survivor of the *Titanic,* opposes plans to disturb it. "It's the graveyard of 1,500 people," she says. "I believe they should be left in peace."

Exercise B
1. My great-grandmother, a survivor of the *Titanic* disaster, told me about the ship's striking an iceberg and sinking.
2. She said, "Let me tell you about my experiences in one of the lifeboats."
3. I told her that I would love to hear her story.
4. John Pierce plans to raise the ship. "The *Titanic,*" he states, "is coming up."
5. "I am dismayed," he said, "by those who say, 'Leave it alone.'"
6. "I have mixed feelings about raising the *Titanic.*" Anna said.

Page 197, Form A
1. Mark Twain stated, "Courage is resistance to fear, master of fear—not absence of fear."
2. Do you know who wrote, "No truth or goodness realized by man ever dies"?
3. "Look out below!" the hikers frantically yelled.
4. "A skid," states the booklet *Winter Motoring,* "reflects poor driving technique."
5. Which President made the statement "If a man starts out to make himself President, he hardly ever arrives"?
6. "Nowadays," explained the nurse, "chemotherapy can be controlled by a small, computer-programmed, implanted device."
7. "How often," inquired Ali, "does a longhaired cat need its fur brushed and combed?"

8. Who was the first person to remark, "A fool and his money are soon parted"?
9. "Aquatic plants," the saleswoman began, "are essential for keeping the fish in aquariums healthy."
10. "I can't believe," exclaimed Anita, "that motion pictures were invented in 1891!"
11. "What do you think of my choice of subject—the ground-nesting snowy owl?" Stephen was asking.
12. Jennifer asked, "Why did John Donne say, 'No man is an island'?"
13. We heard Kareem exclaim, "My sister will be interviewed on Channel 4 tonight!"
14. Didn't Louisa May Alcott's father once say, "One must be a wise reader to quote wisely and well"?
15. Writing a piece of fiction begins with asking yourself, "What if . . . ?"

Page 198, Form B
Exercise A
1. Amy exclaimed, "I found some great quotations for the bulletin board!"
2. Voltaire stated, "The secret of being a bore is to tell everything."
3. "Common sense is not so common," this famous French writer also wrote.
4. Wasn't it Benjamin Franklin who wrote, "Lost time is never found again"?
5. Charles Kettering commented, "We should all be concerned about the future because we will spend the rest of our lives there."

Exercise B
1. fiction!"
2. Correct
3. fiction"?
4. Correct

Page 199, Form A
1. The movie Cyrano de Bergerac is based on Edmond Rostand's play.
2. Edgar Degas, a French Impressionist, created bronze sculptures and produced numerous paintings, among them The Bellelli Family, a group portrait.
3. Markings was a book of diary entries by Dag Hammarskjöld, a United Nations Secretary General; it was published after his death.
4. The title song "The Rose," in the film of that name, has a theme of hope.
5. Millions of Americans read either Time or Newsweek every week.
6. Songs like Paul Simon and Art Garfunkel's "Sounds of Silence" synchronize the talents of the composer and the lyricist.
7. The musical score from the film Chariots of Fire has sold widely on tape cassettes.
8. "Lullaby for Peregrine" is Robert P. Tristram Coffin's poem for the first Pilgrim child born in the New World.
9. "The Life and Death of a Western Gladiator" is an article about a rattlesnake; it was written by Charles Finney for Harper's magazine.
10. Columnist Sydney J. Harris wrote the essay "We're Not Fit to Colonize Space."
11. My favorite episode of the Nova television series is called "Case of the Flying Dinosaur."
12. The title Seventeen was used long ago by Booth Tarkington for a novel about a teenaged boy; it is now the title of a magazine for girls.

13. In Jessamyn West's short story "Sixteen," a girl struggles with the conflicts of growing up.
14. The Song of Roland is the national epic of France.
15. Robert Louis Stevenson, known for his adventure novels, also wrote volumes of essays; one of his most popular essays is "Walking Tours."

Page 200, Form B
1. Pilgrims Landing at Cape Cod
2. Founding Mothers
3. "Nature"
4. Correct
5. Animals magazine; "The Magic of Cedar Swamps"
6. "The Ballad of Late Annie."
7. "The Blue Hotel."
8. Old Possum's Book of Practical Cats; "Growltiger's Last Stand,"; Cats
9. The Golden Girls; "Rose Fights Back."
10. Correct

Skills Assessment 4
Pages 201–203
1. B—rose,"   D—best-known
2. A—Aaron Burr,   D—shot and killed
3. B—no one was   D—surgery.
4. E
5. A—Sheen,   B—whose
6. A—unfortunately,
7. E
8. A—You're   C—Smith; however,
9. A—include   B—Sears Tower in Chicago, Illinois
10. B—enthusiastically,   D—whoever
11. A—that   D—summer
12. B—moons
13. E
14. A—Far East   C—Sony televisions
15. A—inning   D—today?"

16. D
17. A
18. B
19. B
20. A
21. C
22. B
23. A
24. D
25. C

Proofreading

Page 204

Does inteligent [intelligent] life exist elsewhere in our galaxy? Researchers from the National Aeronautics and Space administration [Administration] (NASA), the SETI Institute (Search for Extraterrestrial Intelligence), and the Jet Propulsion Laboratory are working on a major program that may provide an answer to this question. On Columbus Day, 1992, the researchers began the ~~more~~ most intensive search ever conducted, for evidence of extraterrestrial life within our galaxy. They turned on new high-powered equipment that is searching the galaxy for radio signals possibly being transmited [transmitted] by alien civilizations.

The SETI program consists of two search strategys [strategies]—a targeted search and a sky survey. The targeted search uses the ~~most~~ largest radio telescopes in the world to focus on 800 nearby stars and listen for radio signals. The sky survey uses 34-meter antennas to scan the entire sky for signals coming from places not on the targeted search list. The researchers expect the two search strategies to continue until about the year 2002.

According to Deputy Chief Bernard M. Oliver at the SETI program office, "~~Theire~~ There's nothing unique about our sun and its planets that one would not expect to find duplicated in millions of other places in the galaxy." Oliver explains that since there are over 10 billion sunlike stars in the Milky way [Way] alone, a large number of these stars may have planetary systems. Therefore, it is highly likely that within those systems are planets with an earthlike environment that can support intelligent life forms. On the basis of this likelihood, the researchers on the SETI team believes [believe] that it is just a matter of time before contact with a distant civilization will be made.

Page 205

7523 Powers Street

Shelby, Iowa 51570

October 17, 19—

Dear Chef Clarisse:

I like to watch your show, *Cooking with Clarisse,* on saturday [Saturday] afternoons. I especially like when you prepare foods that are popular with kids and teens. I have invented a snack that I make when some of my friends comes [come] over to my house. We all think it's great, and it's real [really] easy to make. Here's the recipe:

Mark's mini-Taco Pizza snacks [Snacks]

10 refrigerator biscuits

1/4 c. of grated cheddar cheese

1 6-oz. can of enchilada sauce

1 choped [chopped] onion

1/2 envelope of taco seasoning

1/2 c. of water

1/2 lb. of ground beef

Preheat your oven to 425°. Brown the ground beef and onion, and drain the fat. Add the taco seasoning and water, and stir the mixture. After you have ~~brung~~ brought it to a boil, Reduce [reduce] the heat and simmer it for 15-20 minutes.

On a greased baking sheet, Flaten [flatten] each biscuit to a four-inch circle and make a rim. Fill the biscuits with enchilada sauce. Add the ground beef and onion. Sprinkle [sprinkle] the cheese on top. Bake them in the bottom half of your oven for 10 minutes. Enjoy!

I hope you make this recipe on your show. Happy cooking!

Sincerely,

Mark Ulrich

Page 206

Most Chicagoans agree that the Chicago Air and Water show is one of their ~~cities~~ *city's* most exciting events. Held every summer on Lake Michigan's spectacul*a*r shoreline, the event attracts hundreds of thousands of spectators. *M*en, women~~s~~, and children all take delight in the show's daring and dramatic performances. Among the most popular attractions are the military groups who demonstrate their special skills, such as parachuting, assault procedures, and rescue operations.

The highlight of each show is the final act. A loud roar seems to come out of nowhere as spectat*o*rs are greeted by the sudden appear*a*nce of a military jet team—the U.S. Air Force Thunderbirds, the U.S. Navy *B*lue *A*ngels, or the Canadian Snow Birds. Members of the team risks their ~~lifes~~ *lives (or life)* as they carry out a series of aerial maneuvers that ~~do not~~ never cease to amaze and excite the crowd. In one thrilling feat, two or more planes fly straight toward each other. *A*t several hundred miles per hour. Loud oohs and aahs can be heard in the crowd as the planes veer away from each other at the last second.

What daring flight hero*e*s and performances will dazzle the crowd at the next Chicago Air and Water Show? Time will tell, but if ~~passed~~ *past* shows are any indication, the star lineup will undoubtedly meet most Chicagoans' expectations. As the show draws near, famil*ies*, couples, and individuals who just wouldn't miss this annual event will be making ~~there~~ *their* plans for another exciting after*noon* on the lake front.

Page 207

Driving on a lonely desert road on a trip to *C*alifornia, Margaret Starr had car trouble. An hour earlier, she had turned off the main highway to take a shortcut. Now ~~her~~ *she* and her two children, eight-year-old Madge and eleven-year-old Andy, were stranded. "How long can the kids and *I* ~~me~~ last without water?" she wondered. It wasn't long before the heat in the car became unbear*a*ble. Margaret opened the trunk and pulled out a blanket. She set about making a half tent by using rocks to secure one end of the blanket to the top of the car and the other end to the ground. *I*n the shade of the shelter, it seemed a little less *hot.* ~~hotter~~

The next day, Margaret knew she had to find water. She drained her car radiator and tasted *the water* ~~it~~. "It's undrinkable," she muttered disappointedly, but she didn't throw it out. She dampened a rag and used it to cool her children's faces. Then she tried digging for water. She didn't find any, but she noticed that the ground was cooler a foot or so down. She asked Andy to help her dig shallow pits for Madge and ~~he~~ *him* to ~~lay~~ *lie* in. Then she covered their bod*ies* with sand and smeared ~~they're~~ *their* faces with cold cream. Later, Margaret slashed pieces of cactus. She and the children squeezed ~~them~~ *those (or the)* cactus pieces to get every bit of moisture.

By the third day, Margaret knew that she and her children could not survive much longer. She set out in the direction of the main high*way*. On the fourth day, two rockhounds whom were out

prospecting found Margaret laying ~~laying~~ *lying* in the road.

They revived her and then rescued her children.

Margaret hadn't never *(or hadn't ever)* thought of herself as a

particularly clever person. However, experts said

that her creative thinking had saved both her and

her children. She and them *they* survived against

incredable *incredible* odds.

Page 208

Inspector Swift was hot on the trail of another

bold and cunning criminal. The night before, there

had been a robbery at the home of Mr. and Mrs.

Howard Smythe, one of the towns' *town's* wealthyest *wealthiest*

couples. A valuable painting had been stolen from

the Smythes' den and the police report suggested

that the robber had broken a window and then had

entered the room. In addition, a tiny peice *piece* of blue

fabric laying ~~laying~~ *lying* next to the glass on the floor

suggested that the robber had tore ~~tore~~ *torn* his shirt as he

crawled through the window. However, on the basis

of his own investigation, Inspector Swift was

convinced that the robber had went ~~went~~ *gone* into the room

through the door, not the window. The Inspector

already knowed ~~knowed~~ *knew* that the outcome of this case

would rise ~~rise~~ *raise* some eyebrows.

"By the end of the day," thought Inspector

Swift, "I will have spoke *spoken* to every one of the Smythes'

household employees. I'll crack this case in no

time!"

None of the employees were spared the

inspector's careful questioning, not even Mrs.

Sedwick, the smythes' *Smythes'* cook and most trusted

worker. Mrs. Sedwick walked into the living room,

where the inspector had been waiting, and set *sat*

down. She sqirmed *squirmed* uneasily and then shouted,

"Leave ~~Leave~~ *Let* me go! I didn't steal no *any (or that or the)* painting!

"On the contrary, Mrs. Sedwick, you did steal

the painting, and I can prove it," replied the

inspector. He held up a plastic bag that contained

fabric like the piece that had been finded ~~finded~~ *found* on the

den floor. "We found this fabric in your sewing

basket; *You you* broke the window yourself and planted

this clue so that the police would believe that

someone had broke *broken* into the house."

Page 209

West Fest

Step into the past and relive the exciting days of

the Old West. Don't miss none ~~none~~ *any* of these thrilling

attractions and activities at the incredibly *incredible* 50-acre

site of Colorado's West fest *Fest* extravaganza. Look

what's in store for you:

Western Stage Show

Enjoy good knee-slapping and foot-stomping

performances by some of the more ~~more~~ *most* talented stars

of todays *today's* country music.

Musical Entertainment

Join in the fun of line dancing and two-stepping to

the livly *lively* music of several excelent *excellent* country bands.

Horseback Riding

Take a trail ride in the beautifuleest ~~beautifuleest~~ *most beautiful* country setting

imagineable *imaginable*.

Square Dancing

Expert caller Joe "Smoothie" Jones always calls

out the dance movements very clear. *clearly.* Even

beginners dance quite good ~~good~~ *well* to Joes *Joe's* directions.

Hearty Cowpoke Supper

Tasty chow will be served between 5:00 and 8:00

pm daily. Hungry cowpokes can wander over to

the ~~most~~ nearest chuck wagon for some real*ly* hearty edibles.

Old-Time Photo Shop

Individuals, couples, and groups can have ~~there~~ *their* pictures taken in period costumes; customers can also have ~~them~~ *those (or their)* photos framed.

General Store

Shop in the supermarket of yesterday. This ~~here~~ store has great gifts and souvenirs.

Call 555-WEST for more details, partner.

Page 210

A.

Unbelievable! Incredible! Wow! Words of surprise like these are frequently uttered by visitors standing ~~above~~ on the rim of the majestic Grand canyon for the first time. Gazing upon the canyon's multicolored cliffs and wondrous vistas is an experience of a lifetime! However no visit to the Grand Canyon is complete without going down in *to* the canyon. Visitors who travel down the mountainous trails in the canyon walls discovers unique and diverse rock formations. They can also observe an abund*a*nce of plants, flowers, and animals that have adapted ~~good~~ *well* to the canyons dessert environment. The more adventur*o*us travelers complete the one-mile descent to the bottom of the canyon, where they are greeted by the raging waters of the mighty Colorado river.

B.

Dear Naomi,

Guess where I went ~~to~~ today! I took a mule trip into the Grand Canyon. What an adventure! My mules' name was Ida, and, oh yes she was stubborn! Of all the mules in the group, she was the ~~more~~ *most* stubborn one, and beside*s* that, she insisted on stopping to nibble at the bushes all along the trail. When I finally got her back in line, she proceeded to walk on the outside of the trail, where the drops were very steep. The guide said not to worry though, because mules are sure-footed. I guess he was right, because Ida didn't loose her footing even once. All in all, the mule trip was thrilling but I'm stiff and ~~soar~~ *sore* from being in*to* the saddle so long. Ouch!

Jan

Page 211

The management team of Teen Scene want*s* to make improvments in its store, and you can help. Please take the time to fill out this survey; your comments will be ~~took~~ *taken* very serious*ly* as the team tries to create a better store for their valued customers.

1. Describe the style of casual clothes you like best. _____

   _____

2. What fabrics are most appealing to you in casual clothes?

   _____

   What types of fabrics does you avoid? _____

3. Check *True* or *False*;
   The clothes at Teen Scene are made real*ly* ~~good~~ *well*. True _____ False _____

4. Check the statement below that tells how you feel about the prices at Teen scene:
   The prices are very good. _____
   Only some of the clothes ~~is~~ *are* within my budget. _____
   I can only look. The prices are much too high. _____

5. Check the statement below that tells how you feel about the service you recieve at Teen Scene:

I always get friendly courteous, and helpful
service. _____

Some of the salespeople give good service but
others act uncaring. _____

The service is always poor. _____

6. Check *True* or *False*.

There are always enough salesclerks during a
sale in the fitting rooms and at the checkout
counters. True _____ False _____

Optional: Write your name and a phone number
where you can be reached at.

_____

Page 212

Wiggling back and forth, many people are
disgusted at the sight of a long, slimy worm.
Indeed, a worm is not a visualy attractive creature
to human beings. In fact the word *worm* has
become a generic name for any lowly life form.
However, such a negative image is undeserved. In
reality, worms are truely amazing little creatures
and serve many useful purposes that far outvalue
their usefulness as fish bait. Knowing ~~them there~~ those (or these)
purposes, worms ~~might be shown~~ people might show the respect and
appreciation they deserve.

Boring their way through the upper soil,
worms are sometimes called natures plow. ~~There~~ Their
burrows allow air and water to pass through the
soil easy, promoting plant growth. In addition,
consuming about 30 percent of their own weight
daily in plant matter and minute animals and dirt,
worms leave
useful excrement ~~is left~~ on the surface of the soil.
The excrement of worms transform barren soil into
rich, fertile loam.

Population figures for worms are staggering!

Researchers estimate that there are more than
four thousand earthworm species varying greatly
in habit and diet and the list grows by a dozen or
so new species each year. While some species
lives in rain-forest treetops and dine on
decomposing material found in Bromeliads, a type
of pineapple plant, other species live as much as
eight feet underground and consume protozoa,
bacteria, and other microorganisms from the soil.
Some species even dine on other earth worms!

Worms are also a good source of protein.
There is no need to, however, worry that
earthworms will become a secret ingredient in
fast food hamburgers. Obtaining the tremendus
number of worms that would be reqired for human
consumption on a regular basis would be much too
costly. (alternatirely, the word however
in the last paragraph may be positioned
to precede the word there or to
follow the word need.

Page 213

Upon entering an Amish settlement, visitors
notice the homes painted white, the horses and
buggies, and the plain clothing of the residents.
The Amish are hard working and gentle people
who practices a simple way of life. Some of the
men are farmers, while others work in various
trades, such as furniture making. The women are
homemakers who spend their spare time making
quilts and other crafts. Both the men and women
are very skilled craftspersons their products are
sold in Amish stores nationwide and are of high
quality.

have
Since the 1600s, the Amish ~~has~~ held firm to
their beliefs and traditions in a world that has made
giant technological advances. They do not oppose
progress but they have rejected much of modern

252   *Answer Key*

technology, including radios and television. Believing that they must be "in the world, but not of it," the Amish have a culture and a value system that emphasizes family and community. Regarding radio and television as a threat to family life, amish families spend their leisure time reading. At mealtime, neither radio nor television interrupt the quiet time needed for family conversation

There are an abundance of good food and social activity in the comunity. The Amish cherishes their families, relatives, and friends and regularly travel to each other's homes for both informal visits and formal occasions such as baptisms, worship services, weddings, and funerals many of the Amish enjoys group games, such as volleyball and baseball.

The Amish also truly model the meaning of community spirit. When a disaster strikes an Amish household, the neighbors does that familys chores for them, takes care of their children, and harvests their crops. When a barn burns down, everyone work together to rebuild it.

Page 214
A.

Some people might call truck driver Chester A. Sutter an ordinary man but the citizens of middleton call him a hero. As Mr. Sutter was driving down Waverly Avenue on the afternoon of May 3 He spotted smoke poring out of the third-floor windows of the Sunset view apartment building. He later told reporters that when he saw two women and a baby on the ledge of one of those windows he knew he had to do something quick. He parked his truck under the window which

was a huge eighteen-wheeler. He climbed on top of the trailer and braced himself with his arms stretched out in front of him.

After only a moment's hesitation, Dina Gardner dropped six month old Kyle down toward Mr. Sutter. He caught baby Kyle, whom was uninjured in the fall. Mrs. Gardner and her sister Rosa, both of who jumped onto the truck, also was uninjured. In recognition of that heroic act, mayor Thorndike has named Chester A. Sutter Middletons Citizen of the week.

B.

There was not a seat at the park that was empty during Saturday's exciting game between the Valesburg Vipers and the Bayberry Bulldogs. Even though the Vipers played very competitive They were held scoreless against the undefeated Bulldogs, whom scored a whoping nine runs. The crowd gave rousing cheers for Ricardo Lopez, the Bulldogs star first baseman, who caught four line drives and hit three home runs. After the game, Lopez talked appreciativly about the crowd, who had cheered him in an interview with a local news reporter.

Page 215

May 15, 19—

Dear Aunt Aiko and uncle hoshi,

My class trip to Washington, d.c., was great! It took us all day and all night to get there I hadn't never slept on a train before. I found out that those berths really are as small as they look in the movies!

We checked into our hotel on Tuesday afternoon. Then we went straight to the white house. I could hardly believe I was walking into the home of the president! I was hoping to see the oval office, the official office of the President, but the public doesn't get to see that. Too bad! We saw five beautiful rooms on the first floor. They are used for formal dinners, big parties, and meetings with goverment [n] dignitarye [ies]. Some of the fancy furniture there don't [doesn't] look very comfortable to sit in, but it is real [ly] pretty. I especially liked the portraits of passed [past] Presidents.

On the second day, we visited the museums at the Smithsonian Institution. In the National Museum of natural history, we saw exibits [exhibits] of animals from all over the world. Believe it or not, there was a [an] enormous skeleton of a Blue Whale on the ceiling! Did you know that blue whales can grow up to 100 feet long?

After the Smithsonian, we went to capitol hill and toured the United States Capital [Capitol]. We saw the chambers where the senate and house of representatives meet and many beautiful works of art that show people and events from american history. We also saw the rotunda, the grand circular room beneath the Capitol's dome.

Well I have to go now because mom needs my help in the kitchen.

Your Loving Niece,

Lee

Page 216

Looking for adventure? Well you don't have to look far. *Adventure on Vintar,* an exciting futuristic thriller, opens Friday in theaters everywhere.

In the opening scene Earth's world leaders and top scientists are meeting with highly advanced creatures from vintar, a distant planet in our galaxy. For several months, a scientific research team on Earth have [has] been transmiting [transmitting] radio messages to the Vintarians through space in order to arrange this historic meeting. Discussion centers on a plan for transporting a group of earths [earth's] top scientists to Vintar, where they will study the Vintarians method of eliminateing [eliminating] starvation, pollution, and illness. In addition, an Earth family that have [has] been chose [chosen] to live in a Vintarian household and experience family life on Vintar will accompany the scientists.

Brian Tuscany and Marlena Muldair give very convincing performances as Willie and Wanda, the two clever teenagers who uncover the real purpose of the Vintarians contact with Earth.

"This is my best role yet," says Muldair, "and I hope the public will begin to see me now as more than just a supporting actress."

Tuscany who had never played a leading role before admits that he was challenged by the role of Willie: "That scene in which I made one last attempt to convince the doubting Dr. Horn that the Vintarians were not the compassionate beings that they presented themselves to be was especially difficult for me Im [; (or me. I'm)] really not an outspoken kind of guy like Willie."

When all seems lost, it is up to Willie and Wanda to save the Earth however they [; (or Earth. However,)] are up against tremendous odds. If you like fast-paced action, don't miss *Adventure on Vintar.* Its [It's] terrific!